# Your Voice Is Your Business

*The Science and Art of Communication*

SECOND EDITION

# Your Voice Is Your Business

*The Science and Art of Communication*

## SECOND EDITION

**ORLANDO R. BARONE, MA**
**CARI M. TELLIS, PhD**

PLURAL
PUBLISHING
INC.

5521 Ruffin Road
San Diego, CA 92123

e-mail: info@pluralpublishing.com
Website: http://www.pluralpublishing.com

FSC
www.fsc.org
MIX
Paper from
responsible sources
FSC® C011935

Typeset in 11/13 Garamond by Flanagan's Publishing Services, Inc.
Printed in the United States of America by McNaughton & Gunn, Inc.

Library of Congress Cataloging-in-Publication Data:

Barone, Orlando R., author.
  Your voice is your business : the science and art of communication /
Orlando R. Barone, Cari M. Tellis.—Second edition.
      p. ; cm.
  Includes bibliographical references and index.
  ISBN 978-1-59756-722-0 (alk. paper)—ISBN 1-59756-722-1 (alk. paper)
  I. Tellis, Cari M., author. II. Title.
  [DNLM: 1. Voice. 2. Communication. 3. Voice Training. WV 500]
  PN4162
  808.5—dc23
                                                    2015029450

# Contents

# Preface

This expanded second edition of *Your Voice Is Your Business* responds to the desire on the part of readers to have us expand many of the topics, illustrations, and techniques they found helpful in the original version. The text updates the science in the dynamic field of speech-language pathology with two brand new chapters. Stylistically, we have made the writing more vivid, powerful, and direct.

A new feature of this edition is the companion website, an interactive and updatable resource offering instructive illustrations, videos, and content that bring the book's topics and exercises to life. Instructors and students will find the website of enormous value in reinforcing learning and enabling practical application of key concepts.

We always believed that our readers were interested in applying the techniques of voice science to the communication needs of people who want a better understanding of interpersonal effectiveness, as well as a guide to self-improvement as communicators. In fact, we experienced a demand for even greater technical knowledge. This edition responds with more depth and content in the application of our knowledge of the human voice.

We co-authors have also expanded our vision since the publication of the first edition. Lonnie has been coaching MBA students in executive leadership at the Wharton School of Business at the University of Pennsylvania. He has encountered there a marked desire of these future leaders for improvement in all areas of interpersonal communication.

Cari has founded the now flourishing Performing Arts Training Academy in Northeastern Pennsylvania. Cari's work with her professional staff of musicians, singers, dancers, and actors—and their work with student performers—has reinforced the need for, and the unqualified usefulness of, knowledge-based applications of voice science to expression and performance at the highest levels.

Both of us have continued our work with speech-language pathology students, leaders, and executives in a wide array of professions and industries, Cari as an associate professor of voice science in her award winning program at Misericordia University, Lonnie as a global consultant to leaders in the private, public, and military sectors. We bring to this edition a fresh and relevant perspective, a wealth of new and confirmed understandings about the fields of voice science and self-presentation.

As a result of these learnings, we have been able to rework a fine book and make it significantly better. It will be a staple in a variety of departments including speech-language pathology, communications, theater and drama, and business. We are grateful to users of the earlier edition who have been kind enough to offer the terrific feedback that has led to this second edition of *Your Voice Is Your Business.*

# Introduction:
# The Search for Your Voice

*How we are educated by children, by animals! Inscrutably involved, we live in the currents of universal reciprocity.*

—Martin Buber, *I and Thou*

## A Troubling Case

At the dawn of the 20th century, when The Victor Company was looking to brand its Victrola record player, it selected a painting by Francis Barraud. The canvas featured a mutt named Nipper, head tilted toward the horn of a wind-up device emanating a sound. What attracts the dog most is as distinctive as a fingerprint, as hypnotic as a dangling pocket watch: It is "His Master's Voice."

There's a reason this picture creates such an indelible impression. We grasp implicitly the importance of the voice, its power to beckon, to describe, to thrill, to enrich. It is life-encompassing sound, primitive as a simian grunt, sophisticated as a Shakespearean soliloquy.

We have assigned some major responsibilities to these little vibrations in the throat. When a friend urges you to "speak in your own voice," to "voice your feelings," those little vibrations encapsulate the very essence of your unique self. They connote the weighty authority of whole nations when a leader summons "the voice of the people." They take on moral qualities, too, like the courage to "lift your voice against tyranny" or the compassion to "voice your concern."

The great religious leader, Oscar Romero, was called "the voice of the voiceless" because he spoke in the name of the poor and oppressed. When the U.S. government created a radio station to broadcast its message into Communist countries during the Cold War, it was called "The Voice of America." When a tire company created a classical music program to tout its unlikely upper crustiness, it was called "The Voice of Firestone." In business circles, the key to understanding quality is intimately bound up with hearing and heeding the "VOC" or "Voice of the Customer" (Pande, Neuman, & Cavanaugh, 2000).

People who work with children know that almost from birth infants are drawn to the human voice, its sounds and the very sight of a mother's lips making those sounds. Researchers have noted that the focusing distance of a newborn's eyes is the exact span from those eyes to mother's lips when nursing (Stephenson, 2013).

Those who enlist you as their ally tell you to "raise your voice," while those who want your obedience warn you to "keep your voice down." And if that is not enough, you are even told to watch your "tone of voice." Nothing the voice does is beneath notice.

As we considered a title for this second edition, we realized that we were embarking on a new stage in our investigation of the ways we humans seek to transmit our intentions to others. We have uncovered new layers of understanding in the past seven years, outgrowths of the expanding science of voice and communication, along with exciting new insights into the artistry involved in reaching an audience and making our intentions present to them.

Science and art, the empirically discoverable and the humanly imaginable—this inseparable duality conspires to produce a profound connection between you and me, the connection of people interacting and all the while seeking to understand and getting it right. The title of this second edition, then, recognizes that successful interpersonal communication requires these two elements. *Your Voice Is Your Business: The Science and the Art of Communication, Second Edition* proposes that interpersonal effectiveness comprises a combination of knowledge, skills, and talent.

The science helps you to learn about and understand the workings of this vital asset, this mechanism called voice. How is it produced? How do you make it louder, quieter? How do you change its tone and quality? How does it help you express emotion and intention? How do you keep it working and meeting your needs? These questions are important to you because it is your voice and it is vital to your art, your communication, and your career. To help you accomplish this aim, we will explore the vocal sciences, cashing in on the rich lode of empirical knowledge about the voice as a physical and physiological reality. Armed with this insight we will travel the haunts and havens where people play and work, brag and barter, whisper, shout, and sing. There we will transform knowledge into skill, skill into competence, competence into creativity. You will learn to use those little vibrations and use them well. You will further learn not only the use of the voice but its care—tending to your voice, maintaining its good working order, and keeping it safe.

Many of our clients both in the vocal rehabilitation world and the corporate world influenced our desire to write this book. All have realized the importance of their voice in some capacity. One corporate client in particular was jolted into the discovery of just how valuable an asset her voice was after comments were made about her voice by her own managers following a bout with laryngitis. She noticed that they were not taking her seriously.

When we serve up examples like this one, we will fabricate names to protect the anonymity of clients, and we are not hesitant to create composites as long as the resulting illustrations are true to our experience with real life clients. This client's alias is Genevieve. She was a high-level manager in a large corporation who enlisted Lonnie's help because she was worried that her employees found her voice weak and lacking in authority. One of this book's co-authors, Lonnie is an executive leadership coach who had conducted a presentation skills workshop for Genevieve's company in the past. She remembered that he talked about voice in the workshop and even had participants practice changing their pitch and loudness. After meeting with Genevieve, Lonnie determined that her voice was stiff and breathy. She had difficulty projecting her voice and often strained to get louder.

Genevieve seemed perplexed when Lonnie recommended that she see a clinical voice team to evaluate and treat her voice issue. If she had torn a ligament or pulled a muscle in her leg, she would have understood and probably expected that physical therapy would be recommended, but to suggest vocal rehabilitation bordered on bizarre. Genevieve appreciated that there was a problem with her voice; the solution just did not seem obvious or normal to her.

xiv   *Your Voice Is Your Business*

Lonnie explained to Genevieve that there are speech-language pathologists and ear, nose, and throat physicians (ENTs), called laryngologists, who specialize in the voice. A comprehensive assessment of her vocal difficulties would result in an accurate diagnosis and plan for vocal rehabilitation, similar to how physical therapists would evaluate and treat an injured muscle or knee. The voice assessment would include quality of life surveys (how the voice issue affects the individual), auditory-perceptual ratings of the voice (how the voice sounds), acoustic and aerodynamic testing (how the voice makes sound), and visual perceptual evaluations (what the voice looks like when it makes sound).

Make no mistake, vocal coaching and training readily address plenty of vocal issues, including dynamics, expression, and mechanics. In fact, after a full evaluation by a clinical voice care team and completion of a course of voice therapy with Cari, a voice therapist and this book's other co-author, Genevieve resumed her work with Lonnie. She began incorporating what she learned in clinical treatment into her interpersonal communication with her managers. Lonnie's professional relationship with Cari had given him the astute ability to recognize an issue that was outside his realm as a presentation coach. The unique aspect of voice is that a clinical disorder like Genevieve's is not adequately treated by a presentation workshop or even by one-on-one coaching alone. Through his referral to Cari, as well as Genevieve's subsequent work with Lonnie, a connection could be formed between the clinical world and the creative outlet. Genevieve's "voice team" now included members (laryngologist, speech-language pathologist, presentation coach) all working toward the overall care of the client.

Unfortunately, for a large number of people in Genevieve's situation, nothing beyond vocal coaching is accepted as the norm. Yet, if people whose voice is germane to their passion and their work desire to restore or sustain vocal health and strength, they must be agreeable to treatments that include behavioral, medical, and possibly surgical management. One objective of this book is to make such recourse expected, not foreign. We want to forge a seamless link between the technical world of voice science and the practical art of interpersonal competency and creativity.

Your journey through this book will lead you to the tools and resources available to you whether your work includes speech-language pathology, vocal coaching and training, or performance/presentation coaching and interpersonal effectiveness. Our intent is to help you communicate powerfully no matter your age. Crucial to that power is your voice, and the power of your voice depends on its compelling use and your constant attention to its care and health. If we are successful, you will enhance a skill set and a competency that is second to none in contributing to the attainment of your hopes and dreams in your work and even in your life.

## Voice Science

Cutting edge voice therapies are a product of the exciting and growing body of empirical voice research. Colleges nationwide are instituting or expanding voice studies departments. If the term *laryngology* has not yet acquired a musical lilt, it has at least become less unfamiliar to the general public. Ear, nose, and throat practices are instituting voice therapy centers, if they are smart, and the future of vocal studies remains one of the most expansive.

Voice science is growing and deepening at a rapid rate. We are beginning to understand ways to heal specific injuries to the vocal folds besides using just voice rest or surgery (Hansen & Thibeault, 2006; Hirano, 2005). We know more today about the actual biochemical and histological properties of the muscles of the larynx than we have ever known. This information gives us insight into the ways these muscles are capable of functioning and what it takes to make them function properly. Through extensive modeling, we also better understand how the interaction of the entire vocal tract, from the trachea to the lips, influences the production of voice (Titze, 2004). This modeling also has given us insight into the underlying scientific explanations of how traditional vocal techniques, like the lip trill and humming, work in the rehabilitation process (Titze, 2006) and how valuable novel approaches can be.

Because of these advances, the reach and effectiveness of voice therapies are also expanding. Many of the techniques can be helpful to those seeking vocal improvement even where no vocal disorder exists. The training and development world provides an ideal setting for individuals pursuing such improvement.

## The Presentation Training and Development World

The world of training and development is one that has seen a revolution in its approach to interpersonal effectiveness. Workshops and coaching in presentation skills are ubiquitous and usually include applications in use of gesture, eye contact, posture, and, of course, voice, although voice work is usually confined to efforts at making the sound less monotonous, more lively, perhaps louder. Still, people who use their voice at work are not at all surprised to find themselves in a class devoted to improving their speaking and presentation skills.

## Vocal and Performance Training and Coaching

Singers and actors are performers who rely on their voices to capture the essence of a song or bring life to a character. Training in voice is essential to their art and their career. Long has there been a disconnect between vocal and performance training and the science of voice production. Many performers do not grasp the full complexity and workings of the vocal anatomy. The breath is still the go-to remedy for support and power, and scales are just scales.

Jo Estill, a brilliant singer and researcher, began a lifelong quest to merge voice science and performance artistry with the inception of her voice-training model (Colton & Estill, 1981; Estill, 1988; Honda, Hirai, Estill, & Takhura, 1994; Steinhauer & Estill, 2008). She understood vocal anatomy and physiology and believed that performance magic was born out of a merger between craft (technical knowledge) and artistry (Klimek, Obert, & Steinhauer, 2005). Her work has even begun to influence voice therapy (Lombard & Steinhauer, 2007; Tellis, 2014). Estill acknowledged that, insofar as her model was based on science, her model would continue to develop with scientific research and advancements.

Current scientific knowledge in voice, including aspects of Estill's work, will be used to provide you with the most up-to-date understanding we have of vocal mechanics. Keep your mind open to the possibilities. Sometimes it is difficult to reconcile what you have learned with what science tells us. Once you do, though, the world opens to you.

## A Comprehensive Approach

The task of merging the knowledge and techniques from the voice science, training and development, and performance worlds is far from complete. Training and development practices rarely, if ever, incorporate the insights and techniques emerging from voice science, just as the vocal sciences seldom offer comprehensive syllabi on the interaction of voice, face, gesture, and drama in the communication process. As a result, many speech-language pathology students emerge from a vacuum in which voice stands alone, as if all human transmission issued from a cell phone relying only on voice. Unfortunately college-level speech communication, theater, and communication disorders departments rarely communicate.

Combining these worlds produces a comprehensive approach which, when integrated, views communication as a unitary act involving the transmission and reception of meaning between humans in real time. Presentation skills then can naturally involve the employment of clinical voice therapies and theatrical performance if they enhance success at the communication enterprise. If you look at any of these fields independently, each can benefit from what the others have to offer. With this merger, the scientific study of voice, like the study of a ligament, will be viewed in its role as an agent of communication teaming with the rest of the body to hurl packages of meaning from one person to another. Performers will understand the true meaning of connecting with their audience, and their voices will stay healthy for their entire careers and beyond.

## How to Read This Book

This book and its companion website have been designed to afford optimum ease of use whether you are a student of voice science or a person desirous of using your communication equipment to its best advantage at work, on stage, or in life.

The text can be read cover to cover with great benefit. You will be cued within the text when a web page illustrates a point in the narrative; once again, you have the option not to rush off to the website. The text is written to be read as an integrated whole.

You can, however, jump to the various sections of the text without reading what went before. Our suspicion is that many readers will want to go to the page most relevant to their aims at a given time. They should feel free to do so.

Anecdotes and stories that illustrate the chapter's theme are found throughout the text. While these stories use fictional names and composite settings, they are all true to our experience and those of our clients and students.

Sometimes a technical amplification of a point in the text is appropriate. That could include scientific data or other clarifications. Technical information is integrated into the text and reviewed at the end of each chapter. It contains terminology and references suitable to the serious student of the voice and will be of interest to many other readers. Technical information is often enhanced by an illustration. These illustrations appear throughout the book and will exemplify a point being made in a nearby text. They are clearly labeled and referenced.

The companion website is interactive and can be utilized with or without the book. Its purpose is to bring to life the key points and themes of the book, so it will also be used with the book to elucidate those points and themes. The text will direct you to the relevant scene on the website when a point is being explored. Again, you will experience no gap if you just continue reading the text. The site, however, is a powerful learning aid.

Here is where science and art commingle. It is our hope that, armed with the tools and resources presented here, you will expand the range and efficacy of resources available to assist you in giving voice and being heard.

# References

Colton, R. H. & Estill, J. (1981). Elements of voice quality: Perceptual, acoustic and physiologic aspects. In N. J. Lass (Ed.), *Speech and language: Advances in basic research and practice* (Vol. V). New York, NY: Academic Press.

Estill, J. (1988). Belting and classic voice quality: Some physiological differences. *Medical Problems of Performing Artists, 3,* 37–43.

Hansen, J. K., & Thibeault, S. L. (2006). Current understanding and review of the literature: Vocal fold scarring. *Journal of Voice, 20*(1), 110–120.

Hirano, S. (2005). Current treatment of vocal fold scarring. *Current Opinion in Otolaryngology, Head Neck Surgery, 13*(3), 143–147.

Honda, K., Hirai, H., Estill, J., & Takhura, Y. (1994). Contribution of vocal tract shape to voice quality: MRI data and articulatory modeling. In O. Fujimura & M. Hirano (Eds.), *Vocal fold physiology: Voice quality control.* San Diego, CA: Singular.

Klimek, M. M., Obert, K., & Steinhauer, K. (2005). *Estill voice training level one: Figure combinations for six voice qualities workbook.* Pittsburgh, PA: Estill Voice International.

Lombard, L., & Steinhauer, K. (2007). A novel treatment for hypophonic voice: Twang therapy. *Journal of Voice, 21*(3), 294–299.

Pande, P. S., Neuman, R. P., & Cavanaugh, R. R. (2000). *The Six Sigma way: How GE, Motorola, and other top companies are honing their performance.* New York, NY: McGraw-Hill.

Steinhauer, K. & Estill J. (2008). The Estill Voice Model™: Physiology of emotion. In K. Izdebski (Ed.), *Emotions of the human voice.* San Diego, CA: Plural.

Stephenson, S. M. (2013). *The joyful child: Montessori, global wisdom for birth to three* (2nd ed.). Arcata, CA: Michael Olaf Montessori Company.

Tellis, C. M. (2014). Integrated implicit-explicit learning approach to voice therapy. *Perspectives on Voice and Voice Disorders, 24*(3), 111–118.

Titze, I. R., (2004). A theoretical study of F0-F1 interaction with application to resonant speaking and singing voice. *Journal of Voice, 18*(3), 292–298.

Titze, I. R. (2006). Voice training and therapy with a semi-occluded vocal tract: Rationale and scientific underpinnings. *Journal of Speech, Language, and Hearing Research, 49*(2), 448–459.

# Acknowledgments

An expanded, fortified second edition of a book like *Your Voice Is Your Business: The Art and Science of Communication* requires many talented hands contributing in a variety of ways. Without their dedication and perseverance as deadlines approached, the superior quality of the final product could not have been attained.

To artist, consultant, and supporter-in-chief Maida Barone, unreserved gratitude for sharing your time and your flair to make the work a thing of beauty that is fun to read. To the best graduate students in the field, Erin Roberts and Tia Spagnuolo, thanks deeply for always being there to make sure the research was spot on, errors were identified, and figures looked amazing and were all in the right spots. Your intelligence, dedication, and perseverance to this project were unmatched.

To Stan Spagnuolo and Jessica Flaim, thank you for taking the time to share your artistic talents. Your creativity brought The 5 Intentions to life. We are forever grateful.

Thanks to the editors at Plural Publishing for your dedication to this edition, our friends and colleagues for keeping us on the straight and narrow, and our families for making the rough ways smooth and the hard road a lot softer.

Our gratitude goes to Dr. Glen Tellis for giving freely of his vast knowledge of speech-language pathology and how to write a book about it. His insight has left more than a trace on every page.

If our second edition surpasses the success of the first, the excellent work of these marvelous collaborators is very much to blame.

*To Maida Barone, mother, spouse, never letting up and never letting down. We love you.*

# SECTION I

# Foundations of Communication

# Chapter 1

# A People Finds Its Voice

*Words mean more than what is set down on paper. It takes the human voice to infuse them with deeper meaning.*

—Maya Angelou

## Variations on Voice

Imagine yourself at a presentation by the greatest speaker you have ever heard. You have a terrific seat, front row center. The topic, Shakespearian tragedies, had not previously been of much interest to you, but you find yourself almost immediately mesmerized by the speaker's imposing presence, intent gaze, graceful gestures, and, most definitely, most enchantingly, her voice.

It rises, falls, belts, whispers, caresses each phrase with a controlled passion that draws you in, makes you feel at one with her and her message. You experience not only the panoply of emotions she is transmitting but a mysterious something that connects you to her and her to you. You sense her fierce need to get herself across to you, and it is personal, intimate. You just know you'll never forget these powerful moments.

Her extraordinary voice echoes in memory long after you leave the auditorium. She made you want to know more about Shakespeare, to be sure, but you also want to find out more about the hold her voice and presence had on you. What made her so impressive? What did she do and how did she do it? You decide to check with the experts.

You have choices since you are on a university campus. The speaker was quite dramatic, so you figure you might find answers in the theater department. A meeting with the long-time acting coach proves interesting. You strike up a warm conversation with the man. You admit you were in a couple of high school theater performances. What you remember is the terrible fear, the stage fright, you felt in the wings, just before going on. He smiles and recollects his old mentor, Stella Adler, the legendary advisor to great actors of her era.

"She always said actors don't like it in the wings; they don't belong there. There is nothing to do there. The stage crew, they belong in the wings, not the actors. Actors belong on stage. That's their turf."

"Turf?" You ask.

He smiles and amplifies. Great actors, he claims, own the stage. The stage is their territory, like the slope to a champion skier, the ring to a boxer, a head of hair to a barber. You agree. That speaker certainly seemed to own the "turf" where she stood. Right, he says. She walked out and asked the question, "Where am I?" When she got the answer she was ready to go to work.

You get the idea. Confidence is generated by comfort, the sense that you are where you belong, and where you are belongs to you. That's not all, though. Actors need to be strong; they aspire upward from their feet up through their spine to their head. Upward. Your body always pulls you up, never down.

Still, you say, it was her voice that captured you. Yes, answers the acting coach. It is the same with the voice. Your voice cannot turn inward; no mumbling! Too big is better than too small. Your voice has to stretch. Remember, he almost shouts, "Talking goes out; you simply cannot talk in. Talking in is madness." He quotes Adler.

"When your body is always pulling you upward and when your voice is strong enough to fill the room, you'll be worthy of standing on the stage. Communication," he continued, "is making someone else see what you see." It is grabbing hold of the picture in your mind and placing it into the other's mind. That speaker, he claimed, made you feel the urgency she felt, the need she had to make you really see what she has seen. That urgency is what pushed her voice out to you. It's the impact or effect you have on your audience. It's almost like magic."

The acting coach gave you a lot of insight on what made that speaker effective. You wonder if a presentation skills instructor might have something to add. You head over to the communication department where your meeting with the instructor of Presentation Skills 101 sheds light on a different perspective.

"When I teach presentation skills," the professor says, "I focus on four aspects of effectiveness: message, voice, face, and gesture. These are what audiences hear and see. That speaker who enthralled you likely used all four superbly."

The instructor reveals that great presenters have a message of importance to deliver and they deliver it exquisitely. The message is foremost. Great presentations not only sound well, they read well. Examples are many. Check out *The Gettysburg Address*, the *I Have a Dream* speech, John F. Kennedy's Inaugural Address.

Great speeches, well written speeches, often have signature lines, sentences that pop out and stay in the mind. Franklin D. Roosevelt's First Inaugural, delivered in the depths of the Great Depression, begins with, "So, first of all, let me assert my firm belief that the only thing we have to fear is fear itself . . . " Dr. King said simply, "I have a dream." John Kennedy suggested you "ask not what your country can do for you. Ask what you can do for your country." Almost every line of Lincoln's Gettysburg Address is immortal.

"But," the professor adds, "a memorable message is only the beginning, the raw material, you might say." The presentations are stirring even when read silently to yourself. When given life by a skilled presenter like that woman you heard, they soar. The tools she commanded constitute the other three aspects of effectiveness: voice, face, and gesture. You learn that the voice is supported by appropriate facial expressions and movements, all of which aid the transmission of the message sent by the presenter. You want to know what it was that held your attention.

The professor says, "Let's start with the sound coming from her lips." He discusses two aspects of the voice, pitch and volume. Pitch refers to the tone of the voice: how deep or high the voice is. Volume is intensity: how loud or quiet the voice is. Mixing and balancing pitch and intensity, a speaker changes inflection and intonation. Talented speakers use this vocal variety to add interest, emphasis, and, ultimately, meaning to what they are saying.

Powerful presenters know how to utilize every asset to best advantage. They combine face, gesture, and voice to deliver a well-crafted message in the most effective manner. They achieve their goal: to give information, to persuade, to build relationships, to affirm themselves, or to evoke an emotion.

"In short," the professor adds in summary, "this is what that fine speaker did and how she did it."

"Can anyone learn to do what she did?"

"Anyone can improve as a presenter," the professor answers. "Even she, terrific as she is, can improve! It's just that we all start at different levels of proficiency. But we all have skill at presenting, and we all employ those skills pretty much every day of our lives. Right now you and I, speaking and listening together, are employing the same skills she employed."

You thank the professor, who added to your grasp of what made that Shakespearean scholar so mesmerizing. You've learned a lot from the drama coach and from the presentation skills instructor. But something is missing. Before you leave you ask, "Can I get a deeper understanding of the voice? Does anyone know exactly what is going on when someone speaks or sings?"

The professor nods. "Sure. There is a science of voice. You'll want to talk to a speech-language pathologist who specializes in the voice. If your puzzle has a missing piece, the SLP can probably supply it."

Now you are really intrigued. You thought speech-language pathologists, SLPs, were concerned only with saying the "r" sound correctly or increasing fluency in someone with a communication disorder like stuttering. You learn that, in fact, the place on campus that houses the speech-language pathology department is the College of Health Sciences!

"Yes," says the SLP professor, "we're part of health sciences. Accent on health, not just disorder! I specialize in voice, and a big part of my job is to research and instruct vocal health, care of the voice. It is a beautiful instrument, but it is complex, dynamic, and delicate."

You tell her what brought you here. "That presenter blew me away. I got a lot of insight from the first people I spoke with."

You mention the drama coach who told you that great actors "own" the stage, belong there. They are confident and strong. Their strength moves from the bottom up. Their voice soars outward; they grab hold of the picture in their mind and put it into the mind of the audience.

"Scientifically," the SLP says, "that drama coach is absolutely right."

"Scientifically? How does strength move up in the body scientifically?" You ask.

"When you lift your soft palate and widen your pharynx you support the voice and create a wider space in your vocal tract for the sound to resonate almost like a megaphone."

"Huh?" You respond.

"Yes, those are all parts of the vocal tract that you can learn to control to strengthen the sound of your voice. That's the upward feeling the drama coach talked about. But strength also comes from a simultaneous downward support or anchor. You can use the muscles of your back, shoulders, and chest to pull downward and extend out."

You now refer to your visit to the presentation skills instructor who revealed that effective presenters marshal their competencies in using facial expression, gesture, and voice to transmit a well-written message of importance to their audience.

You continue, "That person told me that voice has what are called volume and pitch. The instructor said that volume is intensity, the loudness or softness of the voice; and pitch is highness or lowness. Good speakers learn to mesh these and achieve the effects they want to achieve."

The SLP smiles. "Yes, intensity and pitch are the terms often used to describe certain vocal dynamics. In voice science, we look at what happens when these vocal changes occur. Pitch correlates to frequency, the number of cycles per second the vocal folds vibrate. Your vocal folds probably vibrate close to 200 times a second while talking. When you raise your pitch, your vocal folds vibrate more times a second, 300, 400. When you lower your pitch, they vibrate fewer times per second, between 175 and 150. What many call intensity or volume is really the amplitude of vibration, how far the vocal folds blow apart during vibration. If there is a larger amplitude of vibration, the voice is louder. And if there is smaller amplitude . . . "

"The voice is quieter," you finish.

"That's right," she adds. "There is so much more to the voice than pitch and intensity. Those are only two voice features that you can learn to modulate. Quality is another: how clear or breathy the tone is. And then there's resonation: how the sound is shaped."

"There's a lot to voice science." You are intrigued. "But did that Shakespeare presenter need to know all this to be as good as she is?"

"At some level, yes, she needed to know what she was doing. Knowing the science, though, provides the foundation of understanding."

The SLP gives you an explanation. Realizing what the vocal folds are doing when frequency, or pitch, goes up or down tells you precisely what you are controlling and how you are controlling it. It is the same with other aspects of vocalizing like resonance, timbre, or amplitude, which we perceive as loudness.

"So," you say, "The vocal folds tell us what we need to know about voice."

"You might begin there," the SLP says. "But much more is involved, including lungs, airways, vocal tract, tongue, lips, teeth, and resonance chambers. I study the science of voice, and that knowledge is vital in learning how to use the voice properly and care for it throughout your life. The other professionals you spoke with might focus more on the art of presenting yourself."

"It looks like a big field that includes a number of disciplines."

The SLP nods. "Absolutely. And each one contributes valuable insight to your question. Each one tells you something important about why and how that speaker made such a great impact on you."

You agree. "It is a lot to take in."

"It is." She smiles at you. "And you haven't even looked at singing."

## Beginnings: Voice to Speech

Tanya was not entirely sure she wanted to attend the recital. She was a typical woman in her twenties, so opera was not her favorite musical form, but these were billed as among the most promising young artists, and her parents had paid for the ticket. Early in the program, a gorgeous soprano took the stage and smiled as the opening strains of Puccini's "O mio babbino caro" emanated from the orchestra. The diva clasped her hands and opened her mouth. The opening words found moving expression in her resonant voice, reaching easily to the final row.

By the second line of the aria, Tanya was in tears, astonished at what she was hearing and her reaction to it. Her comment to her father as the singer finished: "I didn't know a voice could sound like that." She was still crying, crying at a song in a language she did not know. Somehow, one human to another, a connection had been made—profound, memorable, indescribable—done solely with the voice. It is a power we will never fully comprehend, a mode of communication vaster and more insistent than you would ever think possible from those thin, barely visible vocal folds.

The voice did not emerge "opera-ready." The amazing performance Tanya witnessed was many centuries in the making. The primitive voice had its physiological inception as an assortment of attributes developed to enhance purely biological functions and then borrowed to produce meaningful sound. You can follow the voice's evolution into an instrument not only of communication but also of individual identity and, ultimately, the sustainer of values we all hold dear.

That identity, your matchless self, is intimately and powerfully realized in your voice. Self-affirmation is embedded in your every utterance. When you think of the sound you make, you think of your voice. When others think of the sound you make, it is likewise your voice they bring to mind. Henry was an elderly man who, due to several severe afflictions, lost first his hearing, then his sight. He learned to communicate in deaf-blind sign, a tactual language transmitted and received from hand to hand. Henry was sometimes asked which of the two distance senses, sight or hearing, he missed most. "Hearing," he answered without hesitation. "I miss the voices of those I love far more than their faces. Their faces are fading pictures now, but their voices have touched my soul."

Your voiceprint is as unmistakable as your fingerprint. Your anatomy, especially the size and shape of your resonating chambers and your vocal folds, helps create your unique voice. It is composed of elements that can be heard and elements that can be detected through spectrographic instrumentation (Koenig, 1986). Voice recognition technology is a rapidly spreading component of entry and security systems because of its precision in screening all voices but the one whose owner has authorization. Companies that use voice recognition technology as a security device for customers verify and confirm their customers' identities based on their "voiceprint." For these types of companies, your voice is you.

When you are seeking to get yourself across to others, you are usually referring to the message you are transmitting at that moment. In fact, along with your message, it really is your "self" that you are getting across.

This evolution is remarkable when you consider that there was a time when the vocal folds were not even vocal. The vocal folds serve many vegetative functions such as respiration, pushing and pulling, as well as airway protection. These small curtains of tissue are responsible for guarding the entrance to the trachea, a cartilaginous tube that provides the pathway to the lungs. "Guarding" is more than a metaphor. These folds protect the air passage; the folds open to allow breathing and close to assure that food goes into the stomach and not the lungs.

Sometime during their existence inside the throats of various organisms, as they effectively kept the respiratory and digestive systems from interfering with each other, these organisms noticed that an exhalation of breath could be sent over these folds under certain conditions and sound could be emitted. The noises took the form of grunts, barks, roars, tweets, screeches, and whines. Eventually ears began interpreting these sounds, making sense of them.

Newborn babies emit cries and other sounds right from birth, and caregivers often learn to distinguish a whimper of discomfort from a cry of hunger. Mothers have been responding to their children's voices since well before recorded history.

Infants also have a distinct bias toward listening to speech over other sounds (Vouloumanos & Werker, 2007), so the rudiments of interaction have been in place for a long time. We do not know for sure when adults first utilized the voice as a communication device. What we do know is that, at some point in human history, certain vocal sounds, like grunts, began to take on meaning and were eventually used in communication. How long was it before these vocalizations acquired increasingly specific connotations? How long before grunts became distinct words and words were joined to create phrases and sentences?

There is no question it took a great deal of time. Over that time the usefulness of vocal sounds was significantly enhanced by people's burgeoning ability to call into service other articulators or "sound shapers" like the, lips, mouth, teeth, and, preeminently, the tongue. With these and other features of the anatomy, people learned to make distinct utterances and attach separate meanings to separate sounds. Thus was language—literally "tongue"—born and raised.

## To Voice a Word

To the untrained communicator, and that is most of us, the process of voice production is taken for granted. The construction of a single spoken word is surprisingly complicated. If you have taught a child how to speak, you probably have some notion of this complexity.

As noted earlier, the production of audible language utilizes numerous parts of the anatomy originally—and still—placed for other purposes entirely. Lips, palate, teeth, tongue exist to work with saliva in preparing food for digestion. The larynx and the vocal folds, again, act as a protective mechanism to ensure that food does not enter the lungs. These anatomical structures are indispensable to food absorption, breathing, and swallowing safety, but every bit as important to speech. Say aloud, "The purse snatcher bit my arm," and pay attention to the role of lips, palate, teeth, and tongue in a successful rendition. Evolution has certainly played its part, repositioning these structures and features to make speech easier. There is a price to pay: We choke more easily than other animals that have almost no use for the Heimlich maneuver. The prize is speech, language, history, culture, and the ability to package thoughts and transport them from person to person, nation to nation, epoch to epoch.

For obvious reasons, what is said here about speech applies to the English language. Many languages are partially comprised of sounds never made in English, and some English sounds do not crop up in other languages. The Khoisan languages of southern Africa include clicks never made in English, and the German guttural sound in a word like "*drei* (three)" is not produced in English. The liquid "r" sound in the English word "word" (especially as pronounced by Americans) is missing from lots of languages including Spanish, Italian, and French. Such examples are almost endless and demonstrate the versatility of the total vocal mechanism in producing the amazing array of sounds we call voice.

Voice—vocal sound—begins with a breath. When you inhale you fill the lungs with air. As you squeeze the air out, it passes from the lungs by way of the windpipe or trachea, then through the vocal folds and into the world. If you exhale and no sound emerges, you are likely keeping the vocal folds open. If there is sound, you are closing the vocal folds and stretching them somewhat, an action that makes them vibrate as you exhale. That vibration would constitute nothing more than a soft buzz, except that it echoes through your resonators, the hollow spaces in the throat, head, and nasal cavities (i.e., vocal tract) until it proceeds from your personal loudspeaker, your mouth.

Vowel sounds, like /a/, /o/, /u/, /i/ (English sounds "ah," "oh," "oo," and "ee") are produced by the unimpeded flow of these amplified vibrations into the world (Tables 1–1 and 1–2 provide description of phonetic notations). Each vowel sound is shaped specifically by the tongue, but also with the help of the jaw, lips, and teeth, at a minimum. Say the words "not," "note," and "neat," and pay attention to how your lips maneuver to help make the three distinct vowel sounds. You are also doing some fancy tongue work to make these different sounds.

Consonant sounds, like those represented by the phonemes /k/ and /t/, are usually produced by impeding the airflow in some

**Table 1–1.** The Front Vowels

| Front Vowels | Word Position | | |
|---|---|---|---|
| | *Initial* | *Medial* | *Final* |
| /i/ | east | meat | funny |
| /ɪ/ | is | stick | (not found) |
| /e/* | eight | berate | hearsay |
| /ɛ/ | edge | head | (not found) |
| /æ/ | aggravate | back | (not found) |

*Some linguists consider /e/ as always representing a diphthong.
*Source:* Reproduced with permission from *Speech and Voice Science* (p. 231) by Alison Behrman. Copyright 2007 Plural Publishing, Inc.

**Table 1–2.** The Back Vowels

| Back Vowels | Word Position | | |
|---|---|---|---|
| | *Initial* | *Medial* | *Final* |
| /u/ | **oo**ze | h**oo**t | bl**ue** |
| /ʊ/ | (not found) | sh**ou**ld | (not found) |
| /o/ | **o**mit | m**o**tor | tang**o** |
| /ɔ/ | **a**wesome | d**au**nting | p**a**w |
| /ɑ/ or /a/ | **o**gle | f**a**ther | sp**a** |

*Source:* Reproduced with permission from *Speech and Voice Science* (p. 231) by Alison Behrman. Copyright 2007 Plural Publishing, Inc.

way. With /t/ the tongue stops the airflow in the front of the mouth; with /k/ something is clearly going on back in the mouth. The /t/ sound is called unvoiced because you send the air through unvibrating (open) vocal folds and let it slam into the tongue as it presses behind the upper teeth, an action you can check out on your own. Just say the word "tattoo" a few times. If you perform the same action except you close the vocal folds and "voice" the sound, you will make a /d/ sound, as in "daddy." The same voicing technique will turn a /p/ into a /b/ ("pip" into "bib"), a /k/ into /g/ ("cackle" into "gaggle"), and /f/ into /v/ ("fanfare" into "van valve").

When you teach a child to speak, your task, and the child's, is monumental. The little one has to learn all this and much more to master even the simplest vocabulary of spoken words. For that child and for you, learning to make those sounds—learning to speak—is one of the most difficult skills she and you will ever acquire (Pinker & Jackendoff, 2005).

## To Voice a Thought

Of course, language acquisition does not stop with word mastery. Words combine to form sentences; sentences represent thoughts. How a child gets from a thought to a spoken sentence and vice versa has occasioned reams of fascinating research (Clark, 2009). The point is, it happens with just about all of us. We put our thoughts into sentences and speak these sentences to others. Vocal sounds that may have begun with a grunt and a roar now transmit profound and intricate notions, everything and anything we want badly enough to get across to another. The spoken word has certainly grown up.

To be sure, the spoken word is even more than words strung into sentences. It is spoken. We hear it. Not just words, then, but words and "music." We inflect our words and thus enhance their meaning. Vocal inflection is called "prosody." Take the following simple sentence.

The child will give the dog three pats.

Now notice how the meaning is altered if the speaker emphasizes different words. Emphasis is denoted by capital letters.

The CHILD will give the dog three pats. (Meaning: No one but the child will do this.)

The child WILL give the dog three pats. (Meaning: Despite any protest the child's going to do it.)

The child will give the DOG three pats. (Meaning: the dog, not the cat!)

The child will give the dog THREE pats. (Meaning: three, no more, no less . . . )

The child will give the dog three PATS. (Meaning: pats, not biscuits . . . )

See the companion website for additional examples.

Emphasis or stress on a word is perhaps the simplest form of inflection. The use of more intricate vocal inflection can infuse a sentence with nuance, clarity, and power. The main components of inflection are pitch and loudness. Loudness is the perceptual correlate of intensity, what the volume control on your TV remote allows you to control. It is a function of sound amplitude, how long you keep your vocal folds closed during vibration, how much pressure you build up under your closed folds during each vibration, how far your vocal folds blow apart during vibration, and how many molecules are moved by your vocal folds' vibrations. Many people still believe respiratory effort to be the main determining factor of loudness. You will learn that there are more efficient ways than pushing air to get louder. Pitch is the perceptual correlate of frequency: how many vibrations your vocal folds make in a given unit of time. If you lengthen your vocal folds you increase the number of vibrations per second. The more vibrations per second, the higher the frequency, the higher the pitch. The reverse is true for lower pitches.

You can, with practice, achieve higher or lower frequency (pitch), higher or lower intensity (loudness) levels. Singers train and work to extend their range or pitch and achieve more or less loudness. If you use your voice professionally in speech or song, extending your range of pitch and loudness can greatly enhance your vocal competence and overall communication skill. Most of us can recall an uninspired semester with a monotone teacher whose voice never varied, or at least we recall the few moments when we were awake. Experiences like those give pretty convincing evidence of the importance of vocal range.

For the hearing, voice is crucial to effective communication. You must learn the capacity and the limitations of your own voice to assure that you are taking advantage of all your vocal equipment in your efforts to get yourself across to others. As you shall see, you have probably been ill served by your educational experiences to date in your quest to learn how to employ your voice to its full potential and to care for it throughout a lifetime of constant use.

Moreover, in our quest to become complete communicators, vocal sounds by no means provide the last word. Among us are the deaf, those who employ sign as their primary mode of communication. From this community we learn the immense importance of visual feedback in interpersonal effectiveness. Facial expression, gesture, posture, position, even what we wear has a significant communication impact. If vocal pitch is critical to meaning, so are face and gesture enormous enhancements to what is transmitted and received. Those meanings-beyond-words we call "paraverbals."

Next, perhaps most significantly, your success as a communicator requires that the listener is prepared to accept what you transmit as reliable and trustworthy. You cannot hope to achieve effectiveness in communicating without achieving credibility with your listener. Your words become senseless, your intentions unattainable, if your listener does not believe you. Credibility certainly involves a believing listener, but it is more sophisticated than that. It requires a confident speaker capable of transmitting a message that possesses not only clarity and accuracy but also believability and integrity. This is the definition of the credible speaker, and the credible speaker is our ultimate goal.

In the midst of your message, therefore, is none other than your self. The "I" that exists at the instant you transmit your message. It might include the little tremor in your voice that tells your listener that you are nervous or the intonation of satisfaction that reflects your pride. Other aspects of your self are revealed in your phrasing, gestures, expressions, and body language. The deeper "I" is there, too, the one that points to your moral fiber, the one that will embody your credibility.

## Connecting With Your Authentic Self

The self you want your listener to connect with is the real you, your authentic self. To realize this bond, you must secure a conscious connection between you and your authentic self. Otherwise, the core of your message, you, is being transmitted unwittingly. At one level, this unselfconsciousness is endearing. Nothing is sweeter than a two-year-old child interacting with complete abandon. We certainly detect a self and we may be enchanted by it; it is all the more appealing that the child has no awareness whatever that she is presenting a self.

Ideally, you as an adult will incorporate your authentic self seamlessly into your transmission with no affectation or pretense. That does not mean, however, that you are required to maintain a childlike innocence about the self that is being propelled toward your listeners. The employment of presentation skills presupposes that you have in mind a way you would like your listeners to view you. There is nothing intrinsically deceptive about using presentation skills, as long as you use them to display and not mask who you are.

The ancient philosopher Aristotle got us started with his marvelous work on rhetoric (Honeycutt, 2011). It is he who insisted that your character is an essential player in the effectiveness of your vocal transmissions. He claimed that there are three things in all that inspire your listener to have confidence in you and your message: (1) You have good sense or intelligence; (2) you possess strong moral character; and (3) your listeners like you or at least they have nothing against you.

First, you must have good sense; that means you must talk sense to your audience. If you present poor arguments or give bad advice because you do not know what you are talking about, you are lacking good sense. Your listener has a right to question the value of a message from a person who is ignorant, illogical, or intellectually inadequate.

The second confidence builder is that you are a good person. You do not lie to others or deliberately mislead others. It is interesting that Aristotle positioned this characteristic after good sense. He seemed to feel that, good person or not, if you lack good sense, you should not open your mouth to begin with. Immorality, however, can cause you to say something other than what you know to be correct, thus subverting the whole point of communication.

The only other thing than can cause you to speak falsely or to give awful advice is that you lack goodwill. If you do not like your listener or are not watching his back, as it were, you may be inclined to present your listener with something other than what you know to be in his best interest.

To be sure, you should develop and control the verbals and paraverbals you use to transmit clearly and precisely the message you intend. Aristotle made clear, however, that those with whom you connect through meaning have a stake in your character, your good sense, and your disposition toward them if you are seeking to inform, convince, or affect emotions. When you choose to transmit to them, they have a right not only to make clear what you mean to say—your intention—they are also right to probe your integrity, to clarify that the message emanates from a dependable source.

That Shakespearean scholar, the one whose presentation skills made such a deep impression on you, may have done much more than impress. She took you on a journey into her world, a world that evoked your passion because it was where her passion resided. She offered her vision, her reality, and her truth. Using the various tools and insights peculiar to the actor, the presenter, and the voice scientist, she recreated for you an intimate experience, one that existed in her mind and in her heart.

She spoke movingly in her own voice and, through the astounding power of communication, enabled you to hear it, feel it, and be changed by it. She made you wonder if one day you might have access to a power like that. She sent you on a search, a search for a voice as potent as hers.

And yet, a voice that is all your own.

## Where Do You Go From Here?

There is still so much to learn about the technical aspects of communication: how to gesture effectively; where to put your arms when talking; what kind of movements are acceptable for certain speaking and singing situations; how to produce and modulate voice; how to get louder or quieter; how to achieve a clearer tone; how to anchor, position, and align your body. Chapters in this book are dedicated to the technique, mechanics, and science of communication. These are the components of communication that the SLP and presentation skills instructor helped you identify.

Other chapters are devoted to the artistry of communication—the meaning, feeling, experience you bring to each communication act. There is heart in each interaction. The way you interpret lyrics to a song. The investigation of the character you portray. The emotion you want to evoke in your listener. The things the drama coach spoke about—the beauty, desire, truth that you bring to interactions that comes from within you. Actors are not the only speakers who have access to this skill set—lawyers, ministers, managers, teachers, and health care providers can learn them as well.

The combination of technique and artistry is impact, effect, metaphysics. It's the feeling that was evoked within you when you listened to the speaker on Shakespeare. It's what Tanya felt when the opera singer hit that ethereal note. It's the care you feel when your professor stays after class to explain a difficult concept. As the speaker or singer, you feel it too. Athletes and performers say you're "in the zone"—the moment when your training, knowledge, understanding, and self align. You are fully present in that moment, and your listeners are with you.

How do you get in the zone? Some of it has to do with your innate ability and openness to go there, to try. Then you learn, study, and practice. Your practice must be technically correct and deliberately focused. There is no use practicing the wrong technique 10,000 times or for 10 years unless that is what you want to learn. Seek out teachers who understand the science and appreciate your individualism and creativity. Be willing to change and be open to new developments as science advances. Have fun along the way.

## Review of Key Ideas

- Knowledge and insight about what fine speakers do can be found by investigating various disciplines, including drama, presentation skill development, and speech-language pathology.
- Drama teaches what great actors do. Actors belong on stage. The stage is their territory.
- For the actor, communication is making someone else see what you see. It is grabbing hold of the picture in the actor's mind and placing it into the other's mind, making you feel the urgency the actor feels, the need to make you really see what the actor has seen.
- The presentation skills instructor focuses on four aspects of effectiveness: message, voice, face, and gesture. These are what audiences hear and see. Great presenters have a message of importance to deliver and they deliver it well. The message is foremost.
- The voice is supported by appropriate facial expressions and gestures, all of which aid the transmission of the message sent by the presenter.
- Two aspects of the voice are intensity and pitch. Intensity is loudness or softness. Pitch refers to tone, how deep or high the voice is. By mixing and balancing pitch and volume, a speaker changes inflection and intonation. Talented speakers use this vocal variety to add interest, emphasis, and, ultimately, meaning to what they are saying.
- Anyone can improve as a presenter. It's just that we all start at different levels of proficiency.
- Voice science looks at what happens when vocal changes occur. Pitch correlates to frequency, intensity to loud-

ness. Knowing the science provides an added layer of understanding.

■ The production of audible language utilizes numerous parts of the anatomy originally— and still—placed for other purposes entirely. Lips, palate, teeth, tongue, vocal tract, larynx, and the vocal folds are indispensable to speech production.

■ Vocal sound begins with a breath. When you inhale you fill the lungs with air. As you exhale, air passes from the lungs to the trachea, then through the vocal folds and into the world. Sound is produced by closing the vocal folds, an action that makes them vibrate as you exhale. The vibrations resonate through the vocal tract and out your mouth.

■ Vowel sounds are produced by the flow of amplified vibrations into the world. Each vowel sound is shaped by the tongue with the help of the jaw, lips, and teeth.

■ Consonant sounds are produced by impeding airflow with the articulators at different levels of the vocal tract. Some consonants are voiced and others are voiceless.

■ For children, learning to speak is one of the most difficult skills they acquire.

■ The spoken word is more than words strung into sentences. We inflect words and thus enhance their meaning. Emphasis is perhaps the simplest form of inflection. Prosody is the melody of the voice and also enhances meaning.

■ The main components of inflection are pitch and loudness.

■ Loudness is the perceptual correlate of intensity and is a function of sound amplitude: how many molecules are moved by your vocal folds' vibrations.

■ Pitch is the perceptual correlate of frequency: how many vibrations your vocal folds make in a given unit of time. The higher the frequency, the higher the pitch.

■ Extending your range of pitch and loudness can greatly enhance vocal competence and overall communication skill.

■ Facial expression, gesture, posture, position, even what we wear has a significant impact on communication and can be enormous enhancements to what is transmitted and received. Those meanings-beyond-words are called "paraverbals."

■ Your voiceprint is as unmistakable and is composed of elements that can be heard and elements that can be detected through spectrographic instrumentation.

- Your self is realized most powerfully in your voice.
- The employment of presentation skills presupposes that you have in mind a way you would like to be viewed. There is nothing intrinsically deceptive about using presentation skills, as long as you use them to display and not mask who you are.
- Aristotle claimed that there are three things that inspire confidence in another's character: you have good sense, you are a good person, and you have goodwill.

## References

Clark, E. V. (2009). *First language acquisition* (2nd ed.). New York, NY: Cambridge University Press.

Honeycutt, L. (2011). *Aristotle's rhetoric*. Retrieved from http://rhetoric .eserver.org/aristotle/

Koenig, B. E. (1986). Spectrographic voice identification: A forensic survey. *Journal of the Acoustical Society of America, 79*(6), 2088–2090.

Pinker, S. & Jackendoff, R. (2005). The faculty of language: What's special about it? *Cognition, 95*(2), 201–236.

Vouloumanos, A., & Werker, J. F. (2007). Listening to language at birth: Evidence for a bias for speech in neonates. *Developmental Science, 10*(2), 159–164.

# Chapter 2

# Learning Voice

*Control of muscles . . . is not accomplished by reading, or even theoretical understanding—it's learned by doing . . . and doing . . . and doing. Be patient during this process . . . practice is required for mastery.*

—Jo Estill

## Overview

Voice is central to our presentation workshops and classroom discussions. We get many different answers when we ask people to define voice. Some quickly reply that voice is the sound heard when a person speaks. Others choose to be more metaphorical: Voice is my identity, it's what makes me, me. A few get very technical: Voice is the vibration of the vocal folds in the larynx. Still others say, "it's the voice of reason," "there's passive versus active voice," "a person can be in good voice," or "a singer can have a unique voice." No matter how we look at it, there is one commonality among all the definitions. They all refer to voice as as a channel for being heard, typically as a sound or the act of making sound. We even say that a people that has lost its voice has lost the ability to be heard.

In this chapter we will focus on the actual physical production of voice. We will investigate the inner workings of those tiny folds of tissue within the larynx, how they start and continue vibration, how they transform that vibration into what we hear, and how they facilitate a change in pitch, loudness, and quality. While voice can be produced in many ways, the objective of this chapter is to define and describe typical voice production. The final section of the chapter is dedicated to discussing the development of voice from birth through early adulthood, the mature voice, and the voice appropriate to public speaking and vocal performance.

## Voice as a Dynamic System

Voice is a dynamic system of coordinating structures that work together and influence one another to make the sound uttered by humans as either spoken word or song. Another definition, true, but this one gets us closer to where we are going. Let us break it down. A dynamic system means that the human voice is a complex and interacting mechanism comprised of many structures that are influenced by one another and coordinated to make sound. The idea of coordinative structures gets to the heart of vocal anatomy. In the dynamic system we call voice, we have three primary coordinative structures: respiration or breath, phonation or vocal fold vibration, and resonation, the sound we hear. Some people include articulation as a fourth coordinative structure, but we'll talk more about that during the section on resonation.

Each coordinative structure has its own components and mechanisms of function. In the following sections we will identify how each coordinative structure works, the important parts of your anatomy that make these structures work, and how they all integrate to make sound.

Science does not lie—or at least it does not intend to lie. The study of the voice that we will discuss in this chapter details what voice scientists currently know and understand. This science is based on the research we have to date, as well as cutting edge, ongoing research. To be sure, there is still some debate between the performance and the scientific worlds about the mechanisms of voice. The search for common ground requires us to recognize that the mechanisms involved in a physiological human action must have a scientific explanation, albeit reliant on the technology currently available to the scientific community. The terminology you use may be different from ours, but if the meaning is the same, then we are all going in the right direction. If the meaning is different, then clarification is needed. This chapter is intended to provide such clarification.

## Simple Voicing Mechanics

Your voicing mechanism, in its simplest form, is no more than a system of pipes and valves. That is right, you heard it, pipes and valves. When we talk about the anatomical structures involved in voice production, we are really talking about plumbing. Air is substituted for water in this example, which flows through a tube or pipe as it travels from the lungs to the nose and mouth. Along its pathway to the outside world, air meets valves that can stay open to let air flow freely or close to limit airflow or stop it altogether. The result of this activity is varying air pressure.

Imagine turning on a tap or faucet. As you twist the handle slowly from closed to open, the valve inside the tap releases allowing water to flow out into the basin. You can modify the flow of water by adjusting the handle toward the closed or open position. When turning the tap toward the off position, you cause the valve to restrict the flow of water; the water streams from the tap in a fine line, then trickles, then drips, and finally stops flowing as the valve closes completely. If you slowly move the handle toward the open position, the valve inside the faucet opens and water trickles, streams, and finally gushes from the tap (Figure 2–1).

The valves within your voicing mechanism work similarly, except that your brain controls the valves to position them in the spectrum from open to closed or closed to open. Some valving happens passively, without your control. I know, it is complicated, but that is why we call it dynamic. Air should flow freely into your lungs through your nose and mouth as you inhale. Your lungs fill with air, and pressure builds within them. When you are ready to exhale, air exits your lungs making its way toward the outside world through your trachea or your "windpipe," the first pipe transporting air to your listener's ear. Air acts as water flowing through the tap. If unimpeded on its way out, all the valves stay open and air travels out the nose and mouth.

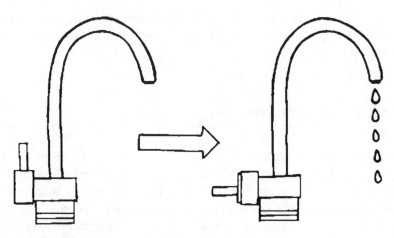

**Figure 2–1.** Valving. Similar to the way a faucet valves the flow of water when turned on and off, the vocal folds valve airflow from the trachea as they adduct (close), abduct (open), and vibrate to make sound.

With the intention to make sound, something different happens to air as it makes its way outside the body. You exhale a bit, sending air from the lungs through the trachea. At the top of the trachea, the air transitions to another tube called the vocal tract. Your vocal tract runs from the bottom of your larynx or voice box through and out your nose and mouth. Nestled within the vocal tract are several valves that manipulate and modify the air from your lungs to make and shape sound.

Air travelling up through your trachea and into the larynx meets the first valve along its path, the vocal folds (Figure 2–2). These folds of tissue close with a muscular contraction and trap the air below them, causing pressure to build. The pressure eventually blows the vocal folds apart. With a careful balance of pressure and airflow, the vocal folds vibrate and create sound waves. As those sound waves move through the vocal tract, they meet bends, curves, and valves along the way. We'll talk more about the vocal tract in the section on resonation.

The following sections delve more deeply into the voicing mechanisms detailing the inner workings of the different coordinative structures that are used to produce voice.

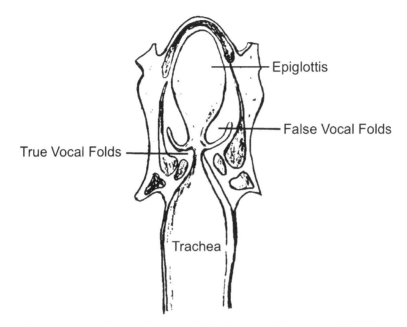

**Figure 2–2.** Coronal view of the larynx. True vocal folds, false vocal folds, and the epiglottis are three laryngeal valves.

## Respiration: "The Source of Power"

### *Quiet Respiration*

Sit and breathe. Pay attention to your breath. Concentrate on the air entering your lungs and then exiting your lungs. We call this "resting breath" or "quiet respiration." Interestingly, when you draw your attention to your breathing, the unconscious, involuntary breath really changes to a more conscious and intentional one. Try it. Do your best not to control your breathing but simply observe it. While you take air in, you inhale and your lungs fill with air as pressure builds up within them. When you exhale, pressure decreases as air exits your lungs.

What you will begin to notice is that your inhalations and exhalations follow a somewhat cyclical pattern—you inhale, stop for a brief moment, then exhale, stop for a brief moment, and then inhale again. The pattern can continue unconsciously, without any of your voluntary control. If you think of this patterned breathing as a circle that starts with your inhale, you begin to notice that about 50% of your circle is the inhale and 50% is the exhale (Figure 2–3).

You may notice that occasionally you have to take a bigger breath. Go ahead and take the bigger breath, and then continue with your 50/50 pattern. What you realize about that bigger breath, though, is that you have the ability to take in more air during your quiet respiration breath than you typically inhale during quiet respiration. This bigger breath is called your inspiratory capacity. You can also exhale past your quiet respiration exhale. If you continue to exhale, you will reach a point where you can no longer exhale and you will stop. If you release muscular control at that point, your lungs will recoil and fill back up with air, and you will start

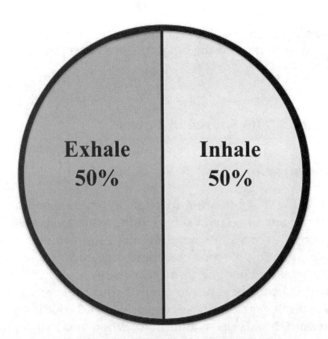

*Figure 2–3.* Quiet respiration. An inhalation and an exhalation comprise a full cycle of respiration. A quiet inhalation is 50% of the cycle and a quiet exhalation is 50% of the cycle.

quiet respiration again. The air left in your lungs after a maximum exhalation is called residual volume. You always have that residual volume in your lungs so that your lungs do not collapse.

As you can see in Figure 2–4, quiet respiration is called tidal volume. With your finger, trace the wave up as you inhale and down as you exhale. Now trace the circle above, start at the top, inhale clockwise around the circle, and as you reach the bottom of the circle, exhale, as your finger traces around the circle back to the top. Continue around. Inhale. Exhale. Inhale. Exhale.

On your next exhale, draw your attention to the point where you stop briefly right before you inhale. Do it again, but this time exhale and be mindful of the spot where you stop briefly before you inhale. It is also the place your finger traces on the wave in Figure 2–4 that is the end of your tidal volume exhalation and the beginning of your tidal volume inhalation. You can trace the same pattern on the circle; as you finish tracing half of the circle through

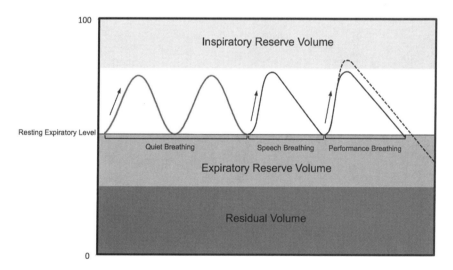

**Figure 2–4.** Lung volumes and capacities. Quiet breathing shows that 50% of the respiratory cycle is an inhalation and 50% of the cycle is an exhalation. In speech breathing the line representing the inhalation has a larger slope, indicating a quicker inhale that occupies less of the respiratory cycle (20%) than the exhalation (80%). Performance breathing often utilizes inspiratory and expiratory reserve volumes.

exhalation, pay attention to the spot on which your finger is positioned before you turn to go around the other half of the circle to begin inhalation. This spot is called resting expiratory level or REL, and is labeled in Figure 2–4 and is denoted by a star in Figure 2–5. Resting expiratory level will be important when we discuss the role breath plays in speaking and singing.

## Respiration for Speaking and Singing

Breath is the primary source of power for sound in human voicing. It is the wind in the sails; without it the vocal folds cannot vibrate. Still, breath is not what necessarily creates powerful speaking or singing. Breath is the starting point for sound, but there is much more to the equation of what creates sound, and more specifically power, than just the breath.

No voice book is devoid of discussion about the impact the diaphragm has on breathing, but we need to set some things straight. When talking about respiration, the diaphragm is a major muscle

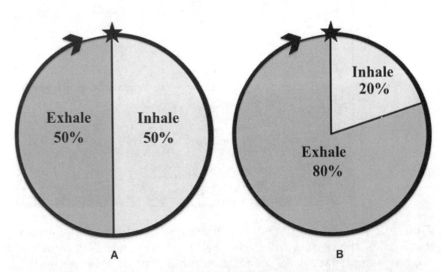

*Figure 2-5.* **A.** Quiet respiration. **B.** Respiration while speaking or singing. Unlike quiet respiration, a smaller inhalation (20% of the cycle) is needed to speak or sing, and most of the cycle is occupied by an exhalation (80% of the cycle).

of respiration, primarily inhalation. During quiet, tidal breathing, your diaphragm contracts and pulls down creating space in the thorax (chest cavity) for your lungs to fill with air. As you exhale, the diaphragm relaxes to its resting position as air is expelled from your lungs. Most of the diaphragm's action in tidal breathing is reflexive and involuntary. As in all organ systems in the human body, though, there is much more to the process of breathing than just a reflexive action.

Let us start with the basic point that all breathing is diaphragmatic because you use your diaphragm every time you breathe. Remember, it is the primary muscle of inhalation. You cannot breathe without your diaphragm. So what do people mean when they talk about diaphragmatic breathing? They want you to divert your breath more towards your abdomen than up higher in your chest.

Place your hand on your breastbone or sternum, the bone right in the middle of your chest. Follow the sternum down toward your belly button. When you reach the end of the bone, push a little as your fingers depress into a cavity within your abdomen. Place your hand across this area. Breathe and see if you can make your hand rise and fall. If you cannot, try this exercise. Blow out all of your air as though you are blowing out birthday candles. Exhale all the way past REL until you have nothing left to exhale, the point of residual volume. Stop, then release, and do not control your inhale. Let your body reflexively inhale. Your inhale should move the area where your hand rests on your abdomen. This type of breathing is said to be "diaphragmatic." The origin of the name probably comes from the fact that your diaphragm is located in this area. Because of the location some people also call it abdominal breathing.

Now try this. Inhale. As your belly rises, push your belly against your hand. When you reach the end of your inhale, hold your belly in that position as you exhale. What you should notice while you do this exercise is that your abdominal muscles hold your belly in that position while your diaphragm goes back to its resting position during your exhale. This abdominal activity is called checking action. The muscles of inhalation check the action of your exhalation so that gravity and recoil do not overrun the exhale as they do during quiet respiration (see the companion website for examples).

What you can take from this discussion is that the phrase "sing, speak, or breathe from your diaphragm" is not accurate and does not really make a lot of sense. Again, all breath is diaphragmatic, because you use your diaphragm during every inhalation. When using your inspiratory muscles to check the reflexive action of your exhalation, your exhalation is slower than your resting exhalation. This action allows you more time in the breath cycle for the exhalation. You do probably have conscious control of your diaphragm during this checking action, though there is limited research on the active, voluntary control we have of the diaphragm. What is known is that during conscious breathing, you do have some control of your diaphragm. When you exhale for speaking and singing, you do have some control of your diaphragm to slow its movement to its resting position, just as you have control of your abdominal, neck, chest, and rib muscles.

During speaking and singing, all inspiratory muscles are more important for exhalation than inhalation. Their action is primarily reflexive for the inhalation when speaking and singing. The act of taking a bigger breath and pushing out your abdominal muscles into a "diaphragmatic or abdominal breath" does not constitute more dependence on the diaphragm. In addition, this type of breath can actually be counterproductive to extended voicing in song or speech (Titze, 2004).

Try this exercise. Take a big, deep breath. You should notice that at the height of your inhale, you held your breath. When you take a deep breath your vocal folds' reaction is to close and hold the air inside the lungs. If you try to talk on that deep breath without exhaling a little before speaking, you notice that the voice sounds slightly pressed and strained. Your chest also feels pressure because you are trying to hold back all that air while speaking. So, a big breath is not usually a good idea; there is too much pressure on the vocal folds, as well as the lungs.

Some people still believe that you need a big breath to sustain voicing for long phrases. The fact is, we breathe in many different ways for different situations and different respiratory, developmental, and vocal demands. There are times you may need a bigger breath, but on the whole your smaller inhalation is going to be more efficient for vocal fold vibration.

Now if someone says "sing from your diaphragm" to indicate that the diaphragm supports or anchors the body during speaking or singing, then the person is no longer talking about the breath. Although the diaphragm has only been shown to contract and possibly support the body during breath holding (Kolář et al., 2009), it is possible that the diaphragm provides some support to the body during speaking and singing. It is more likely, though, that the diaphragm is not so much the primary muscle of support as it is an accessory muscle that works with the intercostal muscles and muscles of the back, chest, and neck to aid in supporting the body.

How do we reconcile all of this new information about the breath? We stop focusing so much on breath. We acknowledge that breath provides power for voicing, but it is not the only means to achieve a powerful voice. Actually, breath is not necessarily the preferred or most efficient way to increase vocal intensity or loudness (Titze, 2004; Titze, 2006). When you increase the velocity of air by pushing air to get louder, you cause increased pressure on the vocal folds. That action decreases their efficiency.

Consider this example. After blowing up a balloon, it is always fun to pull on the sides of the spout to create silly noises as the air exits the balloon. By stretching and loosening the spout, air vibrates the ends of the balloon and the sound changes. Pull the ends of the spout tight and far apart; the sound goes up in pitch to a high squeak. Release tension, and the pitch goes down making a low flapping noise. You do not really worry about how full the balloon is with air. You are more concerned with how the air is "valved" at that spout to make variations in the sound created. Forcing more air out of the balloon by squeezing it does not seem necessary.

If we apply this example to the lungs and vocal folds, the body of the balloon representing the lungs and the spout representing the vocal folds, you can appreciate the relationship between air and pressure. We need to focus more on how the vocal folds valve the air during speaking and singing, and how the vocal folds interact with the vocal tract during voicing (Titze, 2006; Titze, 2008). We will talk about power, loudness, and intensity in the next sections.

## Breath Cycle

During quiet respiration your inhalations are approximately 50% of your breath cycle, and your exhalations encompass the other 50% of the cycle. When speaking and singing, your vocal folds valve the air when they vibrate adjusting those percentages to about 10% to 20% of your cycle for the inhalation and 80% to 90% of the cycle for your exhalation (see Figure 2–5). Notice that the circle is the same as quiet respiration; it is just the percentage of the circle that occupies your exhalation over your inhalation for speaking and singing. You can learn to stay within the cycle of breath by learning to speak or sing within breath cycle.

Here is an exercise to learn to stay within your breath cycle during speaking. Remember that REL (the end of your tidal volume exhale) is at the top of the circle. You need to stay within your breath cycle and not pass REL during your exhale. As you acquire more training, you will learn to compensate for extended speaking and singing that is needed past REL. You will also learn how to stay within breath cycle without people knowing that you are taking a breath. For now, we will learn to stay within breath cycle. Place your finger on the point labeled A in Figure 2–6.

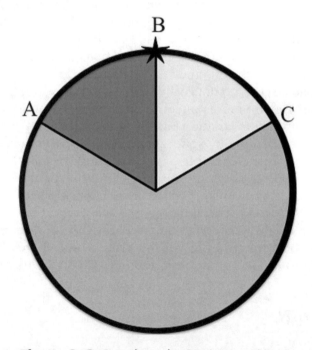

***Figure 2–6.*** Breath cycle. Begin at point **A**, exhale quickly to point **B** (REL), slurp in air quickly to point **C**, count "one . . . two." Repeat. Refer to the associated text for more detailed instructions.

As you move your finger from point A to point B, you are going to exhale quickly, as though you are blowing out a match. Notice that this quick exhale takes you to REL. Again, exhale quickly, blow out the match, then release, and your breath will recoil back in. This time, exhale quickly, moving your finger from A to B, and stop. From point B to C you are going to quickly slurp in, drawing air in past the sides of your tongue between your tongue and cheeks. Keep your tongue high in an /i/ (ee) position during your slurp. Try that a sequence a few times. Exhale quickly as though blowing out a match while simultaneously moving your finger from point A to B. Slurp in (keep your tongue in an /i/ (ee) position) as you move your finger from point B to C.

When you think you have the sequence down, you will add this next step. From point C back to point A you will start counting by twos. Point A, exhale quickly as though blowing out a match to point B. Slurp in, maintaining a high tongue position as though you are saying /i/ (ee), from point B to point C. Count 1 . . . 2 from point C back to point A. Repeat. Exhale quickly, slurp in, count 3 . . . 4. Exhale quickly, slurp in, count 5 . . . 6, and so on. Your own respiratory rate will determine the speed at which you move through the breath cycle.

What you will notice as you do this exercise is that you never exhale past REL and you never take a breath higher than your resting inhalation. If you do take a bigger breath, exhale quickly as though you are blowing out a match, slurp in, and get back on breath cycle. The reason you exhale quickly is that, when you start counting, your vocal folds valve the air and you will have air left to exhale. Remember that you can speak on 80% of your cycle, so by only counting by two, you will still have air left to exhale. Exhaling quickly, as though you are blowing out a match, gets you to REL so you can begin the cycle again. Often a quick exhale is all you will need to get back on breath cycle.

What happens if, instead of counting by two, you count to 30 from C back to A, all on one breath, and at the same rate of speech you were using previously? You should notice that you will probably not be able to count all the way to 30. You go past REL and pressure builds within your chest as you approach residual volume. When you release, you end up taking a big breath and your breathing pattern gets discoordinated off breath cycle. You may also feel out of breath. Exhale quickly, slurp in, and see how you can get back on breath cycle.

Training yourself to not take a big breath when you speak or sing takes time, effort, and practice. As you learn more about how the voice works, you will add on to this basic understanding of the breath. For now, practice counting by twos in breath cycle. Move up to saying the days of the week and then short functional phrases like "How are you?" and "Goodnight." Always remember to exhale first. Often that exhale is one of the most important things you will do.

## Phonation: "The Source of Sound"

As air travels up from your lungs through your trachea, it can either pass through open vocal folds as it does during breathing or it can get caught beneath the vocal folds. If you keep the vocal folds closed, you are holding your breath. If your intent is to make sound, your muscular contraction releases at the level of your vocal folds enough for the pressure to overcome the closure and blow your vocal folds apart. If you maintain a difference in pressure above and below your vocal folds, they will continue to oscillate. This oscillation is called phonation and is the process of making sound via vocal fold vibration.

All vocal fold vibration sounds the same. It is a buzz, like flapping your lips in a lip trill without using your voice or blowing through the mouthpiece of a trumpet without the rest of the instrument attached. Several muscles contract to adduct or close the vocal folds capturing the air below the closed vocal folds. As the air accumulates, pressure begins to build below the folds creating a mismatch between the pressure above and the pressure below. Eventually, the pressure below the vocal folds becomes greater than the pressure above and blows the folds apart, starting from their bottommost edge and working up. As the vocal folds reach their maximum point of displacement apart from one another, their elastic properties, as well as some aerodynamic principles, act to bring the vocal folds back together. This is one cycle of vibration and can take even less than 1/100th of a second (Figure 2–7).

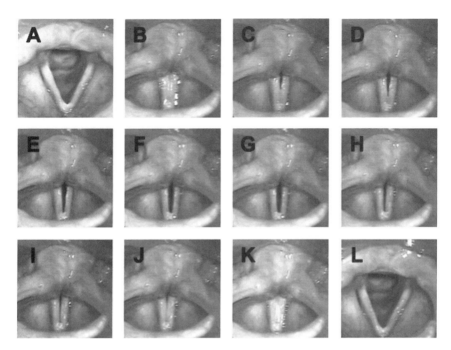

***Figure 2–7.*** Vocal fold vibration. **A.** The vocal folds begin in an abducted position. **B.** Once vibration is initiated, the vocal folds close and pressure builds up beneath the vocal folds. **C–F.** Subglottic pressure becomes greater than atmospheric pressure, blowing the vocal folds apart. **G–K.** The elastic properties of the vocal folds, as well as the quick passage of air through the vocal folds, bring them back together. This sequence is one cycle of vibration and can take less than 1/100th of a second. **B–K.** The cycle repeats. **L.** The vocal folds abduct for you to take a breath. Continuous vibration is called phonation.

## Laryngeal Anatomy

### Cartilages

Four cartilages (Figure 2–8) comprise the voice box or larynx (pronounced, LAR-inks not LAR-niks). They are the cricoid, thyroid, arytenoids, and epiglottis. The cricoid cartilage is a signet-shaped structure that rests on top of, and is distinct from, the uppermost

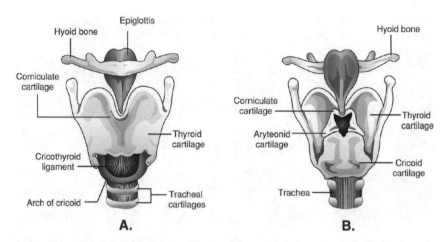

**Figure 2–8.** Anterior (**A**) and posterior (**B**) views of the larynx. There are three main cartilages of the larynx: the thyroid, cricoid, and arytenoid cartilages. Adapted with permission from *The Larynx: A Multidisciplinary Approach* (2nd ed., p. 36) by M. P. Fried. Copyright 1996 by Mosby.

cartilage of the trachea. The thyroid is a paired cartilage fused at the midline that sits directly above the cricoid. Not to be confused with the thyroid gland that sits posterior to it, the thyroid cartilage is the largest structure in the larynx and contains a distinctive prominence on the anterior portion called the thyroid notch or Adam's apple. Males usually have a more noticeable thyroid notch than females because the two halves of the thyroid cartilage meet at a sharper angle. The name thyroid is derived from the Greek word that means "shield-like," which is fitting because this cartilage houses and protects the vocal folds. The thyroarytenoid is the muscle of the vocal folds. This muscle stretches from the anterior (front) portion of the thyroid cartilage to a pair of cartilages found in the posterior (back) part of the larynx called the arytenoids.

Attached to the anterior portion of the larynx and the base of the tongue is an elastic cartilage called the epiglottis. This cartilage acts as a flap to protect the vocal folds during swallowing so that food and liquid are diverted posteriorly to the esophagus (food tube to your stomach) and not into your lungs. When food is said to "go down the wrong tube," it means it found its way past the epiglottis and into the vocal folds. In healthy individuals, that misdirected bolus of food does not usually enter the "wrong tube" or airway because the vocal folds are very sensitive. Coughing or choking is the vocal folds' way of protecting the airway and most times is successful in clearing whatever comes in contact with them.

The epiglottis attaches to the arytenoid cartilages via paired folds of tissue called the aryepiglottic folds. During swallowing, your epiglottis reacts reflexively to protect your airway. You do have voluntary control of the epiglottis during a swallow. The area above your vocal folds is called your supraglottis and contains the epilarynx or aryepiglottic sphincter. Drawing the epiglottis back toward the arytenoids narrows the epilaryngeal space and facilitates vocal fold vibration (Döllinger, Berry, & Montequin, 2006; Titze, 2001; Yanagisawa, Estill, Kmucha, & Leder, 1989). We will discuss this action more in the section on resonation.

## Muscles

There are three sets of muscles that are important to laryngeal function: the intrinsic laryngeal muscles (vocal fold movement), the suprahyoid muscles (larynx raising movement), and the infrahyoid muscles (larynx lowering movement). The suprahyoids and the infrahyoids are part of a group of muscles commonly called extrinsic laryngeal muscles or strap muscles.

You have five intrinsic laryngeal muscles that work together to control and modulate vocal fold movement (Figure 2–9).

1. The thyroarytenoid (TA) muscle is the fan-shaped muscle of the vocal folds and gatekeeper valve to your trachea or airway. It is a paired muscle that runs from the anterior (front) of the thyroid cartilage and inserts into the vocal process of the arytenoids in the posterior (back) part of the larynx. The space between this muscle pair is called the glottis. TA is considered to have two bellies, thyrovocalis (medial, closer to the glottis) and thyromuscularis (lateral). The primary function of the TA muscle is to adduct or close the vocal folds and maintain closure at the midpoint of the vocal folds during vibration. Increasing activation of TA will help to maintain vocal fold closure, especially at higher pitches to decrease breathiness (Chhetri, Neubaer, & Berry, 2012; Chhetri, Neubauer, Sofer, & Berry, 2014; Hirano, Ohala, & Vennard, 1969).

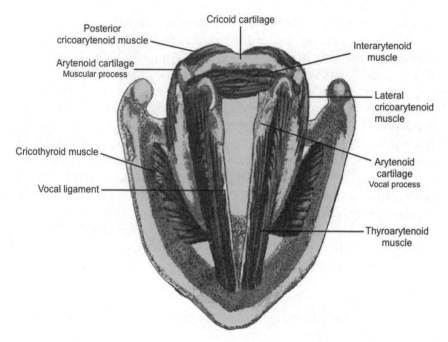

**Figure 2–9.** Superior view of the intrinsic laryngeal muscles.

2. The lateral cricoarytenoid (LCA) muscle is a paired muscle that runs from the cricoid cartilage to the muscular process of the arytenoids. LCA is a vocal fold adductor.

3. The interarytenoid (IA) is a large muscle in the posterior part of the larynx that runs from one arytenoid cartilage to the other. IA is a vocal fold adductor with similarities in muscle composition to skeletal muscle, indicating that it may play a role in maintaining vocal fold position during phonation (Tellis, Rosen, Thedki, & Sciote, 2004). LCA and IA work together to close the posterior glottis during vocal fold vibration (Chhetri et al., 2012).

4. The cricothyroid (CT) is the primary vocal fold tensor that works antagonistic to adductor muscles, TA, LCA, and IA. CT is located in the outside, anterior portion of the larynx and runs from the cricoid cartilage to the thyroid cartilage. When it contracts it pulls the thyroid cartilage forward and stretches the vocal folds, increasing pitch. Of course, CT function cannot be that simple. Results of recent research show that CT contraction

without strong contraction from the adductor muscles actually decreases pitch (Chhetri et al., 2014). We will talk about the implications of this research in later sections.

5. The posterior cricoarytenoid (PCA) is the sole vocal fold abductor and works primarily to open the vocal folds for breathing. The PCA is a paired muscle situated in the outside, posterior portion of the larynx and courses from the cricoarytenoid lamina up to the muscular process of the arytenoids. Some fibers of the PCA course obliquely to the apex of the arytenoid. Contraction of these fibers may indicate involvement of the PCA in positioning and supporting the vocal folds for extended phonation (Hillel, 2001).

Say and hold out the sound /i/ (ee) for three seconds and then breathe. You just activated your TA, LCA, and IA when you said /i/ and then contracted your PCA to take your breath. This time, sing /i/ on any note then slide up to a higher pitch. Now you activated TA, LCA, IA, and then CT. Sing /i/ on any note, slide up to a higher pitch, and then make your voice louder. This time you activated TA, LCA, IA, then CT, and then added more contraction to TA (and probably LCA and IA as well). It is quite likely that you even had some added contraction from PCA, too, but not for abduction until you took a breath. Sing /i/ on any note and then slide to a lower pitch. In this exercise you contracted TA, LCA, and IA, and then activated TA to lower the pitch. If you whimpered while you lowered your pitch, then you activated TA, LCA, and IA to close your vocal folds, and then you released some contraction of those muscles while you contracted CT. If you did the last exercise, whimpered, and got louder, then you probably activated all the muscles at once.

Strap muscles (Figure 2–10) are muscles external to the larynx that have connections with other structures outside the main cartilages of the larynx. These muscles may or may not directly have a connection to the laryngeal cartilages, but do influence their movement in some way. The sternocleidomastoid (SCM) is a strap muscle most people have heard of because it is the largest muscle of your neck. Turn your head to left. You should be able to feel the muscle on the right side of your neck; it runs from just behind your ear all the way down the side of your neck to your collarbone. SCM supports your head on your spinal cord, but can also be used to stabilize the larynx during speaking and singing.

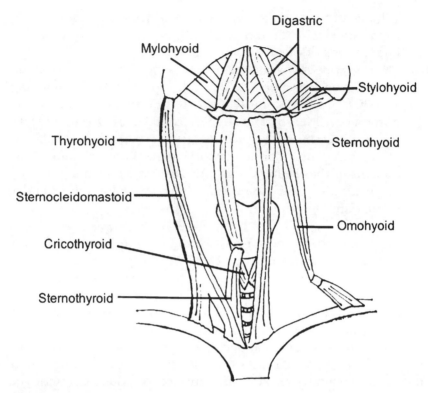

*Figure 2-10.* Strap muscles. Anterior view of the strap muscles or extrinsic laryngeal muscles.

The other strap muscles can be characterized as either laryngeal elevators, called suprahyoids, or laryngeal depressors, called infrahyoids. The main biological function of these muscles is to aid in swallowing. Suprahyoids have their origins on the mandible (jaw) and other processes of the skull. These muscles course downward and insert into different parts of the hyoid bone. This bone is positioned just below the jaw, and is connected by muscles to the larynx. A little tidbit of information is the hyoid is the only free floating bone in your body. When the suprahyoids contract, they pull up on the hyoid thus raising the larynx, moving the larynx forward, and causing the epiglottis to fold over sealing the airway and diverting food and liquid into the esophagus during the swallow.

The infrahyoids pull down on the larynx. Most of their origin points are the sternum (breastbone), clavicle (collarbone), and scapula (shoulder bone). The thyrohyoid is the only infrahyoid with an origin on the thyroid cartilage and insertion to the hyoid bone. The other infrahyoid muscles insert to the thyroid cartilage or hyoid bone. We will talk about the suprahyoid and infrahyoid contribution to voice in the section on resonation.

Place your fingers on your mandible where your jawbone meets in the center under your chin. Push up into the floor of your mouth as you move you fingers back toward your spine. Try not to talk or swallow during this exercise. The first hard structure you meet as you move your fingers back is your hyoid bone. Place your index finger and thumb on each side of your hyoid bone and feel around to get acquainted. Come back to the midpoint of your hyoid bone and move down about a finger-width or less. Your finger should be resting on your thyroid notch. Place your index finger on either side of your thyroid cartilage. If you squeeze the two flat sides of your thyroid cartilage together and say /i/ at the same time you should hear a change in your voice. Your voice changes because you pushed the vocal folds together manually while making sound. Come back to the midline of your thyroid cartilage and move your finger down slightly. You should feel a small space between your thyroid cartilage and the small, thin side of your cricoid cartilage beneath it. Remember, the larger, flat, signet-shaped surface of the cricoid is in the back of the larynx. Below your cricoid cartilage is your trachea. You can move your fingers up and down its bumpy edges.

Place your fingers lightly across your larynx. Swallow and feel your larynx rise up. You should also feel it push out a little against your fingers. As soon as it reaches the height of the swallow, you will feel your larynx fall to its resting position. Get to know your larynx. Notice how tight or loose the muscles are, see if you can move your larynx around in your neck, feel it rise and fall when you swallow, and pay attention to what it does when you speak and sing. Your intrinsic and extrinsic laryngeal muscles control all this movement.

## Nerves

The cranial nerve X is also called the tenth cranial nerve, CN X, and the Vagus nerve. This is one nerve you will not want to forget. The Vagus nerve courses from the brainstem to the periphery and provides motor information to the larynx, as well as sensory information from the larynx to the brain. This exchange of information tells the larynx when and how to move as well as getting information to the brain about what the larynx is feeling. Both right and left Vagus nerves exit the skull base and descend, giving rise to two primary laryngeal nerves, the recurrent laryngeal nerve (RLN) and the superior laryngeal nerve (SLN). There are other branches of the Vagus nerve (auricular nerve, pharyngeal nerve), but we will focus on the laryngeal nerve branches.

***Recurrent Laryngeal Nerve.*** An efferent nerve (motor nerve) to the intrinsic laryngeal muscles, the right and left RLN branches of the Vagus nerve course differently through the body. As these branches split from the Vagus nerve, the right branch diverts straight upward from the aortic arch of the heart into the right side of the larynx as the left branch descends and loops under the aortic arch and up toward the left side of the larynx. Because of its course and increased length, the left RLN is susceptible to injury. Each RLN branch has two subdivisions, the posterior branch and the anterior branch. The posterior branch innervates the posterior cricoarytenoid muscle. There are two subdivisions of the anterior branch. One is called the proximal division that innervates the lateral cricoarytenoid and interarytenoid muscles, and the other is the distal branch that innervates the thyroarytenoid muscle (Figure 2–11).

Because the RLN provides motor information to the intrinsic laryngeal muscles, damage to this nerve will result in a vocal fold weakness or paralysis, observed as impaired movement or complete immobility of one or both vocal folds during adduction (closure) and abduction (opening). Usually damage to the nerve occurs before the anterior and posterior branch divisions, meaning that it will affect both adduction and abduction. In this case, if all neural input is lost to the intrinsic laryngeal muscles at this level, the vocal fold will be rendered completely immobile. If damage results in a paralysis or complete immobility, the vocal fold can be halted in the spectrum anywhere from opened to closed. Individuals with a paralyzed vocal fold in a closed position will have more difficulty breathing than phonating because the vocal fold is in the airway. As the paralyzed vocal fold position moves more laterally away from the glottis, in a more abducted position, individuals will have

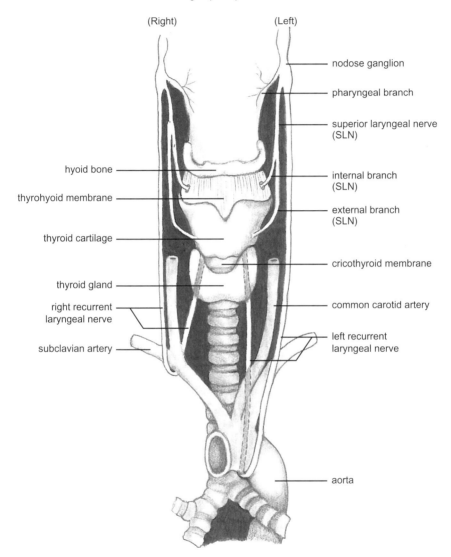

Vagus (CN X) Nerve

(Right)        (Left)

nodose ganglion

pharyngeal branch

superior laryngeal nerve
(SLN)

hyoid bone

internal branch
(SLN)

thyrohyoid membrane

external branch
(SLN)

thyroid cartilage

cricothyroid membrane

thyroid gland

common carotid artery

right recurrent
laryngeal nerve

left recurrent
laryngeal nerve

subclavian artery

aorta

**Figure 2–11.** Vagus (cranial nerve X). The Vagus provides motor information to the larynx, as well as sensory information from the larynx to the brain. Reproduced with permission from *Clinical Voice Pathology: Theory and Management* (5th ed., p. 43) by J. C. Stemple, N. Roy, & B. K. Klaben. Copyright 2014 by Plural Publishing, Inc.

more difficulty with vocal fold vibration and swallowing because the vocal folds do not close completely. Some possible causes of nerve damage are tumor, stroke, virus, surgeries to the head, neck, or chest, and intubation.

***Superior Laryngeal Nerve.*** The superior laryngeal nerve (SLN) is the other laryngeal branch of the Vagus nerve and provides both efferent (motor) and afferent (sensory) information to the larynx. Both right and left SLN originate from the Vagus at the level of the first two cervical vertebrae and have two subdivisions. The internal SLN sends sensory information from the internal larynx, including the superior surface of the vocal folds and the epiglottis (Kiray, Naderi, Ergur, & Korman, 2006), to the brain. This nerve branch possibly provides sensory and motor innervation to the interarytenoid muscle (Sanders & Mu, 1998). Damage to the internal branch could lead to loss of a cough reflex for airway protection.

The external branch of the SLN provides motor information to the cricothyroid muscle. More research is needed, but one study has identified sensory fibers to cricothyroid, as well as other intrinsic laryngeal muscles (Friedman, LoSavio, & Ibrahim, 2002). Damage to the external branch of the SLN will result in a weakness or inability to tense the vocal folds and change pitch, especially an increase in pitch.

### Vocal Fold Anatomy

You have read the term vocal folds many times already and may be wondering if they are the same as the "vocal cords," the structures within the voice box that make sound. Yes, they are, and in the voice science world we call them vocal folds. They are layered folds of tissue about the size of your thumbnail that vibrate together in a wave-like motion. You can think of the vocal folds as being comprised of a cover and a body (Hirano, 1974), but we are going to be a bit more technical than that. The body or innermost layer of the vocal folds is a paired muscle called the thyroarytenoid muscle or vocalis. Contraction of this muscle without antagonistic contraction of other intrinsic laryngeal muscles will shorten the muscle, release tension on the vocal ligament, and bulk up the cover of the vocal fold.

The cover of the vocal folds is composed of four main layers (Figure 2–12). From the most outermost edge of the vocal fold (the part you can see) to the deep region (before the thyroarytenoid muscle) are the epithelium, superficial lamina propria, intermediate lamina propria, and deep lamina propria (Hirano, 1974). You will also learn about the basement membrane zone and the vocal ligament.

Working in from the outermost layer is the epithelium, the most superficial layer of the vocal folds. The epithelium is covered in mucosa and is a very thin layer at approximately 0.05 to 0.10 mm thick. This layer helps to keep vocal fold shape and regulates vocal fold hydration. The concept of hydration will be detailed later when we discuss vocal care and vocal hygiene. The next area is called the basement membrane zone (BMZ) (Gray, Pignatari, & Harding, 1994). The BMZ is susceptible to injury due to its positioning and is often the site for benign vocal fold lesions like nodules. The BMZ secures the epithelium to the next layer called the superficial lamina propria.

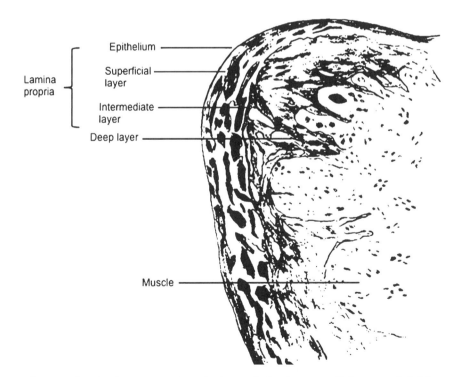

*Figure 2–12.* Cross-sectional view of the layers of the vocal folds.

The superficial lamina propria or Reinke's space is 0.5 mm thick toward the midsection of the vocal fold (Hirano, 1974). It is gelatinous, loose, and pliable, making it ideal for vibration. A disorder created by an unusually thick fluid build up in the superficial lamina propria is called Reinke's edema. A common source of this type of edema (swelling) is exposure to the toxins in cigarette smoke. The vocal folds become big and stiff, limiting the vibratory capacity of the vocal folds and giving rise to the characteristically husky "smoker's voice."

The intermediate lamina propria is about 1 mm thick and contains elastic fibers. Hirano (1974) said this layer was like "soft rubber bands." Consisting primarily of collagenous fibers and likened to a "bundle of cotton thread," the deep lamina propria is the most durable of all the layers. The intermediate and deep lamina propria layers (about 2 mm thick) comprise the vocal ligament, a band of tissue used to position the vocal folds and support vocal fold vibration at high pitches (Hirano, 1975; Titze & Hunter, 2004; van den Berg, 1958).

## Vocal Fold Biomechanics

Your vocal folds serve five primary physiological functions; we call them the five Ps: pulmonary function, pushing, pulling, protection, and phonation. All five are important to know about and understand to be fully knowledgeable about how these tiny folds of tissue work.

### Biological Function

Although this book is about the sound your voice makes and how it can be used to convey your message, your vocal folds' most important life-sustaining, biological functions are for pulmonary utility, pushing, pulling, and protection. We have mentioned many of these purposes in the previous section in this chapter, but they merit further discussion.

***Pulmonary Function.*** Your vocal folds sit on top of your trachea or airway. They are the gatekeeper valve to let air in and out of the lungs during respiration or breathing. In an abducted (open) position, the posterior cricoarytenoid contracts to pull the arytenoid cartilages apart and away from the midline of the glottis (Figure 2–13). If you watch the vocal folds during quiet breathing, you will notice some baseline movement following your inhalations and exhalations. Your vocal folds should, however, stay primarily in their abducted position while breathing (see Figure 2–13).

Some people experience intermittent adduction or closing of the vocal folds during breathing. Often misdiagnosed as asthma, this voice disorder is what pulmonologists (breathing doctors) call vocal cord dysfunction (VCD), what is known in the voice world as paradoxical vocal fold motion disorder (PVFMD) (Altman, Mirza, Ruiz, & Sataloff, 2000; Campainha, Ribeiro, Guimarães, & Lima, 2012; Ibrahim, Gheriani, Almohamed, & Raza, 2007). In either case, the vocal folds, which should stay open during breathing, reflexively close causing shortness of breath, tension in the throat and chest, chronic cough, voice changes, and sometimes laryngeal spasms. Respiratory retraining and patterned breathing exercises with voice therapy by a speech-language pathologist often are extremely helpful in management of this disorder (Al-Awan & Kaminsky, 2012).

When you hold your breath, typically it is assumed that your vocal folds adduct or close. Adduction occurs when the thyroarytenoid, lateral cricoarytenoid, and interarytenoids contract to draw

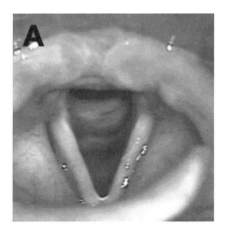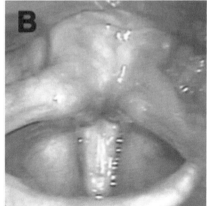

***Figure 2–13.*** **A.** Abducted vocal folds. **B.** Adducted vocal folds. Vocal folds are abducted during breathing and adducted during swallowing and phonation.

the arytenoid cartilages together completely to the midline of the glottis, trapping the air beneath them.

Try this exercise. Say "Ah" without any voice, just as you would after taking a long drink of cold lemonade on a hot day. Put extra emphasis on the first sound; this is called a glottal pulse or stroke. Repeat the whispered "Ah" sound quickly five times in succession and feel the sensation of the glottal pulse in your throat. Remember, do not add your voice. On your sixth trial, go to make the sound, but do not release. Let the pressure build up in your throat. In this posture, you are closing your vocal folds to hold your breath. Release when you are ready and try again until you can feel the closure at the level of your vocal folds.

Breath holding, however, can be accomplished without closing your vocal folds. Actually only about half of the people tested in one study closed their vocal folds when asked to perform relaxed breath-holding (Mendelsohn & Martin, 1993). Results of another study reported that when participants were asked to voluntarily hold their breath without further instruction, only 17% of participants achieved full vocal fold closure; however, that number rose considerably when subjects were told to "hold your breath hard" (Martin, Logemann, Shaker, & Dodds, 1993).

During speech you incidentally hold your breath without closing your vocal folds while making the sounds /p/, /t/, and /k/. Try this exercise. Start to say the word "pop," but do not release the first /p/ sound. Let the pressure build at your lips and the back of your mouth until airflow is at a standstill. In this posture, you are, in essence, holding your breath without bringing your vocal folds together in an adducted position. Now, release the pressure at your lips. You should feel airflow out your mouth without a glottal effort in your throat. Remember not to use your voice. Repeat a few times and concentrate on the flow of air past your vocal folds during the release.

While air is stopped at closed lips for the /p/ sound, the /k/ sound as in "key" is produced by placing the back of the tongue high against your velum (soft palate) and stopping the flow of air at that point. The sound /t/ in "tea" falls to the same fate, but your breath is now held where the tip of your tongue meets your alveolar ridge, which is the place on the roof of your mouth directly behind your front teeth. Try making these three sounds, build pressure at their respective constriction points (lips, alveolar ridge, velum), stop airflow, and hold your breath. Stopping the flow of air is important. You want to make sure you do not allow air to exit through your nose while making these voiceless sounds.

What happens if you force your vocal folds closed? Try this exercise. Hold your tongue while saying /k/ but do not release the air. Build up pressure at that point in the back of your mouth called your velum. Now bear down and hold your breath hard. Feel the pressure build deep in your throat. You should also begin to feel your throat constrict and close and your stomach muscles tighten. You have strongly closed your vocal folds to hold your breath. Now, drop your tongue and release muscular effort. Air should flow quickly and forcefully out your mouth. Repeat this exercise. Remember not to use your voice.

Repeat the beginning of the previous exercise. Hold your tongue to your velum while saying /k/ and build pressure at that point in your mouth. Without releasing air through your mouth or nose, raise your eyebrows, feel your velum rise. Reapply light tongue pressure to your velum, as you consciously start the onset or beginning of a yawn. Feel your throat open all the way to your vocal folds. Do not bear down or tense your stomach muscles. Release your tongue into a /k/ sound. You should notice that you had more control of the force the air was released at the constriction point between your tongue and velum than you did in the previous exercise. Practice until you can sense open movement in your throat all the way to your vocal folds. Then, practice the same exercise with /t/ and /p/. All of these activities should be done without voice.

There are reasons to build up pressure at your lips, alveolar ridge, and velum to open your pharynx and reduce pressure at the level of your vocal folds when speaking and singing, but we will get into that later the book. Right now, we are still talking about holding your breath, although you should start to see the transfer of this biological function to other tasks.

***Pushing and Pulling.*** Two of the five Ps make up another biological function of the vocal folds: pushing and pulling. Just as in breath holding, the vocal folds adduct and build up pressure beneath them to generate force for physical activities like bearing down, heavy lifting, as well as others. Actually, the grunt you may make when lifting a heavy object or when rising from a seated position is made by your vocal folds (Figure 2–14). This maneuver

**Figure 2–14.** Valsalva maneuver scenario. During moments of pushing, pulling, or heavy lifting, such as during a game of tug-of-war, the vocal folds close and build up pressure to help generate force to complete these activities. Adapted with permission from *Clipart Of LLC* by R. Leishman. Copyright Clipart Of LLC.

is a called a Valsalva, a strong exhale against closed vocal folds. The Valsalva maneuver is used in swallowing therapy to forcibly close the vocal folds to decrease the risk of food or liquid entering the lungs during the swallow.

For weight lifters this maneuver should only be used for high exertion efforts of short duration. When performing repetitive, low intensity lifts like bicep curls and stomach crunches, individuals should be instructed to breathe. If you hold your breath during these exercises, blood pressure can rise to dangerous levels causing blood vessels to burst and the risk of fainting to increase.

Individuals with vocal fold closure issues—like vocal fold paralysis, paresis, and atrophy—often have difficulty generating the force needed to perform activities like walking up steps, lifting a mattress to make a bed, and moving heavy objects: They cannot engage the Valsalva maneuver. Learning to hold their breath by blocking the air with the back of their tongue in a /k/ sound may help to support these individuals during such activities. If they need to perform repetitive, low intensity lifts, then using the muscles of the chest, back, or abdomen while exhaling will help to facilitate the lift.

You should avoid using vocal fold adduction exercises like pushing and pulling with individuals who have trouble achieving appropriate vocal fold closure for voicing because of the risk of strain and inefficient effort they place on the vocal fold valve. These exercises also lack any treatment efficacy data to support their use in voice therapy. Vocal folds that do not close completely during vibration will only have more air escape between them as you bear down and force air into the system. Remember, this is what happened in the exercise in the last section. If the vocal folds cannot valve air efficiently, you should not add more air. You achieve vocal fold closure first by teaching clients how to close their vocal folds without bearing down, pushing, or pulling. Exercises like the glottal pulse exercise in the last section may be an option to try.

***Protection.*** Another biological function of the vocal folds is airway protection. You do not want anything but air to go into your lungs. In healthy individuals, your body will work hard to make sure to protect the lungs and keep them safe. One important layer of protection is the vocal folds. Not to be a myth buster, but the hot tea and honey, the tablespoons of olive oil, the lozenges, numbing sprays, and other "remedies" of the sort used to soothe the voice do not ever touch your vocal folds. If they did, you would cough uncontrollably and probably end up irritating the vocal folds more. They do coat, numb, and potentially soothe the throat (or pharynx). You might then release muscle strain and, in turn, perhaps achieve better vocal fold closure for voicing. The effect, however, is only temporary unless you learn better vocal technique. Before ingesting herbal or alternative remedies for the voice, identify possible pharmacological negative side effects.

Besides the vocal folds, there are two other layers of closure in the larynx used to provide protection to the lungs. They are the vestibular or "false" vocal folds and the epiglottis. The vocal folds, false vocal folds, and epiglottis work seamlessly together to valve, close, and protect the airway every time you swallow. In a typical swallow the vocal folds close, then the false vocal folds close, and finally the epiglottis folds over to secure the protection of the airway. As you can see in Figure 2–15, the vocal folds are sometimes called "true vocal folds" to distinguish them from the false vocal folds. Typically, though, when people say "vocal folds" they mean the true ones. Directly above your true vocal folds, in the supraglottic

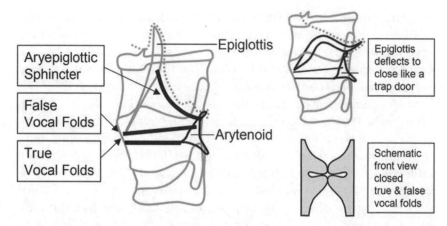

**Figure 2-15.** Three layers of laryngeal protection. The true vocal folds and false vocal folds close and the epiglottis flips down to protect the trachea (airway). Reproduced with permission from *The Estill Voice Training System Level One: Compulsory Figures for Voice Control* (p. 14) by M. M. Klimek, K. Obert, & K. Steinhauer. Copyright 2005 by Estill Voice Training Systems International, LLC.

space called the vestibule, are paired tissue called the "vestibular" folds or false vocal folds. They are called "false" because they look like the true variety but are not.

## Phonation

The final physiologic function of the vocal folds, and the final "P," is phonation or vocal fold vibration. Phonation is not necessarily a biological function at all. It is a voluntary, conscious, learned, motor behavior used mostly for speech and singing. Flap your lips as though you are making a lip trill but do not add sound. This voiceless lip trill is the closest external example to how your vocal folds vibrate inside your larynx. Your lips close lightly and, as you begin to exhale, air gets trapped behind them. You purse your lips to generate pressure until the pressure is so great that it is expelled between your lips and out your mouth. If you keep the correct balance of airflow and pressure, your lips continue to flap until you open your mouth to take a breath. As your lips part, the vibration stops. Close your lips, start your lip trill, open your mouth, and your trill stops.

During vocal fold vibration your vocal folds do the same thing your lips do when they trill. You exhale a little. Your intrinsic laryngeal muscles contract and close your vocal folds by bringing the arytenoid cartilages together. You continue to exhale and air gets trapped beneath the vocal folds. Pressure begins to build. The pressure below your vocal folds is called subglottic pressure. Once that pressure is greater than the pressure above the vocal folds, the vocal folds blow apart and air is expelled in tiny puffs. During vibration, the arytenoids stay together as your vocal folds go through a vibratory cycle from closed phase to open phase.

Just as you breathe in a cycle, so is there a cycle for vocal fold vibration. Depending on the type of sound you want, your vocal folds stay open for part of the cycle and remain closed for part of the cycle. The pressure builds during the closed phase and is released during the open phase. Do not confuse the closed phase of vibration with vocal fold closure for phonation. Once the vocal folds close (arytenoids pulled into an adducted position), the vocal folds can start vibrating (Figure 2–16). The vocal folds stop vibrating when the arytenoids part and you take a breath, as you do when opening your mouth after the lip trill.

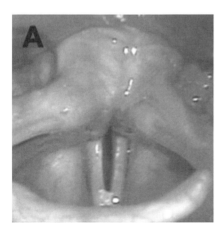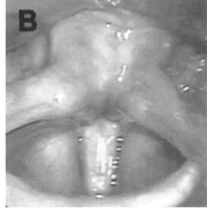

***Figure 2–16.*** Phases of vocal fold vibration. Phases of vibration are moments in time where the vocal folds are open (**A**) and closed (**B**) during phonation. These phases are different from abduction and adduction of the vocal folds, which refer to arytenoid movement that opens and closes the vocal folds (see Figure 2–13).

The myoelastic aerodynamic theory of voice production is one of the longest-standing theories of voice production and includes discussion of a linear, single-mass model of vocal fold vibration (van den Berg, 1958). "Myo" indicates the muscular forces of the intrinsic laryngeal muscles that act to bring the vocal folds together via arytenoid adduction. "Elastic" is a property of the vocal folds that allows for their movement when blown apart and their return back together during vibration. "Aerodynamic" is the airflow and pressure needed to facilitate and continue vibration. The Bernoulli effect is one of the primary physical principles that is assumed to maintain vocal fold vibration in this theory.

When you blow air across a piece of tissue paper, the paper starts to move up and down. When your leg gets too close to the shower curtain, the curtain gets sucked against your leg. When you drive a smaller car past a truck on a highway, the car gets pulled closer to the truck. All of these are examples of the Bernoulli effect: As air passes through a narrowed constriction created by two masses, the velocity of the air increases, causing a negative pressure that brings the two masses together. The vocal folds are the two masses in this theory that, once blown apart, come back together due to an increase in the velocity of airflow that passes through them during the open phase of vibration. The vocal folds are each considered a unitary, vibrating mass in this single-mass model (Flanagan & Landgraf, 1968).

In the early 1990s Story and Titze (1995), departing from the traditional theory, proposed a three-mass model that takes into account the body-cover theory by Hirano (1974). In this model, the body (thyroarytenoid muscle) is one mass, and the upper and lower portions of the vocal fold cover are the other two masses. The vocal folds do not blow apart and come back together in only a lateral, horizontal motion; rather, the vocal folds have three vibratory actions or undulations when transitioning through the closed and open phases of vibration:

- Horizontal (medial to lateral, middle to side)
- Longitudinal (posterior to anterior, back to front like a zipper)
- Vertical (inferior to superior, bottom to top)

These undulations of vibration are called the mucosal wave.

The myoelastic aerodynamic theory of voice production is described by a linear source-filter theory (Fant, 1960), which assumes no interaction between the "source" of sound (vocal folds) and the "filter" (vocal tract). The nonlinear source-filter theory of voice production is a more current theoretical model that takes into account the body-cover influence on vocal fold vibration (mucosal wave) and adds interaction and influence of an acoustical filter (vocal tract) to the facilitation of vocal fold oscillation (Titze, 2008). Although the myoelastic aerodynamic theory is still taught in many speech-language pathology programs, the nonlinear source-filter theory of voice production is more accurate and relevant to current thinking in voice science (Figure 2–17). We will address influence of the vocal tract on voice in the next section on resonance.

***Voiced and Voiceless Sounds.*** Try this exercise. Place your fingers across your larynx and say the sound /s/ as in "snake." Hold out the /s/ sound. You should hear the air travel past your tongue and out your mouth but you should not feel any sensation on your fingers. Now hold out the /z/ sound, as in "zebra." This time, you should feel a buzz or vibration on your fingers. As you switch back and forth from saying the /s/ sound to the /z/ sound, you should notice the sensation comes and goes. What you are feeling is vocal fold vibration or what can be called your "motor." You can also try this exercise with /f/ and /v/. In these examples, the /s/ and /f/ sounds are called voiceless sounds because their sound is not made through vocal fold vibration. The /z/ and /v/ sounds are called voiced sounds because they are produced by the addition of vocal fold vibration or voicing.

When you say the phrase, "We mow our lawn all year," all the sounds you say are voiced. Feel your larynx while you repeat the phrase. Now if you say the phrase, "Sing Sophia a song," you should notice that some sounds are voiced and some are voiceless. Can you pick out the voiceless sounds? That is right, the /s/ and the /f/ sounds in "sing," "Sophia," and "song" are voiceless. Your vocal folds are the sound generator for your voice or what we call the source of sound.

***Pitch or Frequency.*** When phonating your vocal folds open and close once to complete one cycle of vibration. The number of cycles per second that your vocal folds vibrate is called frequency.

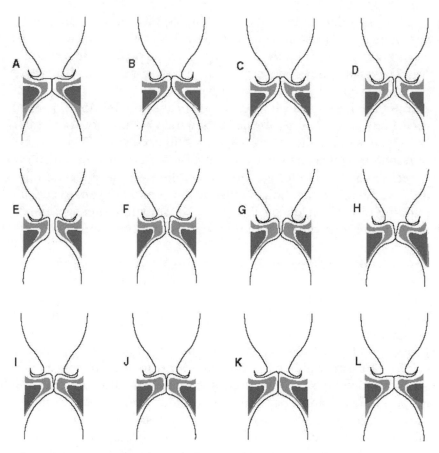

***Figure 2–17.*** Coronal view of vocal fold vibration. The general pattern of vocal fold vibratory motion is represented in this schematic. Once vocal fold vibration begins (**A–E**), the vocal folds blow open from bottom to top, then come back together (**F–L**). This vibratory pattern continues during phonation. Reproduced with permission from *Speech and Voice Science* (p. 145) by A. Behrman. Copyright 2007 by Plural Publishing, Inc.

Frequency is measured in hertz (Hz). The perceptual correlate of frequency is pitch, the tone of your voice. A pure tone such as one created by a tuning fork has the same number of cycles per second every second (100 Hz is 100 Hz always). A complex periodic sound wave, such as the one created by the human vocal folds, has many different frequencies (pure tones) combined together (e.g., 100 Hz, 200 Hz, 300 Hz). These frequencies are called harmonics or overtones.

The lowest frequency in a complex wave (100 Hz in this example) is called the fundamental frequency (F0). During continuous speech, the average fundamental frequency is called the speaking fundamental frequency. The average speaking fundamental frequency for an adult male is around 100 Hz; for an adult female, 200 Hz; and for children, 300 Hz.

There are different ways to change vocal pitch. As you learned previously, contraction of the cricothyroid muscle is a primary method used to alter pitch. When this muscle contracts, it rocks the thyroid cartilage forward and stretches the vocal folds. With complimentary tensing of the vocal folds via the thyroarytenoid and other intrinsic laryngeal muscles, the result is often an increase in the frequency (cycles per second) of vocal fold vibration—more vibratory cycles per second equals a higher perceived pitch. Releasing contraction of the cricothyroid muscle will reduce the stretch of the vocal folds and lessen the tension, thus lowering the frequency of vibration and the perception of pitch (Figure 2–18).

Let us go back to your lip trills. Listen to the sound of your lips flapping as air passes through them during the trill. Remember not to add your voice. When you are ready, purse your lips tighter. Listen to the sound change. Then, release tension at your lips and notice the difference in the sound. When you purse your lips, tension increases, your lips increase the number of times they flap a second, and the pitch goes higher. As you release tension, your lips flap fewer times a second, and the pitch goes lower. Continue practicing moving from higher to lower pitches during your lip trill by increasing and releasing tension at your lips.

Stop trilling your lips and now use your voice. On the vowel /i/ (ee), glide up to your highest pitch, like the high notes on a piano, and then glide all the way down to your lowest pitch. When you do this exercise, you should notice that you sound like a siren on a fire truck or ambulance. As your pitch rises, frequency increases as your vocal folds stretch and tension increases. As your pitch lowers, frequency lowers as tension is released and your vocal folds shorten. Continue practicing these pitch glides to increase vocal fold flexibility.

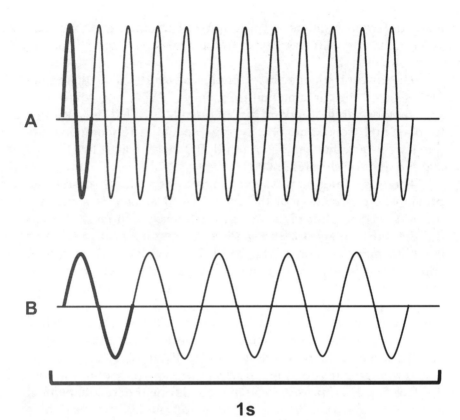

**1s**

*Figure 2–18.* Frequency of vocal fold vibration. **A.** An increase in frequency (more cycles of vibration per second) results in a higher-pitched voice. **B.** A lower frequency (fewer cycles of vibration per second) results in a lower-pitched voice. The frequency of vocal fold vibration is measured in cycles per second or Hertz (Hz). One cycle per second is differentiated by a darkened line in waveforms.

*Loudness or Intensity.* Intensity level is another dynamic of phonation and is related to the amplitude of vocal fold excursion during vibration—how far the vocal folds blow apart during vibration. The further the vocal folds are blown apart, the more intense the sound; the less they are blown apart, the less intense the sound. As you probably guessed, the perceptual correlate of vocal intensity is loudness.

Intensity level is a quantifiable, objective measure while loudness is subjective. What one person hears as loud may not be what another perceives as loud. Age is definitely a factor in the perception of loudness. You and your grandfather will not perceive sounds with the same intensity level as having the same loudness level. Sounds with the same intensity level but different frequencies may also be perceived as being louder than others. The human ear hears the frequencies between 1000 and 5000 Hz very well. If presented with a 20,000 Hz tone at the same intensity level as a 2000 Hz tone, individuals will hear the 2000 Hz tone as louder than the 20,000 Hz tone. Distance from the source of sound is also a factor in loudness. Sounds lose intensity as they move further from the source. Usually, though, the higher the intensity level, the louder the sound; the lower the intensity level, the quieter the sound.

Sometimes "volume" is used as a term for vocal intensity, referring to what your TV remote does to control the loudness level— higher volume, louder sound. In voice science we do not usually use this term because its physical property is different from intensity level, but now you know what someone means when they say "volume," "intensity," "amplitude," or "loudness."

As stated, intensity level is a function of the amplitude of vocal fold vibration—how long your vocal folds stay closed during a cycle of vibration, how much pressure is built up under your closed folds during each vibration, how many molecules are moved by your vocal folds' vibrations, and how much respiratory effort you are providing during vocal fold vibration. Because we want to avoid an increase in respiratory effort to make the voice louder, we will primarily rely on increasing or decreasing the closed phase of vibration at the vocal fold level to adjust vocal intensity.

There are four basic vocal fold closure patterns in healthful voicing (Klimek, Obert, & Steinhauer, 2005a) that are consistent with the body-cover theory mentioned in a previous section (Hirano, 1974; Titze, 1988). Thick true vocal fold closure is closest to what is considered modal speech or chest voice in singing. This closure pattern has a longer closed phase of vibration than open phase, the mucosal wave is larger, and the amplitude of vibration is bigger. Perceptually, a thick closure pattern is loud and clear. If you increase tension on the true vocal fold cover, decrease the mucosal wave, and make the open and closed phases of vibration almost equal, you end up with a thin closure pattern. Thin closure is still clear but is much quieter than thick. This closure pattern is synonymous with head voice in singing.

By further increasing vocal fold tension and slightly separating the posterior part of the vocal folds near the arytenoids, you make the vocal folds stay open during vibration, allowing a constant flow of air during voicing. This closure pattern is called stiff and is perceived as breathy and quiet. Singers will relate this closure pattern to falsetto or loft voice. The last closure pattern is called slack and is used in producing glottal fry or creak. The closed phase of vibration is much longer than the open phase, but the unique, inconsistent vibratory pattern of slack makes it perceptually quieter than thick.

In these past sections, you learned about two dynamics of voice, pitch and loudness. In the following chapters, you will learn how to create meaning by using these dynamics—how to start and stop sound to change meaning, how loudness influences the emotion you want to evoke in your listener, and how pitch portrays confidence, timidity, or assuredness. There is one other vocal dynamic that we have not discussed much yet and that is vocal quality. This dynamic is often influenced by vocal fold closure pattern, but vocal quality also relies on vocal tract configurations. The next section is the last of the coordinative structures for voice. We call this coordinative structure resonation, the manipulations of your vocal tract that influence speech and vocal quality.

## Resonation: "The Filter"

The last coordinative structure of voicing is called resonation. On the same pitch, say the vowels, /i/ (ee), /a/ (ah), /u/ (oo). Listen for the difference in sound. If you do not change your pitch, the difference you perceive is not a result of a change to the rate of vocal fold vibration; the difference is due to manipulations you make primarily to your tongue and lips as you change vowel sound. Your tongue rises in the back and your lips spread into a smile to say /i/. Your tongue drops a bit and your lips round to create the /u/ sound. These manipulations are made to the vocal tract or filter; you are changing your resonance pattern to create these different vowel sounds.

Now maintaining the vowel sound /i/, raise and lower your pitch (Figure 2–19).

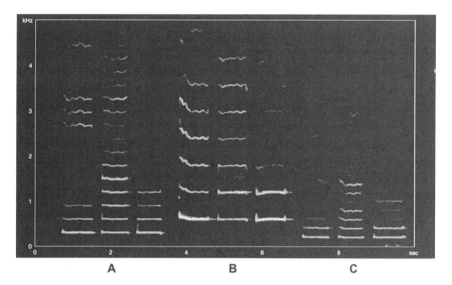

***Figure 2–19.*** Narrowband spectrogram of /i, a, u/ at different pitches. **A.** Frequency display for /i, a, u/ at a conversational pitch. **B.** Frequency display for /i, a, u/ at a high pitch. Notice that fundamental frequency (F0), denoted by the bottom-most line on the spectrogram, increases. **C.** Frequency display for /i, a, u/ at a low pitch. Notice that F0 decreases.

You should not hear much of a difference in vowel sound from pitch to pitch—/i/ still sounds like /i/ at higher and lower pitches. The vocal mechanism is a dynamic and interconnected system, but there are certain primary functions of the vocal folds that are somewhat independent from the vocal tract, although some would say that there is always an effect of one on the other. Pitch comes from the source; it is the rate at which vocal folds vibrate per second, their frequency of vibration. When you change pitch in this exercise, you are changing the source without necessarily changing the filter. Try this exercise. Sing "Twinkle, Twinkle Little Star" but sing the song on the vowel sound /i/ and not the words. This is an example of changing your source, your pitch, without modifying the filter too much.

When you add back in the words to the song, you are changing your source (pitch) and your filter (resonation). There are primary vocal tract functions that do not necessarily influence vocal fold vibration or, at least, the frequency of vibration. Vowel production is driven by the vocal tract or filter, particularly the tongue and lips. If you say /i/ and then drop your tongue to the bottom of your mouth, the sound will change from /i/ to something resembling /ɪ/ as in "it." Now say /i/ and then purse your lips, listen to the way the sound changes. These are vocal tract or resonance manipulations. Most of our speech sounds are created with these types of vocal tract manipulations. Say /m, n, k, d, p, l, r/ and pay particular attention to how your tongue and lips move to create these sounds.

Vocal tracts come in different sizes and shapes; no two vocal tracts are the same. Generally, though, males have longer and larger vocal tracts, measuring about 17.5 cm in length, compared to females at 15 cm. Children and infants have the smallest and shortest vocal tracts measuring approximately 9 cm, almost half that of the female vocal tract.

You should be beginning to recognize that the there are certain distinctions you can make between the source and the filter. For typical human voicing, the vocal folds are the vibratory source, the buzz, or the source of sound energy of the voice. If listening to just the vocal folds, the buzzing sounds are very similar from person to person. This similar sounding buzz can be compared to blowing into the mouthpiece of a trumpet without the rest of the instrument attached or trilling your lips as you have done in previous exercises.

A resonator is something that is forced into vibration by another vibratory source. It is not the source of sound, but it does modify the sound made by the source. In typical human voicing, the resonator is the vocal tract. It is what gives you your unique voice, just like putting the rest of the trumpet back on the mouthpiece. There are certain frequencies or harmonics that come from the source that resonate better than others in certain vocal tracts. These are called resonant frequencies or formant frequencies.

Longer and larger vocal tracts will resonate lower frequencies better than high frequencies. The reverse is true for shorter vocal tracts where higher frequencies find their home. As long as the source is vibrating at a consistent frequency, all the same frequencies will enter the vocal tract. Some of these frequencies will resonate or be admitted better depending on the length and shape of the filter.

Listen to a violin. If you pluck the strings on the violin when not attached to the violin, you will hear the buzzing vibration of the string. When you attach the strings to the violin and pluck the string again, you now hear the characteristic sound of the violin. The strings are the source of sound and the air filled chamber of the violin body is the resonator. If you do the same to a larger string instrument like the cello, you notice that the tone is warmer and mellower—this tone occurs because the lower frequencies of the string resonate better in the body of the cello than the high frequencies you hear resonating from the violin body. A double bass will resonate even lower frequencies than the cello (Figure 2–20).

Your vocal tract is similar to the bodies of these string instruments. It is an air-filled chamber that is open at one end (the nose and mouth) and closed at the other (down below the vocal folds).

**Figure 2–20.** Resonance. Smaller cavities, such as a violin or a child's vocal tract, resonate higher frequencies better. Larger cavities, like a double bass or a man's vocal tract, resonate lower frequencies better. Adapted with permission from *Principles of Voice Production* (p. 186) by I. R. Titze. Copyright 1994 by Prentice-Hall.

The difference is that the vocal tract is a modifiable chamber or what is called a variable resonator. Whereas the violin has a defined shape, size, and length, vocal tracts can change to create different shapes, sizes, and lengths.

Variations in vertical laryngeal position will change the way your voice sounds (Klimek et al., 2005a; Sundberg & Nordström, 1976; Titze, 1993). You can make your voice sound like a violin by raising your larynx and spreading your lips—higher frequencies resonate better in this shorter vocal tract. You can change the sound by dropping your larynx or pursing your lips—now your voice sounds warmer and mellower like the cello because lower frequencies resonate better in this vocal tract configuration. Say /i/, /a/, and /u/ again and listen now to the difference in sound. Consider the varying nature of the vocal tract—how your tongue moves in your mouth and how your lips change to make these vowels.

### Vocal Tract Anatomy

You can think of the human vocal tract like the letter "F." The stem of the "F" depicts the bottom of the vocal tract at the level of the vocal folds up to the top part of the throat. The horizontal lines of the "F" show how the vocal tract continues out the mouth and nose (Figure 2–21).

There are movable structures and nonmovable structures along the length of the vocal tract that work together to resonate and produce different sounds for speech or song (Table 2–1).

Because many of these structures are used to produce speech sounds, articulation is sometimes considered a fourth coordinative structure. Articulation is a fourth coordinative structure for speech; in voice production, however, there are only three coordinative structures that we will focus on: respiration, phonation, and resonation (power, source, and filter).

Some of the movable structures valve the air as it moves throughout the vocal tract to change the sound of the voice. The sections below will focus on some of the more important valves for voicing. To learn more about all the component parts of the vocal tract and how they can be manipulated to create different sounds, you can refer to Estill Voice International™ (Klimek et al., 2005a, Klimek et al., 2005b).

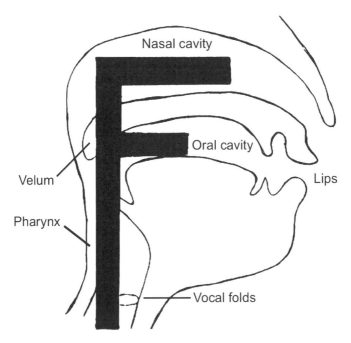

**Figure 2–21.** Vocal tract. The vocal tract is shaped similarly to the letter "F." The tube running from the level of the vocal folds to the throat resembles the stem of the "F"; the nasal and oral cavities resemble the horizontal lines of the "F."

**Table 2-1.** Movable and Nonmovable Structures of the Vocal Tract

| Movable Structures | Nonmovable Structures |
|---|---|
| Lips | Cheeks |
| Tongue | Teeth |
| Velum (soft palate) | Mucous in nasal cavity and sinuses |
| Faucial pillars | Palatine tonsils |
| Pharynx | Adenoids |
| Aryepiglottic sphincter | Epiglottis |

## False Vocal Folds

The false vocal folds occupy the space in the vocal tract directly above or superior to the true vocal folds. In the section on phonation, you learned that the false vocal folds are important for airway protection during the swallow. You also have voluntary control of false vocal fold movement during voicing (Klimek et al., 2005a). Try this exercise. Grunt as you do when you bear down to pick up something heavy. The straining sound you make while grunting includes constriction at the level of the false vocal folds.

You can learn to modify the false vocal fold valve to move it from a constricted position to a more retracted position by increasing the width of the supraglottic space. Because false vocal fold constriction is a main component in the perception of vocal strain, it is important to learn to control valving at this level. Bear down again and hold out /i/, then release while continuing to say /i/. Notice the distinct change in sound (Figure 2–22).

You should also recognize a release in pressure at the level of your true vocal folds. By constricting the false vocal folds while talking and singing, you are limiting the vibratory capacity of the vocal fold cover because the false vocal folds create a backpressure against the true vocal folds. By releasing the constriction and

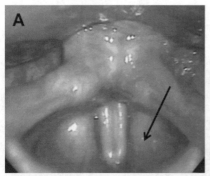 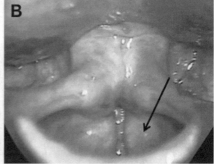

*Figure 2–22.* False vocal folds or vestibular folds. **A.** The false vocal folds in a mid position during voicing. **B.** The false vocal folds in a constricted position during voicing. The false vocal folds are the folds of tissue above the true vocal folds and provide protection for the airway during a swallow. Constricting the false vocal folds during phonation causes backpressure on the vocal folds and limits vibratory motion.

drawing the false vocal folds out of the way, airflow is not restricted and the true vocal folds are able to move more freely. For many years, voice teachers when training singers have used open throat posturing and false vocal fold abduction such as the one used in this example.

**Epilaryngeal or Aryepiglottic Sphincter Narrowing**

A little further in the larynx, just superior to the false vocal folds, is the next valve—the epilarynx or what some refer to as the ary-epiglottic sphincter (Figure 2–23). Similar to the valving that happens during a swallow, the epiglottis is drawn posteriorly toward the arytenoid cartilages, narrowing the epilaryngeal space but not constricting the false vocal folds. Yangisawa and colleagues (1989)

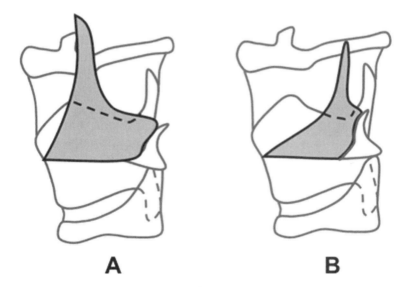

**A**         **B**

***Figure 2–23.*** Aryepiglottic folds (AES) or epilarynx in wide (**A**) and narrow (**B**) positions. The AES or epilarynx is the tube formed above the vocal folds by the aryepiglottic folds. Narrowing of this tube—moving the epiglottis moving toward the arytenoids—makes the voice sound clear, bright, and twangy. Reproduced with permission from *The Estill Voice Training System Level One: Compulsory Figures for Voice Control* (p. 87) by M. M. Klimek, K. Obert, & K. Steinhauer. Copyright 2005 by Estill Voice Training Systems International, LLC.

used fiberoptic imaging and determined that aryepiglottic sphincter narrowing was a defining characteristic of the vocal quality called twang. Many researchers have investigated the production (Titze, Bergan, Hunter, & Story, 2003; Yanagisawa et al., 1989), perception (Sundberg, 2005; Titze, 2001; Yanagisawa et al., 1989), and use of twang in both singing (Sundberg & Thalen, 2010) and voice therapy (Lombard & Steinhauer, 2007; Titze, 2001). See Lott (2014) for a comprehensive review of twang.

Often called the singer's formant, epilaryngeal narrowing results in an increase in spectral energy between 2800 and 4300 Hz, correlating to the resonant frequency of another air-filled acoustic resonator in your body called the external auditory meatus or ear canal. In essence, when you narrow your epilarynx you are making your listener's ears ring. This narrowing results in a tube within a tube effect (epilarynx within the pharynx or throat), creating an inertive vocal tract, sustaining vocal fold vibration, and increasing the closed phase of vibration (Titze, 2001).

People usually perceive twang as loud (Lott, 2014), although loudness is not always the prominent perceptual feature. Twang is also characterized as bright and clear. Generally, the smaller the epilaryngeal space the brighter the perceived sound (Titze & Story, 1997). In voice clients with inefficient vocal fold closure, adding epilaryngeal narrowing to a person's voice results in a return to their "typical" sounding voice. You can learn to adjust the amount of epilaryngeal narrowing in your voice to satisfy different vocal needs.

There are many facilitators that can be used to achieve epilaryngeal narrowing. Attempting to imitate any of the following characters will get you close to the twang quality: Fran Drescher, SpongeBob, and Curly from The Three Stooges. Other facilitators you can try are making a teasing sound like "nyeah, nyeah, nyeah," imitating a bagpipe or an electric guitar, and quacking like a duck. Many people confuse twang quality with nasality. There is a definite distinction that needs to be made between twang and nasality that you will learn below in the section on velum.

### Pharynx

The pharynx comprises most of the vocal tract and is often colloquially called the throat. You can divide the pharynx into three sections. The area closest to the vocal folds is called the laryngopharynx. The area in the back of the mouth is the oropharynx, and the area in the posterior part of the nasal passage is the nasopharynx. A series of pharyngeal constrictor muscles comprise the pharynx, making it ideal for food and liquid transfer during swallowing. Another biomechanical property of the pharynx is conduction and diversion of air into and out of the lungs during breathing (Figure 2–24).

When you have a sore throat, you have pharyngitis or a swelling in your throat. Pharyngitis can make swallowing painful. You can have laryngitis (swelling of your vocal folds) along with pharyngitis. Your voice will sound hoarse when you have laryngitis. Remember that the throat lozenges you take for your sore throat coat, numb, and soothe your pharynx, not your vocal folds. Rest and hydration are probably the best remedies for laryngitis. If hoarseness persists longer than three weeks or worsens in intensity, then it is time to see the doctor.

For speakers and singers, the pharynx plays an important role in the quality of the sound. Good vocal sound has mainly been attributed to openness in the throat (Bartholomew, 1934; Titze, 1998). Debate does exist on terminology and technique related to how to achieve "openness" during singing and speaking (Mitchell,

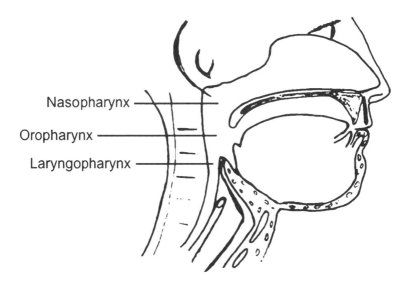

*Figure 2–24.* Divisions of the pharynx.

Kenny, Ryan, & Davis, 2003). Some use inhalation examples: "retracted breathing," "smell a bouquet of flowers," "inhale and act surprised." Many achieve open posturing of the pharynx by yawning, lowering the larynx, or feeling as though there is a bubble in your throat. You already learned that retracting or opening the false vocal folds can also give you the feeling of an open throat.

Because you are dealing with a dynamic system, openness in the throat during speaking and singing is probably a combination of actions associated with many anatomical parts in the vocal tract including the false vocal folds, pharynx, and velum (soft palate), as well as the extrinsic and intrinsic laryngeal muscles and the muscles of the tongue. Head and neck anchoring (Klimek et al., 2005a) is a method used to engage all of these muscles.

Try this exercise. Exhale and sustain the vowel /i/. Continue saying /i/ as you inhale and bring air back into your lungs. Yes, it should feel strange. You will be inhaling and phonating at the same time, which is counterintuitive to typical voicing. Phonation usually occurs on your exhale. Do not gasp the air in, try to make the same sound on your inhale as you do on your exhale. Keep your tongue high in the /i/ position to maintain space in the mid to lower part of your pharynx. Lifting up your eyebrows should also help to create space. If you are doing this exercise correctly you should feel a muscle pull in the middle of the back of your head at the base of your skull, where your neck meets your skull. When you get good, try to raise and lower your pitch while doing the inhaled phonation. Keep practicing. You should begin to feel your pharynx widen, your soft palate rise, and your false vocal folds retract on your exhaled phonation.

### Velum

Put your tongue up to the roof of your mouth. You should feel a flat, bony structure. This is your hard palate. If you slide your tongue back along your hard palate, you will transition to a squishy structure. This is your soft palate or velum. Your velum ends in a rounded point called the uvula. Yes, the thing that dangles in the back of your mouth. The velum is another valve in your vocal mechanism and is located at the top of the vocal tract.

The main biomechanical purpose of the velum is to rise and tense during chewing and swallowing so food and liquid pass through the pharynx and into the esophagus, not up into the nasal cavity. There are two main muscles used to raise and tense the velum: levator veli palatini (raise) and tensor veli palatine (tense). The area between the velum and the pharynx is a sphincter called the velopharyngeal port. For speech, the velum works with the pharyngeal constrictor muscles in the nasopharynx to determine whether sound energy is directed mainly into the nasal cavity, into both the nasal and oral cavities, or only into the oral cavity.

Say the sounds /m/ as in "mom," /n/ as in "none," and /ŋ/ as in the end of the word "sing." Hold out any of those sounds and then plug your nose. What you should notice is that the sound stops when you plug your nose. Try it for each of the sounds. These are the nasal sounds in the English language. The reason they are called nasals is because the sound energy used to make these sounds resides exclusively in the nasal cavity. The velum is in a low position and the velopharyngeal port is open to make these sounds.

Now say /i/ again. If you plug your nose when you say /i/, you should still continue to make the sound. If you cover your mouth while saying /i/, you should be able to stop the sound. You can continue to push the sound out of your mouth if you tried, but for the most part the sound should stop. All vowels are called oral sounds because the sound energy is transmitted strictly through the mouth. The velum is raised and tensed, and the velopharyngeal port is closed to make these sounds. Go back and forth from /ŋ/ to /i/ while you quickly plug and unplug your nose. You should feel the sound energy enter your nose (for /ŋ/) and leave your nose (for /i/).

You can also maintain a velar posture that is somewhere in the middle of raised and lowered; some of the sound energy will go through the nose while some simultaneously goes through the mouth. When oral sounds are constantly produced with sound energy in the nose, it is called nasality. Say the phrase "mon ami" with your best French accent. What you should notice is that the vowels contain some of the nasal sound of the surrounding /m/ and /n/ sounds.

Say /i/ and hold your nose. Make sure all the sound is coming through your mouth. Your velum is raised in this production. Now add some of the /ŋ/ sound into the /i/ sound without going all the way to /ŋ/. Check your nose. If you plug your nose and feel sound energy in your nose but the sound does not stop, then you are doing this mid posture correctly. Now say /ŋ/ without any /i/ sound present. Plug your nose and make sure all the /ŋ/ sound stops. If the sound stops, then you know that you have succeeded in completely lowering your velum and blocking sound energy from entering your oral cavity. To reduce nasality in your voice, you will want to gain more strength and control of the muscles of the velum. Sometimes nasality is a function of an accent or dialect (Figure 2–25).

If air is constantly diverted up to the nasal cavity during speech due to velar or pharyngeal weakness or a cleft palate, then it is called hypernasality. If you say, "Nine new neckties" and you notice air leakage out the nose on the /k/ and the /z/, there may be an issue with hypernasality. A trip to the ENT may be warranted. If you say the same phrase and have sound energy in your nose during the end of the word "neckties," your velum stays in a mid velar position for speech. Again, this is not a disorder; it may just be a dialectal variation. Most nasalization of vowels in American English happens when the vowel is adjacent to a nasal sound, like the /o/ in "mom." If you find that you nasalize the sounds further from the vowel, try holding out the last vowel sound in "neckties" and plug your nose. Try to raise your velum until there is no sound energy in your nose (you feel no vibration in your nose). You have succeeded in creating an all-oral sound.

Singers sometimes drop their velar position from primarily raised to mid when singing up a scale from lower to higher pitches, or when singing high pitches compared to lower ones. Sound energy diminishes at those higher pitches because some of the energy is diverted into the nose and gets damped (or lessened) by the structures in the nasal cavity. Training singers to have more control of their velar position during singing is important to assure that singers have the ability to maximize sound output, especially when wanted (because it is called for in the song) or required (because of the singing environment).

Nasality should not be confused as epilaryngeal narrowing. The twang quality can be made in all velar positions. Twang is twang and nasality is nasality. Practice narrowing your epilarynx and then changing the position of your velum as you did in the exercise above. You will see that the two are separate. Fran Dre-

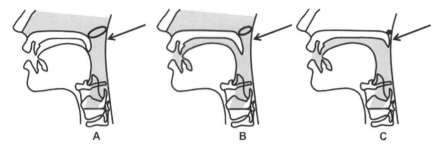

*Figure 2–25.* Velar positions. **A.** When the velum is low, the velopharyngeal port is open, creating nasal resonance for sounds /m, n, ŋ/. **B.** When the velum is in a mid position, the velopharyngeal port is partially open, allowing both nasal and oral resonance. **C.** When the velum is high, the velopharyngeal port is closed, sealing off the nasal cavity and allowing only oral resonance. Adapted with permission from *The Estill Voice Training System Level One: Compulsory Figures for Voice Control* (p. 72) by M. M. Klimek, K. Obert, & K. Steinhauer. Copyright 2005 by Estill Voice Training Systems International, LLC.

scher's voice is a good example of twang quality with nasality. Most British speakers do not have any twang quality in their voices, though some accents do have nasality.

Now that you have learned about the anatomy and physiology of the vocal mechanism, the following chapters will apply this information to voice production and communication.

## Review of Key Ideas

- Voice is a vital component of communication and is often defined in many different ways.
- The tiny folds of tissue that vibrate to create sound are called vocal folds and are housed within the larynx or voice box.
- Voice production relies on a dynamic system of anatomic and physiologic structures, meaning that multiple structures interact and are coordinated with each other to create sound.
- The three coordinative structures for voice production are respiration, phonation, and resonation.

- The vocal mechanism can be compared to a system of pipes and valves. The trachea and vocal tract can be likened to different pipes, whereas your vocal folds and articulators can be associated with valves.
- The first of three coordinative structures for voice production is respiration and is the source of power for initiating and sustaining voicing.
- Quiet respiration is the pattern of breathing that exists unconsciously as you are inhaling and exhaling at rest. In quiet respiration, the inhale and exhale each take up approximately 50% of the cycle of breathing.
- Your body is capable of taking in a bigger breath than you do during quiet respiration. This bigger breath is called inspiratory capacity.
- You can never exhale all the air from your lungs; if you did they would collapse. The air that is always left in your lungs after a maximal exhale is called residual volume.
- The natural pause that occurs between a tidal exhale and a tidal inhale is called resting expiratory level (REL).
- The primary muscle of respiration is the diaphragm. The diaphragm contracts and pulls down during inhalation to create more space in the thorax for the lungs to fill with air. During exhalation, the diaphragm relaxes to its resting position.
- You do not have much volitional control of your diaphragm.
- "Diaphragmatic breathing" is somewhat redundant, as you use your diaphragm every time you breathe.
- The idea that a big breath helps to better sustain extended voicing in speech or song is actually counterproductive; taking in an excess of air builds up too much pressure behind the vocal folds and within the lungs, creating a strained, less efficient voice.
- When speaking or singing, your vocal folds valve air to adjust the 50/50 pattern of breathing in quiet respiration. This adjustment allows for 10% to 20% of the cycle for inhalation and 80% to 90% of the cycle for exhalation.
- Developing a breath cycle that follows the 20/80 pattern of breathing ensures that you will not speak past REL. Always begin speaking or singing with an exhale (that takes you to REL), followed by a small intake of air.

- The second coordinative structure for voice production is phonation or the source of sound.
- The vocal folds adduct and valve air beneath them, thus building air pressure. When the air pressure below the vocal folds becomes greater than the air pressure above, the vocal folds are blown apart and set into vibration. Vocal fold vibration is referred to as phonation.
- Vocal fold vibration can be compared to a voiceless lip trill or the buzz that is created when you blow through the mouthpiece of a trumpet without the rest of the instrument attached. All vocal fold vibration sounds the same.
- The larynx is composed of four main cartilages: the thyroid, cricoid, arytenoids, and epiglottis.
- The vocal folds stretch from the thyroid cartilage in the anterior portion of the larynx to the paired arytenoid cartilages in the posterior portion of the larynx.
- The epiglottis is a cartilaginous flap that is vital for protection of the vocal folds and airway during a swallow.
- There are three categories of muscles that are important to laryngeal function: intrinsic laryngeal muscles, suprahyoid muscles, and infrahyoid muscles.
- There are five intrinsic laryngeal muscles: thyroarytenoid (TA), lateral cricoarytenoid (LCA), interarytenoid (IA), cricothyroid (CT), and posterior cricoarytenoid (PCA).
- TA is the muscle of the vocal folds and is divided into two bellies: thyrovocalis and thyromuscularis. It functions to adduct the vocal folds and maintain appropriate medial closure during phonation.
- LCA and IA are both vocal fold adductors.
- CT is the primary tensor of the vocal folds, aiding in adduction and enabling pitch change.
- PCA is the sole abductor of the vocal folds and is important for opening the vocal folds to allow respiration to occur.
- Suprahyoid muscles elevate the larynx, whereas infrahyoid muscles depress the larynx.
- The most important nerve that innervates the larynx is cranial nerve X (CN X) or the Vagus nerve. The Vagus descends from the brainstem and splits into two primary laryngeal nerves: the recurrent laryngeal nerve (RLN) and the superior laryngeal nerve (SLN).

- RLN transmits efferent (motor) information from the brain to the larynx. RLN and its various subdivisions innervate PCA, LCA, IA, and TA.
- SLN transmits efferent and afferent (sensory) information to and from the larynx. Its internal branch is responsible for transmitting afferent information from the internal larynx to the brain, whereas the external branch innervates CT and is vital for pitch change.
- The vocal folds are composed of multiple layers. These layers, from outermost to innermost, are as follows: epithelium, basement membrane zone (BMZ), superficial lamina propria, intermediate lamina propria, deep lamina propria, thyroarytenoid.
- The vocal folds are responsible for the five Ps or five primary physiological functions: pulmonary function, pushing, pulling, protection, and phonation.
- One of the longest standing theories of voice production is called the myoelastic aerodynamic theory. "Myo-" refers to the muscular forces involved in vocal fold adduction; "elastic" refers to the property of the vocal folds that allow for vibratory movement; "aerodynamic" refers to the balance of airflow and pressure needed to sustain vocal fold vibration.
- One main component of myoelastic aerodynamic theory is the Bernoulli effect. This states that as air passes through a point of constriction (e.g., the glottis), velocity of airflow increases, creating a negative pressure that draws two masses (e.g., the vocal folds) together.
- During vocal fold vibration, the vocal folds transition between open and closed phases with three different types of movement: horizontal (medial to lateral), longitudinal (posterior to anterior), and vertical (inferior to superior).
- The most current theoretical model for voice production is the nonlinear source-filter theory. This model assumes interaction between the source (vocal fold vibration) and the filter (vocal tract).
- Both voiced and voiceless sounds are used in speech; the vocal folds are vibrating when producing voiced sounds, such as /z/ and /d/, while the vocal folds are abducted when producing voiceless sounds, such as /s/ and /t/.

- Frequency is defined as the number of times your vocal folds vibrate each second and is measured in Hertz (Hz). The perceptual correlate of frequency is pitch.
- The lowest frequency in a complex wave (e.g., the human voice) is called the fundamental frequency (F0).
- Intensity level or amplitude is defined as how far the vocal folds blow apart during a vibratory cycle. The perceptual correlate of amplitude is loudness.
- Increasing the closed phase of vibration results in a larger displacement amplitude of the vocal folds, thus causing an increase in loudness.
- There are four vocal fold closure patterns: thick, thin, stiff, slack.
- Thick true vocal fold closure has a longer closed phase of vibration, larger mucosal wave, and larger amplitude of vibration. Perceptually, it is loud and clear.
- Thin true vocal fold closure occurs when the vocal folds are tensed, which decreases the mucosal wave and equates the open and closed phases of vibration. Perceptually, it is clear but much quieter than thick.
- Stiff true vocal fold closure occurs when the vocal folds are tensed and arytenoids are slightly abducted, allowing a steady flow of air to pass through the vocal folds during phonation. Perceptually, it is breathy and quiet.
- Slack true vocal fold closure occurs when closed phase of vibration is long but vocal fold vibration is inconsistent. This is often referred to as glottal fry.
- The third coordinative structure for voice production is resonation. The source (vocal fold vibration) and filter (vocal tract) interact with one another to shape the buzz created by the vocal folds to create your voice.
- Pitch comes from the source (vocal folds). The filter does not change pitch.
- Resonant or formant frequencies are the frequencies that resonate best in each individual's vocal tract.
- Larger cavities (e.g., longer vocal tracts) resonate lower frequencies better, while smaller cavities (e.g., smaller vocal tracts or the ear canal) resonate higher frequencies better.

■ The vocal tract, composed of various valves, can change the way your voice sounds depending upon which manipulations are made.

■ Estill Voice International™ provides an anatomical and physiological model, detailing the specific manipulations that can be made to the source and filter to change vocal quality.

■ False vocal folds are folds of tissue that are superior to the true vocal folds (the folds that vibrate during phonation). The false vocal folds' primary biological function is protection of the vocal folds during a swallow.

■ False vocal folds can move from a constricted position (when you bear down or lift a heavy object) to a more retracted position. Retraction of false vocal folds alleviates backpressure on the true vocal folds.

■ The aryepiglottic sphincter or epilarynx is just superior to the false vocal folds and is the space between the epiglottis and the pharyngeal (throat) walls.

■ When the epiglottis is drawn posteriorly toward the arytenoid cartilages, the aryepiglottic sphincter is narrowed, creating the "singer's formant," or an increase in acoustic energy between 2800 and 4300 Hz. Narrowing of the aryepiglottic sphincter or epilarynx is a vital component of twang.

■ Epilaryngeal narrowing can be used to improve the voices of individuals with insufficient vocal fold closure.

■ The pharynx or throat is divided into three cavities: laryngopharynx, oropharynx, and nasopharynx. These cavities play a significant role in producing the sound quality of your voice.

■ Openness in the pharynx is noted as one of the keys of good vocal sound. Openness is likely achieved through a combination of movements of many anatomical parts in the vocal tract.

■ The velum is the soft, squishy structure on the roof of your mouth. Its main biomechanical function is to rise, sealing off the nasal cavity during a swallow.

■ The velum can be held in three different positions to alter sound: high, mid, or low. A high or raised velum directs all airflow during speech through the mouth; a low velum directs all airflow during speech through the nose; a mid velar position allows passage of air through both the nose and mouth during phonation.

▪ Vowels are oral sounds, meaning that the velum is raised and airflow is directed exclusively through the oral cavity when they are produced.

▪ Nasal sounds, such as /m/, /n/, and /ŋ/, require a low velum, as airflow passes primarily through the nose when they are produced.

▪ Some accents, such as French, and dialects utilize a mid velar position.

▪ Hypernasality occurs when there is constant passage of air through the nose on both nasal and oral sounds.

▪ Twang (epilaryngeal narrowing) and nasality should not be confused with one another.

## References

Al-Awan, A., & Kaminsky, D. (2012). Vocal cord dysfunction in athletes: Clinical presentation and review of the literature. *Physician and Sportsmedicine*, *40*(2), 22–27.

Altman, K. W., Mirza, N., Ruiz, C., & Sataloff, R. T. (2000). Paradoxical vocal fold motion: Presentation and treatment options. *Journal of Voice*, *14*(1), 99–103.

Bartholomew, W. A. (1934). A physical definition of "good voice quality" in the male voice. *Journal of the Acoustical Society of America*, *5*(3), 25–33.

Campainha, S., Ribeiro, C., Guimarães, M., & Lima, R. (2012). Vocal cord dysfunction: A frequently forgotten entity. *Case Reports in Pulmonology*, *2012*, 1–4. doi:10.1155/2012/525493

Chhetri, D. K., Neubaer, J., & Berry, D. A. (2012). Neuromuscular control of fundamental frequency and glottal posture at phonation onset. *Journal of the Acoustical Society of America*, *131*(2), 1401–1412.

Chhetri, D.K., Neubauer, J., Sofer, E., & Berry, D. A. (2014). Influence and interaction of laryngeal adductors and cricothyroid muscles on fundamental frequency and glottal posture control. *Journal of the Acoustical Society of America*, *135*(4), 2052–2064.

Döllinger, M., Berry, D. A., & Montequin, D. W. (2006). The influence of epilarynx area on vocal fold dynamics. *Otolaryngology—Head and Neck Surgery*, *135*(5), 724–729.

Fant, G. (1960). *Acoustic theory of speech production.* The Hague, Netherlands: Mouton.

Flanagan, J. L., & Landgraf, L. (1968). Self-oscillating source for vocal-tract synthesizers. *IEEE Transactions on Audio and Electroacoustics, 16*(1), 57–64.

Friedman, M., LoSavio, P., & Ibrahim, H. (2002). Superior laryngeal nerve identification and preservation in thyroidectomy. *Archives of Otolaryngology—Head and Neck Surgery, 128*(3), 296–303.

Gray, S. D., Pignatari, S. S., & Harding, P. (1994). Morphologic ultrastructure of anchoring fibers in normal vocal fold basement membrane zone. *Journal of Voice, 8*(1), 48–52.

Hillel, A. D. (2001). The study of laryngeal muscle activity in normal human subjects and in patients with laryngeal dystonia using multiple fine-wire electromyography. *The Laryngoscope, 111*(S97), 1–47.

Hirano, M., Ohala, J., & Vennard, W. (1969). The function of laryngeal muscles in regulating fundamental frequency and intensity of phonation. *Journal of Speech and Hearing Research, 12*(3), 616–628.

Hirano, M. (1974). Morphological structure of the vocal cord as a vibrator and its variations. *Folia Phoniatrica et Logopaedica, 26*(2), 89–94.

Hirano, M. (1975). Phonosurgery: Basic and clinical investigations. *Otologia (Fukuoka), 21,* 129–440.

Ibrahim, W. H., Gheriani, H. A., Almohamed, A. A., & Raza, T. (2007). Paradoxical vocal cord motion disorder: Past, present, and future. *Postgraduate Medical Journal, 83*(977), 164–172.

Kiray, A., Naderi, S., Ergur, I., & Korman, E. (2006). Surgical anatomy of the internal branch of the superior laryngeal nerve. *European Spine Journal, 15*(9), 1320–1325.

Klimek, M. M., Obert, K., & Steinhauer, K. (2005a). *Estill voice training system level one: Compulsory figures for voice control.* Pittsburgh, PA: Estill Voice International.

Klimek, M. M., Obert, K., & Steinhauer, K. (2005b). *Estill voice training system level two: Figure combinations for six voice qualities workbook.* Pittsburgh, PA: Estill Voice International.

Kolář, P., Neuwirth, J., Šanda, J., Suchánek, V., Svatá, Z., Volejník, J., & Pivec, M. (2009). Analysis of diaphragm movement during tidal breathing and during its activation while breath holding using MRI synchronized with spirometry. *Physiological Research, 58,* 383–392.

Lombard, L. E., & Steinhauer, K. M. (2007). A novel treatment for hypophonic voice: Twang therapy. *Journal of Voice, 21*(3), 294–299.

Lott, J. (2014). The use of the twang technique in voice therapy. *Perspectives on Voice and Voice Disorders, 24*(3), 119–123.

Martin, B. J., Logemann, J. A., Shaker, R., & Dodds, W. J. (1993). Normal laryngeal valving patterns during three breath-hold maneuvers: A pilot investigation. *Dysphagia, 8*(1), 11–20.

Mendelsohn, M. S., & Martin, R. E. (1993). Airway protection during breath-holding. *Annals of Otology, Rhinology, and Laryngology, 102*(12), 941–944.

Mitchell, H. F., Kenny, D. T., Ryan, M., & Davis, P. J. (2003). Defining 'open throat' through content analysis of experts' pedagogical practices. *Logopedics Phoniatrica Vocology, 28*(4), 167–180.

Sanders, I., & Mu, L. (1998). Anatomy of the human internal superior laryngeal nerve. *The Anatomical Record, 252*(4), 646–656.

Sundberg, J. (2005). Vocal tract resonance. In R. Sataloff (Ed.), *Professional voice: The science and art of clinical care* (pp. 275–291). San Diego, CA: Plural.

Sundberg, J., & Nordström, P.-E. (1976). Raised and lowered larynx—The effect on vowel formant frequencies. *STL-Quarterly Progress and Status Report, 17*(2–3), 035–039.

Sundberg, J., & Thalen, M. (2010). What is "twang"? *Journal of Voice, 24*(6), 654–660.

Story, B. H., & Titze, I. R. (1995). Voice simulation with a body-cover model of the vocal folds. *Journal of the Acoustical Society of America, 97*(2), 1249–1260.

Tellis, C. M., Rosen, A., Thekdi, A., & Sciote, J. J. (2004). Anatomy and fiber type composition of human interarytenoid muscle. *Annals of Otology, Rhinology, and Laryngology, 113*(2), 97–107.

Titze, I. R. (1988). The physics of small-amplitude oscillation of the vocal folds. *Journal of the Acoustical Society of America, 83*(4), 1536–1552.

Titze, I. R. (1993). Raised versus lowered larynx singing. *National Association for Teachers of Singing Journal, 50*, 37.

Titze, I. R. (1998). Voice research: The wide pharynx. *Journal of Singing, 55*(1), 27–28.

Titze, I. R. (2001). Acoustic interpretation of resonant voice. *Journal of Voice, 15*(4), 519–528.

Titze, I. R. (2004). Theory of glottal airflow and source-filter interaction in speaking and singing. *Acta Acustica-Acustica, 90*(4), 641–648.

Titze, I. R. (2006). Theoretical analysis of maximum flow declination rate versus maximum area declination rate in phonation. *Journal of Speech, Language, and Hearing Research, 49*(2), 439–447.

Titze, I. R. (2008). Nonlinear source-filter coupling in phonation: Theory. *Journal of the Acoustical Society of America, 123*(5), 2733–2749.

Titze, I. R., Bergan, C. C., Hunter, E. J., & Story, B. H. (2003). Source and filter adjustments affecting the perception of the vocal qualities twang and yawn. *Logopedics Phoniatrics Vocology, 28*(4), 147–155.

Titze, I. R., & Hunter, E. J. (2004). Normal vibration frequencies of the vocal ligament. *Journal of the Acoustical Society of America, 115*(5), 2264–2269.

Titze, I. R., & Story, B. H. (1997). Acoustic interactions of the voice source with the lower vocal tract. *Journal of the Acoustical Society of America, 101*(4), 2234–2243.

van den Berg, J. (1958). Myoelastic-aerodynamic theory of voice production. *Journal of Speech and Hearing Research, 1*(3), 227–244.

Yanagisawa, E., Estill, J., Kmucha, S. T., & Leder, S. B. (1989). The contribution of aryepiglottic constriction to "ringing" voice quality—A videolaryngoscopic study with acoustic analysis. *Journal of Voice, 3*(4), 342–350.

# Chapter 3

# Vocal Care and Awareness

*The voice is an instrument that you really must take time to develop. It is like a good red wine. Give it time.*
—Cecilia Bartoli, World famous mezzo soprano

## Voice Science: Developing Voice and Developing Your Voice

You know the voice now as a physical entity, centered on the two little folds vibrating in the larynx to produce sound. The scientific study of that physical entity involves many disciplines, the two core fields being vocology, the study of the voice, and laryngology, the study of the larynx (or voice box). An ongoing explosion of knowledge informs these important fields, which scrutinize not only the biology, chemistry, and physics of the larynx but also the etiology, diagnosis, and treatment of disorders and issues related to the voice.

### *Typical Vocal Development*

Every voice, from an infant's to an adult's, is composed of the same physical accouterments, yet every voice is unique. The adult male voice is different enough from the adult female voice that most people believe they can tell one from the other when they hear someone on a telephone. The adult male voice has a lower average pitch than the female voice, although there are wide variances within the sexes.

There is not much dimorphism in vocal development between males and females from birth to age six years, nine months (Vorperian et al., 2005). In infants the vocal folds are short in length—about 1.25 to 3 mm (Hirano, Kurita, & Nakashima, 1983). In adolescents, the male's vocal pitch lowers as his larynx enlarges and his neck increases in length. Typically, the post-adolescent male voice drops a full octave. The young man's new voice thus can deepen quite dramatically, whereas the female voice pitch stays relatively higher, although acquiring the richness and texture characteristic of adult women. Adult female vocal folds develop to a length of 11 to 15 mm, whereas adult male vocal folds end up between 17 and 21 mm long (Hirano et al., 1983). Vocal tract length develops from 10 to 12 cm in children to 15 cm in adult woman and 17.5 cm in adult men (Vorperian et al., 2005).

The voice changes as individuals continue to age. Some believe that as they age, their voice must become ragged, hoarse, and creaky. Any imitation of an older person always includes a degraded and wobbly pattern of speech to match the facial wrinkles and stooped spine. So how is it that a crooner like Tony Bennett can win a Grammy for a CD recorded at age 80? Bennett may be an exception. His longevity, however, and that of phenoms like the late Lena Horne and Luciano Pavarotti, certainly provides evidence that the voice need not grow feeble with age. Legendary newscaster Walter Cronkite maintained a powerful speaking voice into his 80s.

When listening to someone talk without any visual input, listeners are able to estimate with fairly good accuracy the age of the person who is speaking (Linville & Fisher, 1985; Ramig, Scherer, & Titze, 1984; Ryan & Burk, 1974; Shipp & Hollien, 1969). Many factors contribute to an individual's perception of age related to speech. These factors include articulation, speaking rate, word choice, and voice (Baken, 2005). Although voice appears to be most useful in determining the age of the speaker when heard in conjunction with speaking rate (Harnsberger, Shrivastav, Brown, Rothman, & Hollien, 2006), there is something about the voice that makes it especially useful in determining a speaker's age.

As men and women age, speaking fundamental frequency (average fundamental frequency during speech) has been shown to decrease (Baken, 2005; Mysak, 1959; Mysak & Hanley, 1958; Ramig & Ringel, 1983). Perceptually this decrease in speaking fundamental frequency may be observed as a decrease in pitch. Both genders, however, show a slight rise in speaking fundamental frequency during the latest stages of development (i.e., 80 to 90 years old), with men experiencing a greater effect at an earlier age than females. Perturbations of frequency (jitter) and amplitude (shimmer) also show an increase with age (Linville & Fisher, 1985; Ramig & Ringel, 1983).

Research on observations of the vocal folds conducted through videostroboscopy revealed that older women have decreased glottal closure as well as decreased amplitude of vibration compared to their male counterparts (Biever & Bless, 1989). Changes to the vocal folds due to hormone fluctuations following menopause also may lead to roughness and hoarseness of the female voice (Abitbol, J., Abitbol, P., & Abitbol, B., 1999; Honjo & Isshiki, 1980). Limited research, however, exists on how the voice ages when the individual considers and cares for the voice. With the knowledge you take with you from reading this book, you may help change the course of the aging voice (Figure 3–1). You may even affect future research.

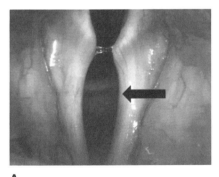 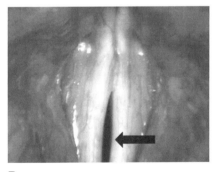

**A**                                        **B**

*Figure 3–1.* Open (**A**) and closed (**B**) phases of vibration in an aging voice. Vocal fold atrophy is common in the aging process where thinning of the vocal folds is present, causing decreased glottal closure. Videostroboscopy depicts male vocal folds with bilateral atrophy.

## Vocal Choice

There are many aspects of your voice that you do not choose. You are born with a particular predestined anatomy and map for laryngeal development (Laver, 1968). Without any vocal training you will develop a unique vocal pitch, tone, resonance, and quirkiness that enable your friends and family to distinguish your voice from that of other people. Your adult voice becomes an essential component of the self that others perceive. When people observe your visual features they may judge you to be imposing, slight, cuddly, ripped, or square-jawed. When they hear you talk, they determine that you are boisterous, shy, bombastic, mealy-mouthed, or well spoken. In a dramatic sense, your voice is a big part of who you are in the eyes—and ears—of the world.

There are unconscious, untrained choices you may make about your vocal quality—aspects and characteristics you pick up from your family, coworkers, and friends. You may even find that your voice quality changes unknowingly when you are with different people and in different environments. You may also make conscious decisions about your voice quality for particular situations and settings. You probably do not speak the same way in a loud cafeteria as you do when talking to a family member or friend after a long day. As you gain knowledge and training about voice, you will begin to realize just how many different vocal qualities you can choose to produce.

Because of the perceptual nature of evaluating voice quality, there is still much debate about terminology, methods of assessment, listener agreement, and voice quality production (Fex, 1992; Kreiman, Gerratt, & Khan, 2010; Sofranko & Prosek, 2014; Sonninen & Hurme, 1992). We do know that as far back as the Roman era there are writings documenting discussions on voice quality. Some of these ancient terms are used today, including breathy, hoarse, weak, dull, and bright (Austin, 1806/1966; Kreiman et al., 2010). Studies throughout the ages have identified the myriad of psychoacoustical, physical, social, neuropsychological, and emotional characteristics that constitute perception and production of voice quality (Kreiman & Sidtis, 2011). Many researchers and clinicians have called for a link between the perception and production of voice qualities (Laver, 1968; Fex, 1992). Descriptive modeling of voice quality was introduced in the 1960s and was based on findings from several researchers suggesting that voice quality should be approached phonetically, taking into consideration laryngeal anatomy and physiology (Abercrombie, 1967; Fairbanks, 1960; Garvin & Ladefoged, 1963; Honikman, 1964; Laver, 1968). Laver (1968) divided the anatomy into laryngeal settings and supralaryngeal vocal tract settings. These divisions have physiological parameters that can be manipulated to create different vocal qualities.

Colton and Estill (1981) identified five primary vocal qualities that are derived from a combination of different anatomical and physiological laryngeal conditions: speech, falsetto, belt, twang, and opera. Estill continued to develop her model of voice training through the early 2000s and included two new qualities, sob and cry, as well as concepts of nasalization (oral-twang, nasal-twang) (Klimek, Obert, & Steinhauer, 2005). These qualities provide a perceptual anchor for identifying voice quality. Learning how to produce the individual conditions of each anatomical figure—and then combining them—allows the speaker or singer to create numerous variations in voice quality based on communication environment and personal preference. Continued research is needed on how perception and production influence each other.

## Mainstream Education Loses Its Voice: Practice Breaks From Science

While all this voice science is pretty cool, some resist mainstreaming the science into practice. At first such resistance seems odd. Other parts of our anatomy are happily subjected to the ministrations of therapeutic science. Are you a marathoner? If so, you welcome the incursion of the applied sciences that teach you how to exercise effectively and safely; how to care for muscles, bones, and joints; and how to avoid strain, pain, and damage. Should damage occur the services of trained professionals, clinicians, physicians, therapists, and trainers are sought without embarrassment. To do otherwise is deemed foolish and self-destructive, because it is.

The same enlightened attitudes prevail with respect to care of the eyes, ears, even the gastrointestinal tract. There is an accepted continuum of care from routine self-applied maintenance, usually seen as "common sense," to the summoning of high-level surgical skills when such remedies are advisable.

Unfortunately, where the voice is concerned there is a widespread ignorance of even the most basic science. Our biology classes teach us to marvel at the body's interactive array of neurons, muscles, ligaments, and skeletal structure that make human activity possible, down to the movement of the little finger. The eye is dissected into rods and cones, retina, lens, cornea—components of the miracle that is sight. Yet, most high school graduates have no recollection of studying the voice and grow into adulthood with little awareness of that particular miracle, as if nothing very notable occurs when we give voice to a thought, even a thought as profound as Martin Luther King Jr.'s dream.

This neglect is compounded by the meager instruction we receive on the use of the voice, how to make speech effective and powerful, varied and interesting. Nothing akin to rhetoric is taught. In fact, unless you were in the choir or had an especially enlightened debate coach, very little about your voice was taken seriously. One study of university communication and education professors indicates that more than 70% of them do not include aspects of vocal care and vocal hygiene in their classes (Tellis & Conklin, 2007). It is astounding but not surprising, then, that as an adult you attend a presentation skills workshop and find yourself unable to lower your pitch or raise your loudness level when asked to do so.

Still, we allow our voices to develop without conscious cultivation and, in many cases, the results are predictably substandard, whether we are aware of them or not. Meanwhile, the science of voice has accelerated and expanded but has moved away from public consciousness altogether. Returning instruction on voice to the forefront of training in the art of speaking is imperative to the effectiveness of communication, the power of performance, and the longevity and health of the voice.

When the benefits of voice science make themselves felt in the life of an individual in need, we get a glimpse of a world in which these benefits are routinely accessed. Beth is such an individual (see companion website). A woman who makes heavy demands on her voice as both a speaker and a singer, Beth reached a crisis point where attention had to be paid to the voice issues that threatened her effectiveness as a professional and a performer.

Her journey to improvement required behavioral voice therapy, including substantive lifestyle changes, altered vocal practices, and applied understanding of her unique instrument. Beth's is the remarkable story of someone who heard the warning bell and responded successfully.

Those warning bells resonate throughout the culture. Political campaigns always feature exhausted candidates overworking their voices into a painful whisper as Election Day nears. Politicians repeatedly and publicly lose their voices after weeks of hard campaigning. Teachers, singers, coaches, and drill sergeants, many of whom make unremitting use of their voices, threaten their vocal health and longevity. Some of these individuals seek professional help but it is usually a stopgap move made to get them "back on the stump."

A single instance of misusing the voice, such as singing out of range, cheering for your favorite sports team, talking to your friend at a rock concert, or yelling upstairs to your children, can lead to an injury to the vocal folds. Vocal fold polyps (Kleinsasser, 1982) and vocal fold hemorrhaging (bruising) (Figure 3–2) are two of the more common forms of "one-instance" types of vocal fold

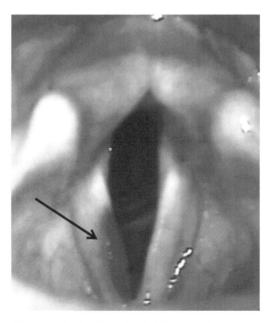

**Figure 3–2.** Vocal fold hemorrhage. The arrow identifies a right vocal fold hemorrhage.

injury (Boone, McFarlane, & Von Berg, 2005). Often individuals can identify the exact moment their voices changed. "It was the third inning. Bases were loaded and, that batter, he watched a third strike. I started yelling at the umpire because obviously he needed glasses and then I felt a pop. My voice was hoarse from then on and it's just never been the same since." Continuous overuse and inefficient use of the voice can lead to chronic voice disorders and, if left untreated, may cause permanent damage to the vocal folds.

Our unawareness of voice science carries a hefty price. Clear symptoms of treatable vocal disorders are overlooked or shrugged off, and a minor voice problem develops into a severe malady. "Common sense" care of the voice does not happen because we do not commonly acquire the sense to do the caring. Few of us would tolerate an untreated leg injury that could have been healed so as to avoid a lifelong limp; however, many of us live with wounded voices that limp for life, that are neither as compelling nor as pleasant as they should have been. The very least of these consequences is a voice that is simply less interesting and less listenable than it could be.

## Results of Vocal Neglect

It is difficult to know just why applied voice science has not made it into the mainstream, but the resulting vocal mismanagement, prevalence of harmful myths, and compromised vocal health all give testimony to the need for a major change.

The first change is to be aware of riskier vocal practices and bad vocal advice. Pop singer Kelly Clarkson avoided oblivion by what she herself called a "miracle" as she vied with nine competitors during the inaugural season of "American Idol." During a brief interview just after a successful performance, Clarkson, in a shockingly hoarse speaking voice, disclosed her battle with laryngitis. She had been unable to sing at all just a few hours earlier.

Laryngitis and vocal fold hemorrhaging have become recurring themes on this and other talent shows, and a few afflicted contestants since Clarkson have not fared as well as she did. At the height of a competition these youthful singers are probably driving their voices as they never have in their lives; the contest becomes one of vocal stamina as much as talent. The possibility of vocal injury is ever present.

Clarkson seems to have recovered from the extreme stress placed on her voice during her "American Idol" competition. Singers like Adele, John Mayer, and Sam Smith also made headlines because of issues related to their voices that caused them to cancel concerts or take a break from singing all together. Surprisingly, the only news reported to the public is of the surgeries they had to "fix" their voice problems. There is no mention of the voice therapy they received to regain their voices or the voice training they require to continue performing without risking further incident.

Becoming hoarse after performing a show or during intensive theater camps is sometimes seen as a badge of honor. Often we hear "I know it's a good show if I'm hoarse at the end of it," "Everyone gets hoarse in their first year of this camp, you know you are working hard if you do," or "Wow, that's cool, we're all hoarse." Unique, hoarse voices also get attention. We remember the raspy voice quality of actor Demi Moore and singer Macy Gray. In the hit show, "The Voice," we have heard some of the coaches say, "I love that raspy quality in your voice. You can't put that in, you just have to have it." While we are not the ones to determine what everyone should deem as an aesthetically pleasing voice quality, hoarseness is one symptom that should not be ignored or sought after. Proper vocal training and technique can minimize the risk of hoarseness, while still maintaining the artist's or speaker's desired voice quality.

Because of the remitting and recurring pattern of hoarseness that often accompanies vocal performance, it is not until hoarseness persists, voices do not return to "normal," or performers can no longer sing or speak the range of notes they used to be able to sing and speak that people start to worry. The issue is that the worrying should have started the first time the individual became hoarse after speaking, performing, or singing to determine what was causing the hoarseness. Neglecting the problem can make management more difficult and recovery harder to attain.

## When to Seek Help: Don't Wait

Hoarseness is not a diagnosis; it is a symptom and sometimes it is the symptom of a much larger and pressing issue than originally suspected (Sulica, 2014). Visualization of the larynx is absolutely necessary for a comprehensive and accurate assessment of hoarseness. Unfortunately, some published guidelines for assessment do not always support clinical practice and expert opinion (Keesecker, Murry, & Sulica, 2015).

The American Academy of Otolaryngology Clinical Practice Guidelines for hoarseness allows up to a 3-month waiting period for individuals with hoarseness to be evaluated via laryngoscopy (an instrument used to view the structures and function of the larynx) (Schwartz et al., 2009). A recent survey of otolaryngologists, however, discovered that the longest specialists actually delay the laryngoscopy procedure is only approximately 13 days (Paul, Branski, & Amin, 2012). Another recent survey indicated that members of the American Broncho-Esophagological Association, the American Laryngological Association, and the European Laryngology Society mandated that individuals with hoarseness or any new voice disturbance undergo a laryngoscopy procedure within one week to one month from the time the voice issue is first noticed (Sadoughi, Fried, Sulica, & Blitzer, 2014).

Here's the bottom line: If an individual notices a voice issue including hoarseness, strain, change in singing or speaking vocal range, or any other voice issue, the individual should be seen by a specialist for a comprehensive evaluation including laryngoscopy (and more specifically, laryngoscopy with stroboscopy) within one week to one month post recognition and no longer than two months post recognition of the voice issue.

## Who to See: Voice Care Team

So now that you know when to see a specialist, let us talk about whom to see. In the last section you saw the word "otolaryngologist" many times. If you got the sense that this is a physician of some sort, you are correct. The term is actually otorhinolaryngologist: 'oto' meaning ear, 'rhino' meaning nose, and 'laryngo' meaning larynx (or the place where your larynx resides, meaning throat). The shortened form is ear, nose, and throat physician or ENT.

After you detect a voice issue, a trip to the primary care physician is usually a customary first line of defense. It would be highly unlikely for a primary care physician to have a laryngoscope. Usually a diagnosis of laryngopharyngeal reflux (LPR) is made, and a course of reflux medication is prescribed, even without indication of gastroesophageal reflux disease (Ruiz et al., 2014). When the voice issue does not subside with reflux medication, a referral is made to an otolaryngologist who will potentially perform laryngoscopy. Even after visualizing the larynx, many otolaryngologists attribute hoarseness to LPR when laryngoscopy does not reveal an obvious cause (Sulica, 2014).

If accessible and available, the appropriate referral should be made to a subspecialist of otolaryngology called a laryngologist. These physicians have fellowship training in laryngology and all things related to the voice. Unfortunately, the majority of patients have seen one to two physicians before seeing a laryngologist (Keesecker et al., 2015). Some speech-language pathologists with specialty training in the evaluation of voice disorders are also able to evaluate patients and refer when necessary. Speech-language pathologists who specialize in voice are called vocologists, voice pathologists, or voice therapists.

The best-case scenario is accessibility to a voice center. Usually residing in a large university hospital system, a voice center is composed of a voice care team, a team of laryngologists and speech-language pathologists who work together in the assessment and treatment of individuals with voice issues. If you search "voice center" in any internet search engine, you will be able to locate the voice center closest to you. These highly trained professionals are best equipped to comprehensively assess and treat any type of voice problem.

A routine voice evaluation consists of several important steps. The speech-language pathologist will listen and rate your vocal quality, test parameters of your voice related to its sound and function, and get a sense of how much the voice problem is affecting your life. The laryngologist or speech-language pathologist will conduct a laryngoscopy evaluation to look at your vocal folds. Together they make a diagnosis and a plan of treatment is formulated. Treatment usually consists of some combination of behavioral voice therapy, medical management (e.g., medications), and/or surgical intervention.

Viewing laryngeal structures and function is one of the most important aspects of the voice assessment. Typically voice centers use a procedure called laryngoscopy with videostroboscopy. The laryngoscope is the part of the instrument used to access the larynx (Figure 3–3). There are two different types of laryngoscopes. A flexible laryngoscope is a flexible, fiberoptic tube that is inserted

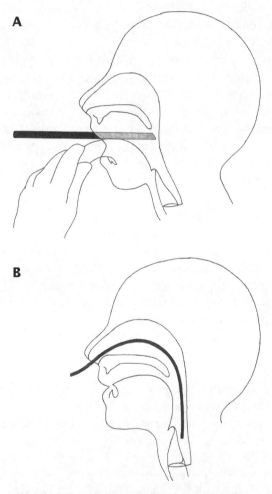

***Figure 3–3.*** **A.** Rigid laryngoscope. **B.** Flexible laryngoscope. Reproduced with permission from *Clinical Voice Pathology: Theory and Management, 5th edition* (p.174) by J. C. Stemple, N. Roy, & B. K. Klaban. Copyright 2014 by Plural Publishing.

in the nasal passage, passed through the velopharyngeal port, and positioned above the vocal folds. With this laryngoscope, the voice care team can view both structure and function of the larynx during breathing, phonation, speaking, and singing. This laryngoscope is ideal for observing the function of the larynx. A rigid laryngoscope is the other variety and is inserted into the mouth to view the larynx. Because of its positioning in the mouth, the rigid scope is excellent for close, clear viewing of the mucosal wave and appearance of the vocal folds. It is very difficult to sing and speak with a rigid scope in your mouth.

A camera is attached to either laryngoscope and makes a video recording during the examination. You will be able to watch the video and review findings with the voice care team at the completion of the evaluation. Stroboscopy is the light source. Otolaryngologists that employ flexible laryngoscopy typically use an LED light to view the larynx. The strobe light, however, is the better choice for assessing voice disorders because, when the strobe matches the frequency of vocal fold vibration, it provides a mechanism to view the mucosal wave during voicing. Lesions like vocal fold scar, atrophy, sulcus vocalis, nodules, cysts, and many others are much more easily identified with stroboscopy (Keesecker et al., 2015).

A recent study found that revisions were made to the incoming diagnosis of almost half of patients after reevaluation with stroboscopy (Keesecker et al., 2015). Most of the incoming diagnoses were edema (swelling) and LPR. Final diagnoses after reevaluation with stroboscopy were paresis, sulcus, atrophy, scar, malignancy, and behavioral voice issues. The bottom line in assessment is that as soon as you notice a chronic change in voice, the best place to be assessed is at a voice center or by a voice specialist who is equipped to perform a comprehensive voice evaluation that includes flexible or rigid laryngoscopy with videostroboscopy.

## Rehabilitation of Voice Issues

Following the identification of a voice problem, a plan of care will be established. Usually vocal rehabilitation includes a combination of behavioral voice therapy, medical management, and/or surgical intervention.

## *Voice Therapy*

Performed by a certified and licensed speech-language pathologist (voice therapist), voice therapy can be very effective in treating many different types of voice problems. Voice therapy involves the learning and repatterning of behaviors that reestablish adequate vocal fold closure patterns and balance airflow and subglottal pressure during vocal fold vibration. Voice therapy may also focus on vocal hygiene (e.g., increasing hydration, decreasing poor vocal behaviors), respiratory retraining (e.g., for vocal cord dysfunction or paradoxical vocal fold motion disorder), public speaking voice, singing voice, and resonance disorders. Here are some typical vocal hygiene strategies:

- Drink water. Although the body may be capable of providing hydration to the vocal folds when needed, increased consumption of water can help to thin mucus, as well as maintain the flexibility and pliability of the vocal fold layers.
- Minimize throat clearing and coughing. Persistent throat clearing can be damaging to the vocal folds; every time an individual clears his or her throat, the vocal folds slam together, an action that may cause further irritation to the folds.
- Minimize yelling and screaming. Unless proper technique is used, constant yelling and screaming can be harmful to the voice.
- Maintain good posture. Stand or sit upright, with shoulders back and down.
- Decrease talking over loud noises.
- Do not whisper for long periods of time. Whispering is speaking without phonating. After long periods of whispering, surrounding muscles of the larynx and neck can become strained and tired.
- Properly treat gastroesophageal reflux disease and laryngopharyngeal reflux. This treatment may take the form of medical management and/or lifestyle changes.
- Keep allergy symptoms under control. Get tested for allergies. Minimize exposure to known allergens. Treatment may include medical management and allergy shots/drops.
- Do not smoke and minimize exposure to secondhand smoke.

Professional voice users—like singers, aerobic instructors, and, particularly, teachers—have an increased risk for developing voice disorders compared to professionals who do not rely on their voices for their work (Roy et al., 2004; Williams, 2003). Scheduling your day so you can conserve your voice is one way to combat the vocal rigors of professions like teaching, sales, and other occupations where voice use is a priority. Pharmaceutical sales representatives are instructed to do the bulk of their talking when in physicians' offices. The time spent in their cars can be used to rest their voice and limit time talking on the cell phone.

If you are an elementary school teacher, you can arrange your day to build in "vocal time-outs." One example is to alternate talking times with voice rest periods. Start the day with quiet play, then use your voice for circle time, then let students work independently while you move around the room to help individual students with their work, then do reading circle (if with older students, have them take turns reading). If you need to do recess or lunch duty, do not yell across the lunchroom or recess yard—walk over to the student instead. If you are a middle school or high school teacher, alternate lectures with labs and independent or group work sessions. Use the labs or work sessions as your time-outs. When the students are between classes or at lunch, recess, library, or chorus, use the time to rest your voice instead of talking. Let another teacher do the talking at that time. Remember also to have water with you throughout the day (and keep drinking it) or consider using amplification devices when teaching.

Some of the more notable voice therapy approaches are vocal function exercises, Lessac-Madsen Resonant Voice Therapy (LMRVT), and Lee Silverman Voice Treatment Program (LSVT). Vocal function exercises are used to balance the coordinated structures of voice production with a concrete, prescribed process of vocal exercises. (Stemple, Lee, D'Amico, & Pickup, 1994). LMRVT is taught by integrating vibratory sensations of the oral cavity with easy phonation (Lessac, 1997; Verdolini, Druker, Palmer, & Samawi, 1998). LSVT is a highly researched therapy protocol and was determined to be effective in improving the voice quality of individuals with Parkinson's disease (Ramig et al., 1988). Other recent voice therapy approaches include an implicit-explicit approach to voice therapy, an approach that integrates contemporary research and thinking in motor learning with traditional voice therapy methods (Tellis,

2014); stretch-and-flow therapy used to treat muscle tension dysphonia (Watts, Hamilton, Toles, Childs, & Mau, 2015); and twang
therapy (recently reviewed by Lott, 2014). Voice therapy strategies
will be integrated into this book in sections entitled, "Voicing Intention" throughout the latter chapters.

## Medical Management

Prescribed by a medical doctor, medications are sometimes required
to reduce or eliminate medical diagnoses that interact and inter-
fere with the health and functioning of the voice. Allergies and
gastroesophageal reflux disease (GERD) are two of the more common diagnoses that may require medical management to treat
their symptoms. Antihistamines, nasal sprays, and inhalers may
be prescribed to manage the symptoms of allergies. Proton-pump
inhibitors (e.g., omeprazole) and H2-blockers (e.g., ranitidine) may
be prescribed to treat gastroesophageal reflux disease and laryngopharyngeal reflux.

In some cases the medicines a patient takes could exacerbate a
voice issue. It is very important to check with your doctor or phar-
macist when starting a new medication to determine the potential
side effects the medication may have on the voice. Work with
your doctor to establish the best course of action to effectively treat
the medical condition, meanwhile limiting any negative effect on
your voice.

## Surgical Intervention

Most voice care teams will prescribe a course of voice therapy and/
or medical management before surgical intervention is discussed.
There are clearly some diagnoses that require immediate surgical
attention, for example, potential carcinoma, Reinke's edema, vocal
fold paralysis, or lesion (if breathing is compromised), and laryngeal papillomatosis. Pesky benign vocal fold lesions (e.g., nodules,
pseudocysts) respond very well with voice therapy and do not
often need surgical intervention.

When performed by a laryngologist, many microlaryngoscopic
surgical procedures are conducted in the clinical office with topical

anesthesia, eliminating a trip to the operating room. Examples of surgical procedures are lesion removal (Sulica & Behrman, 2003), vocal fold augmentation (bulking up a vocal fold for atrophy, paresis, or paralysis) (Rosen et al., 2007), and KTP/532 pulsed laser (cauterizing vocal fold hemorrhage) (Hirano, Yamashita, Kitamura, & Takagita, 2006). General anesthesia is needed for some surgical procedures like medialization laryngoplasty (Zeitels, Mauri, & Dailey, 2003) and some laryngeal carcinomas. Before surgery a couple of preoperative voice therapy sessions with the voice therapist are scheduled. A course of voice rest is usually required after surgery and then more voice therapy.

## Reinstating Vocal Awareness

Everyone has an obligation to care for his or her voice, but those whose professions place them in a position to render advice on voice use and care must be educated to do no harm and give guidance in keeping with sound, healthful practice. Singing coaches, presentation skills consultants, and voice therapists must be certifiably knowledgeable about what is good and bad for the voice.

Society's vocal attentiveness must be ratcheted up significantly so that individuals will recognize symptoms of incipient voice disorders and get them diagnosed when therapies would be most effective. When tenor José Carreras contracted leukemia, his sophisticated vocal awareness and the brilliance of his doctors enabled him to tune his treatment to avoid damage to his voice. His return to health was considered close to miraculous, but the resumption of his splendid career with his voice intact may have been even more so. Far too often, happy results that might have been do not come about simply because vocal health never makes it to the front burner.

Vocal ignorance, as with all ignorance, generates foolish misconceptions that harden in the public mind and block the paths to vocal health. Prominent among these is the myth that the voice is something we should "just take for granted." It is what it is and cannot be improved or altered. Professional singers know this assertion is ridiculous, but the rest of us, even if we dislike the sound of our own voice, too often believe there is nothing we can do about it. So we seek self-enhancement in every area except the voice. Ironically, the voice is remarkably susceptible to structured programs of improvement. Participants in our Presentation Practicum, which has been delivered to hundreds of organizations over the last 35 years, uniformly report marked improvement in speaking and interpersonal effectiveness, as do their managers and colleagues. Samples of the workshop appear throughout the accompanying companion website.

It is imperative to give vocal awareness the prominence it warrants. Three dimensions of awareness must be cultivated simultaneously if the quest for vocal vitality and health is to be the norm rather than the exception: voice science must intrude assertively into public consciousness, education from the earliest years must incorporate sound vocal instruction, and the rhetorical arts must stage an effective and enduring comeback.

Voice science belongs in the forefront of our conversation about health and fitness as well as effective communication. This rapidly expanding field provides critical insight into vocal function and wellness. It supplies key data on the components of speech that meld with other communication faculties to transmit and receive thoughts and feelings.

An argument could be made that lay people need not grasp the science as long as they follow the prescriptions that science has generated. A baseball pitcher is under no obligation to learn the anatomy of his pitching arm or the physiology of motion to throw a curve ball correctly, nor is he required to appreciate the value of rest, icing, and a structured exercise program. Ignorance of these scientific insights is allowed. Such ignorance is not wise. Absent a solid grasp of the relevant science, he literally will not know what he is doing when he throws a curve ball. He will not know what he is putting at risk and what it means to minimize the risk. There is a lot at stake for a major league pitcher. He needs more than a working knowledge of the biological sciences pertinent to his craft. Major league pitchers typically seek and acquire that knowledge.

Very few of us operate our arms like a major league pitcher and few of us rely on our curve ball for our livelihood. The voice is a different matter. We definitely depend on our vocal abilities to function in work and social settings. That pitcher learns how to use his body, especially his arm, to retire opposing batters; how to develop his body to possess the strength, stamina, balance, and skill to pitch well; how to care for his body to maintain the health and fitness necessary to pitch nine innings or more and to remain productive nine years or more. He learns how to seek professional help from coaches, physicians, therapists, and others when they are needed. Professional voice users should view their voices the way pitchers view their arms.

If the rest of us were to begin thinking of the voice in the way that a pitcher thinks of his arm, a few propositions would start to look like common sense. School curricula from grades K through 12 should incorporate age-appropriate voice education along with instruction on the rest of the anatomy. Opportunities to use the voice and to practice speech should abound. Obviously, teachers themselves should receive instruction that qualifies them to promote this learning.

The integration of voice science at the college level complements learning in a variety of fields. Any course in oral communication and presentation skills should involve the science as it applies to those skills. Academic programs in biology, singing (vocal arts), business communication, law, drama, theater, and speech communication all provide a suitable venue for voice science.

Then there is rhetoric. It is tempting to advocate a full reintegration of the rhetorical arts into our basic concept of what education is about. Compelling as the idea may be, it is not likely to catch on in the near term. A more modest approach seeks to revive key elements of rhetoric into the life-learning enterprise. After all, rhetoric stakes its territory on the terrain of the voice in use, the voice in communication, the voice caught in the act of persuading, informing, inspiring, and connecting.

Instruction and skill in the rhetorical arts are as essential to speakers as instruction and skill in the vocal arts are to professional singers. If voice science provides the understanding, rhetoric provides the reason to understand. Rhetoric begins to address the question that must be answered before voice science can gain wide acceptance as a fundamental field of study: Why bother? We will address rhetoric in the next chapter.

Your voice is a critical means of communication and self-expression. Maintaining its vitality and robustness throughout life is worth every effort you expend on it. Vocal mismanagement and fallacious beliefs—all the products of ignorance—will compromise the health of this irreplaceable faculty.

## Review of Key Ideas

- Males and females follow a similar trajectory of vocal development until age 6:9.
- Adolescent male voices deepen by about one octave as males transition into adulthood and their vocal tract, larynx, and vocal folds become larger.
- Adult female voices remain higher pitched than those of males because a woman's vocal tract and vocal folds are shorter, and larynx is smaller, than a man's.
- Voice, especially speaking fundamental frequency, is one of the key features used to approximate an individual's age.
- It is a fallacy to believe that the voice as it ages inexorably becomes ragged, hoarse, and creaky. The longevity of many famous voices gives evidence that the voice need not grow feeble with age.
- An individual can choose to manipulate his or her anatomy to create various vocal qualities.
- Voice science and education about vocal hygiene is often overlooked in mainstream education and voice training, which can often lead to vocal injury.
- Vocal injury can occur during one instance of vocal misuse or through maladaptive vocal strategies used over time.
- Hoarseness is one of the most common symptoms of a vocal injury. Hoarseness should be investigated by a medical professional specializing in the voice and should not be ignored for longer than two months.
- Voice centers, composed of a team of laryngologists and speech-language pathologists, are the best places to go to further evaluate a voice issue.
- One of the most important aspects of voice assessment is viewing the structures and functions of the larynx via laryngoscopy. Laryngoscopy that uses videostroboscopy is one of the most favorable and most comprehensive voice evaluation procedures.
- Treatment of voice disorders typically utilizes a combination of behavioral voice therapy, medical management, and surgical intervention (if necessary).
- There are three key dimensions for improved vocal awareness: (1) Voice science must intrude assertively into public

consciousness; (2) education from the earliest years must include sound vocal instruction; and (3) the rhetorical arts must stage an effective comeback.

■ College courses in oral communication and presentation skills should involve voice science as it applies to those skills. Academic programs in biology, singing and vocal arts, business communication, law, drama, theater, and speech communication all provide suitable venues for voice science.

## References

Abercrombie, D. (1967). *Elements of general phonetics* (Vol. 203). Edinburgh, Scotland: Edinburgh University Press.

Abitbol, J., Abitbol, P., & Abitbol, B. (1999). Sex hormones and the female voice. *Journal of Voice, 13*(3), 424–446.

Austin, G. (1966). *Chironomia.* Carbondale, IL: Southern Illinois University Press. (Original work published 1806).

Baken, (2005). The aged voice: A new hypothesis. *Journal of Voice, 19*(3), 317–325.

Biever, D. M., & Bless, D. M. (1989). Vibratory characteristics of the vocal folds in young adult and geriatric women. *Journal of Voice, 3*(2), 120–131.

Boone, D. R., McFarlane, S., & Von Berg, S. L. (2005). *The voice and voice therapy* (7th ed.). Boston, MA: Allyn & Bacon.

Colton, R. H., & Estill, J. A. (1981). Elements of voice quality: Perceptual, acoustic, and physiologic aspects. In N. J. Lass (Ed.), *Speech and language: Advances in basic research and practice* (Vol. 4, pp. 312–402). New York, NY: Academic Press.

Fairbanks, G. (1960). *Voice and articulation drillbook* (2nd ed.). New York, NY: Harper and Row.

Fex, S. (1992). Perceptual evaluation. *Journal of Voice, 6*(2), 155–158.

Garvin, P. L., & Ladefoged, P. (1963). Speaker identification and message identification in speech recognition. *Phonetica, 9*(4), 193–199.

Harnsberger, J. D., Shrivastav, R., Brown, W. S., Jr., Rothman, H., & Hollien, H. (2006). Speaking rate and fundamental frequency as cues to perceived age. *Journal of Voice, 22*(1), 58–69.

Hirano, M., Kurita, S., & Nakashima, T. (1983). Growth, development, and again of human vocal folds. In D. M. Bless & J. Abbs (Eds.), *Vocal fold physiology* (pp. 22–43). San Diego, CA: College-Hill Press.

Hirano, S., Yamashita, M., Kitamura, M., & Takagita, S. (2006). Photocoagulation of microvascular and hemorrhagic lesions of the vocal fold with the KTP laser. *Annals of Otology, Rhinology, & Laryngology, 115*(4), 253–259.

Honikman, B. (1964). Articulatory settings. In D. Abercrombie, D. B. Fry, P. A. D. McCarthy, N. C. Scott, & J. L. M. Trim (Eds.), *In honour of Daniel Jones* (pp. 73–84). London, England: Longman.

Honjo, I., & Isshiki, N. (1980). Laryngoscopic and voice characteristics of aged persons. *Archives of Otolaryngology, 106,* 149–150.

Keesecker, S., Murry, T., & Sulica, L. (2015). Patterns in the evaluation of hoarseness: Time to presentation, laryngeal visualization, and diagnostic accuracy. *The Laryngoscope, 125*(3), 667–673.

Kleinsasser, O. (1982). Pathogenesis of vocal cord polyps. *Annals of Otology, Rhinology, and Laryngology, 91*(4), 378–381.

Klimek, M. M., Obert, K., & Steinhauer, K. (2005). *Estill voice training system level two: Figure combinations for six voice qualities workbook.* Pittsburgh, PA: Estill Voice International.

Kreiman, J., Gerratt, B. R., & Khan, S. U. (2010). Effects of native language on perception of voice quality. *Journal of Phonetics, 38*(4), 588–593.

Kreiman, J., & Sidtis, D. (2011). *Foundations of voice studies: An interdisciplinary approach to voice production and perception.* West Sussex, UK: John Wiley & Sons.

Laver, J. D. M. (1968). Voice quality and indexical information. *British Journal of Disorders of Communication, 3,* 43–54.

Lessac, A. (1997). *The use and training of the human voice: A bio-dynamic approach to vocal life.* Mountain View, CA: Mayfield.

Linville, S. E., & Fisher, H. B. (1985). Acoustic characteristics of perceived versus actual vocal age in controlled phonation by adult females. *Journal of the Acoustical Society of America, 78,* 40–48.

Lott, J. (2014). The use of the twang technique in voice therapy. *SIG 3 Perspectives on Voice and Voice Disorders, 24*(3), 119–123.

Mysak, E. D. (1959). Pitch and duration characteristics of older males. *Journal of Speech and Hearing Research, 2,* 46–54.

Mysak, E. D., & Hanley, T. D. (1958). Aging processes in speech: Pitch and duration characteristics. *Journal of Gerontology, 13,* 309–313.

Paul, B. C., Branski, R. C., & Amin, M. R. (2012). Diagnosis and management of new-onset hoarseness: A survey of the American Broncho-Esophagological Association. *Annals of Otology, Rhinology & Laryngology, 121*(10), 629–634.

Ramig, L. A., & Ringel, R. L. (1983). Effects of physiological aging on selected acoustic characteristics of voice. *Journal of Speech and Hearing Research, 26,* 22–30.

Ramig, L., Mead, C., Scherer, R., Horii, Y., Larson, K., & Kohler, D. (1988). *Voice therapy and Parkinson's disease: A longitudinal study of efficacy.* Presentation at Clinical Dysarthria Conference, San Diego, CA.

Ramig, L. A., Scherer, R. C., & Titze, I. R. (1984). Acoustic correlates of aging. *Journal of the Acoustical Society of America, 76*(S1), S59.

Rosen, C., Gartner-Schmidt, J., Casiano, R., Anderson, T. D., Johnson, F., Reussner, L., . . . McWhorter, A. (2007). Vocal fold augmentation with calcium hydroxylapatite (CaHA). *Otolaryngology-Head and Neck Surgery, 136*(2), 198–204.

Roy, N., Merrill, R. M., Thibeault, S., Parsa, R. A., Gray, S. D., & Smith, E. M. (2004). Prevalence of voice disorders in teachers and the general population. *Journal of Speech, Language, and Hearing Research, 47*(2), 281–293.

Ruiz, R., Jeswani, S., Andrews, K., Rafii, B., Paul, B. C., Branski, R. C., & Amin, M. R. (2014). Hoarseness and laryngopharyngeal reflux: A survey of primary care physician practice patterns. *JAMA Otolaryngology–Head & Neck Surgery, 140*(3), 192–196.

Ryan, W. J., & Burk, K. W. (1974). Perceptual and acoustic correlates of aging in the speech of males. *Journal of Communication Disorders, 7*(2), 181–192.

Sadoughi, B., Fried, M. P., Sulica, L., & Blitzer, A. (2014). Hoarseness evaluation: A transatlantic survey of laryngeal experts. *The Laryngoscope, 124*(1), 221–226.

Schwartz, S. R., Cohen, S. M., Dailey, S. H., Rosenfeld, R. M., Deutsch, E. S., Gillespie, M. B., . . . & Patel, M. M. (2009). Clinical practice guideline: Hoarseness (dysphonia). *Otolaryngology-Head and Neck Surgery, 141*(3), S1–S31.

Shipp, T., & Hollien, H. (1969). Perception of the aging male voice. *Journal of Speech and Hearing Research, 12*(4), 703–710.

Sofranko, J. L., & Prosek, R. A. (2014). The effect of levels and types of experience on judgment of synthesized voice quality. *Journal of Voice, 28*(1), 24–35.

Sonninen, A., & Hurme, P. (1992). On the terminology of voice research. *Journal of Voice, 6*(2), 188–193.

Stemple, J. C., Lee, L., D'Amico, B., & Pickup, B. (1994). Efficacy of vocal function exercises as a method of improving voice production. *Journal of Voice, 8*(3), 271–278.

Sulica, L. (2014). Hoarseness misattributed to reflux: Sources and patterns of error. *Annals of Otology, Rhinology, and Laryngology, 123*(6), 442–445.

Sulica, L., & Behrman, A. (2003). Management of benign vocal fold lesions: A survey of current opinion and practice. *Annals of Otology, Rhinology, and Laryngology, 112*(10), 827–833.

Tellis, C. M. (2014). Integrated implicit-explicit learning approach to voice therapy. *Perspectives on Voice and Voice Disorders, 24*(3), 111–118.

Tellis, C. M., & Conklin, J. (2007, November). *Voice: What are professors teaching prospective professional voice users?* Presentation at the

American Speech-Language Hearing Association (ASHA) Convention, Boston, MA.

Verdolini, K. Druker, D. G., Palmer, P. M., & Samawi, H. (1998). Laryngeal adduction in resonant voice. *Journal of Voice, 12*(3), 315–327.

Vorperian, H. K., Kent, R. D., Lindstrom, M. J., Kalina, C. M., Gentry, L. R., & Yandell, B. S. (2005). Development of vocal tract length during early childhood: A magnetic resonance imaging study. *Journal of the Acoustical Society of America, 117*(1), 338–350.

Watts, C. R., Hamilton, A., Toles, L., Childs, L., & Mau, T. (2015). A randomized controlled trial of stretch-and-flow voice therapy for muscle tension dysphonia. *The Laryngoscope, 125*(6), 1420–1425.

Williams, N. R. (2003). Occupational groups at risk of voice disorders: A review of the literature. *Occupational Medicine, 53*(7), 456–460.

Zeitels, S. M., Mauri, M., & Dailey, S. H. (2003). Medialization laryngoplasty with Gore-Tex for voice restoration secondary to glottal incompetence: Indications and observations. *Annals of Otology, Rhinology, and Laryngology, 112*(2), 180–184.

# Chapter 4

# Verbals and Paraverbals

*"I told no lies, and of the truth all I could," said Frodo. "I do not blame you," said Faramir. "You spoke with skill in a hard place, and wisely, it seemed to me. But I learned or guessed more from you than your words said."*

—J. R. R. Tolkein, *The Lord of the Rings: The Two Towers*

*And don't underestimate the importance of body language. Ha!*

—Ursula, *The Little Mermaid*

## More Than Voice

The previous chapters stressed the importance of voice to communication. A book on the effectiveness of human connection through communication, however, cannot just be about the voice. Communication is more than the sound your voice makes. Even the mere act of speech involves more than voice. Your brain develops a thought that you intend to transit. Your lips and tongue move to articulate sounds. Your eyes show interest, enthusiasm, or boredom. Your body too has a language all its own. Your hands, your posture, and your physical presence all have meaning, intended or not. Then there are sounds: words, phrases, sentences put together in a nice little package delivered to the listener. What the listener does with the message—and the subsequent interactions between speaker and listener—constitute communication. This chapter will focus on some of these other aspects of communication. You will learn how they can be used to enhance the voice and how they can be enhanced by the voice.

## The Two Grand Categories

Aspects of communication can be grouped into two main categories: *verbals*, the words you use when communicating, and *paraverbals*, everything else that accompanies the words. Verbals is derived from the Latin word *verbalis*, meaning "by means of words," or *verbum*, meaning "word." Language is composed of words from which are derived paragraphs, sentences, phrases—the items accessed not only during speech but also through written form in essays, stories, texts, and e-mail messages.

Voice, tone, gestures, and facial expressions are also employed during speech. These terms are called paraverbals. The word nonverbals has received more use in this context but is actually less precise because it refers only to things that are not words. The term paraverbals connotes that words may be present in the transmission but that, along with the words, there are also other sensory realities that communicators call on to enhance meaning, to "scent" the message, as it were.

Individuals who are deaf or hard-of-hearing place the visual front and center, literally, with sign language, whereas individuals who are both deaf and blind rely on *tactuals*, the sense of touch. For the hearing, direct communication is primarily oral/aural, mouth to ear. Sights and tactuals serve as paraverbals, enhancing meaning. Sometimes paraverbals act as verbals, literally phrases. You probably do not need interpretation of the conductor's look when your cell phone rings during the piano concerto at a performance. The conductor's paraverbal says it all.

## Linguistics: Speech and Parts of Speech

Linguistics is the study of language meaning and structure. Language is the mechanism for communication. It's how you organize what you intend to say and prepare it for its trip from your mind to others. Syntax encompasses the rules of sentence structure within a language. It regulates language, shapes it, and molds it into a form that enables communication. The sentence, "I heard that he a song sang," is an example of incorrect English syntax. If you heard someone speak those words, you could probably figure out what the speaker intended but it would strike you as obviously odd sentence structure. "I heard that he sang a song" should bring music to your ears.

The basic component of language is the *morpheme*, the smallest unit of meaning. Morphemes are made up of linguistically distinctive sound units called phonemes. A morpheme may be bound or free. A bound morpheme cannot stand alone. Consider the word "unreachable." The bound morphemes are "un" meaning "not" and "able" meaning "having the ability." The free morpheme is "reach," because "reach" can stand alone. Linguists call units like "reach" lexemes. We will call a *lexeme* a word. In English, as in many languages, a word is a discrete part of speech. A word can name a thing or concept: *house, tree, elephant, beauty, word.* It can denote action: *move, attack, sneeze, fall, stand.* It can describe a characteristic: *lovely, squeamish, affable, large.* When we speak of verbals we are speaking about these units of language called words.

One word can express a complete thought. "Go!" is a command, a sentence. A sentence expresses a thought that contains a subject (what the sentence is about) and a predicate (what the sentence has to say about the subject). Although a sentence, as we see, can contain only one word, it can theoretically run to an infinite length. If the word is a basic unit of language, then the basic unit of syntax can be said to be the sentence. (Some would say it is the clause, which is not always a sentence, but that distinction is not really necessary.)

Although it is clear that sentences express our thoughts, there is ongoing debate about the connection between thoughts and sentences. Does a child's acquisition of language, his ability to connect a word and a sentence with what we adults know they mean, signal the onset of thinking (Whorf, 1956)? Or does thinking precede language acquisition? Most linguistic scholars today believe the latter (Pinker, 2000). Researchers observe a good deal of thinking capability already in place prior to a child's earliest use of linguistic symbols. It is pretty clear that thoughts are not words.

You can think of the spectacles that help you see distance and at the same time be thinking about the two drinking containers sitting on the counter and not be confused that the word "glasses" is the same word used to refer to each. "Glasses" is one word that can encompass two different thoughts, so thoughts go beyond words.

Activist and author Temple Grandin wrote about visual thinking in her famous book entitled, *Thinking in Pictures*. She states,

> I think in pictures. Words are like a second language to me. I translate both spoken and written words into full-color movies, complete with sound, which run like a VCR tape in my head. When somebody speaks to me, his words are instantly translated into pictures. Language-based thinkers often find this phenomenon difficult to understand, but in my job as an equipment designer for the livestock industry, visual thinking is a tremendous advantage." (Grandin, 2006, p. 3).

The controversy about the relationship between thinking and language will go on. The curious can read the works of Chomsky, Whorf, Larsky, and Pinker, but the debate will be left to those linguists who continue to study language. For the purposes of this book, words comprise the atoms of language; sentences, the molecules. A connected string of these "molecules" is a paragraph.

A paragraph is a relatively short, tightly connected series of thoughts encompassing one intelligible idea. As this entire book is built of words, sentences, and paragraphs, you are awash in examples. Beyond the paragraph there is the *essay*. Every essay has a thesis or purpose— what the speaker intends to get across when he or she sets out to speak at a particular moment. Like a written essay, the oral essay can be of variable length and range from well-prepared and highly formal (e.g., "The Gettysburg Address") to spontaneous and ephemeral (e.g., the very next thing you say to your best friend). Every time you speak, you produce an essay of sorts.

The thesis of an essay is the core of an intended message. The essay, then, involves words, sentences, paragraphs, and paraverbals —all the parts of speech that can carry your intended message. Without an essay and an intended message, all speech becomes babble. Intended meanings inform, give sense to language.

## Meaning of Sounds, Sounds of Meaning

The linguistic components that form communication merit a close inspection; they are the source of successful communication. They begin with things that strike the ear. The paraverbals most closely associated with the spoken words are intonation and inflection. When you recite a sentence you do so with inflection, utilizing variations in pitch and intensity to make your meaning clearer. In tonal languages, not typically in English, inflection can actually change the word itself. In Thai the word for *far* is *glai*, as is the word for *near*, its opposite. Although the two words contain the same sounds, they are intoned differently. The word *far* is *glai* said with a mid tone; the word *near* is *glai* said with a falling tone.

English boasts almost none of that tonal subtlety. Almost. The verb *refer* ("to make an allusion to") is pronounced the same as *reefer* (an archaic term for a marijuana cigarette) with one exception: The accent is on a different syllable. Just as very few English speakers confuse their allusions with their recreational drugs, people from Thailand get along quite well with their tonal language.

Although the English language is not tonal like Thai, inflection is crucial to meaning. In Chapter 1 you explored the sentence, "The child will give the dog three pats." We noted the alterations in meaning consequent to stressing different words in the sentence. How you inflect your sentences can have a dramatic effect on your communication transmission. You can test this for yourself by reading the following three sentences aloud. Put the major stress on different words in each sentence and ask yourself how this inflection affects the meaning.

Throw the bums out.

I didn't say you stole the pickles.

Shirts and shoes will be worn at all times.

Let us consider the first sentence, "Throw the bums out." Say you asked your friend, "Do you want me to make a polite request that the bums leave?" It would not be confusing for your friend to answer, "No, THROW the bums out," accenting the word "throw."

You might, on the other hand, ask, "Should I throw the honest folks out?" "No," your friend might rejoin, "throw the BUMS out."

Now, can you think of a question appropriately answered by "Throw the bums OUT," accenting the final word? Once you do that, then try constructing questions answered by the second and third sentences with varying accented words. In this activity you are exploring inflection in English. Unlike Thai, English rarely affords you the opportunity to change a word by simply changing tone. In English tone and inflection are paraverbals, placing emphasis on words that alter and enhance the meaning of sentences, adding texture and nuance.

Connecting inflection to the thesis is critical; these emphases are true paraverbals only if they foster and enhance your intended message. Success at deciphering inflection requires a profound familiarity with (American) English prosody and the distinctions it conveys. Native speakers usually absorb this facility along with language acquisition, whereas non-native speakers must work diligently to "get the music right."

Look at the second sample sentence above, "I didn't say you stole the pickles." Place the main stress on each word in that sentence and the sentence actually takes on seven quite different connotations. Consider the underlined word to be the one stressed and read the sentences below.

"I didn't say you stole the pickles." Meaning: someone other than I said it.

"I didn't say you stole the pickles." Meaning: despite your accusation that I did say it, I did not.

"I didn't say you stole the pickles." Meaning: I may have hinted that you stole them, but I never actually said it.

"I didn't say you stole the pickles." Meaning: the pickles were stolen, but I never said you were the thief.

Now, stress each of the final three words (*stole*, *the*, and *pickles*) in the sentence, and try to detect the three different implications. This seemingly simple sentence can convey a number of different intended meanings.

Stress and inflection involve changing the pitch and intensity (loudness) of the voice, termed *prosodic fluency*, the ability to vocalize sentences in a manner that imbues them with the meanings you intend. This basic skill, of course, is learned at a young age and is informed by the voices children hear around them. Many individuals perform these nuances of speech without even being aware that they are utilizing them. Some speakers, however, are often completely unaware that they are lacking this skill. Have you heard someone who has monotone speech? These individuals fail to utilize pitch and intensity during speech and can appear to lack interest or be bored.

There are a number of exercises designed to evoke awareness of stress and inflection, as well as improve the basic ability to distinguish pitch and intensity in your own voice. Once vocal awareness is achieved, extending your range is a matter of practice and application. An especially effective example uses a simple chart called the "P-L Chart" (Figure 4–1). It combines pitch and loudness into four logical categories: (1) low pitch and low loudness; (2) high pitch and low loudness; (3) low pitch and high loudness; and (4) high pitch and high loudness. These categories can occupy the four corners of the P-L Chart.

## Pitch and Loudness

Let us review pitch and intensity before you proceed with the P-L Chart activity. The perceptual correlate of intensity is loudness. If you speak at a typical conversational intensity, you are speaking at about 65 to 70 dB. You are not loud and you are not quiet. A loud voice begins at about 75 dB and a shouting voice at about 85 to 90 dB. When someone asks you to "project your voice," they are basically asking to you to get louder and stay loud. A quiet voice is 60 dB and lower without going to a whisper. Try holding out /i/ ("ee") in your typical conversational intensity, and switch from loud back to typical and then to quiet voice.

There are many ways to achieve a loud voice. The basic mechanism, though, is that you have to increase the proportion of the closed phase of the vocal fold vibratory cycle compared to the proportion of the open phase. Remember that the vocal folds open and close within a cycle of vibration. The longer the vocal folds stay closed within that cycle, the more molecules get trapped below the vocal folds, the more pressure builds, the larger the amplitude of

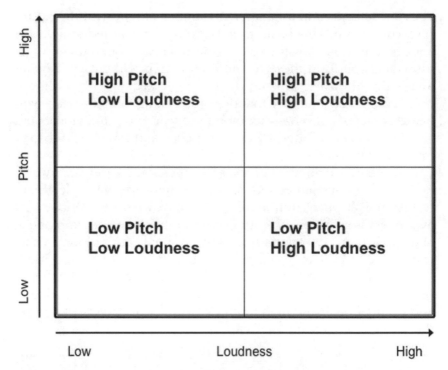

**Figure 4-1.** The P–L Chart. The P-L (Pitch-Loudness) Chart is used to help with practice in extending vocal range, moving from higher to lower pitch (or frequency), while also increasing and decreasing loudness or amplitude.

vibration of the vocal folds once the pressure is released, and the louder the voice.

Many people equate loudness to respiratory effort—the more you drive or push air, the louder you will be. While you might get louder in this way, increasing airflow can lead to vocal strain. There is an increase in air pressure below the vocal folds when achieving a loud voice, but the release of that pressure does not have to equal an increase in airflow. It is just more pressure upon those air molecules, pressure driving them to vibrate stronger, not pushing them to induce the molecules to flow out faster. Though tiny, vocal folds are mighty, but even their might has limits. This concept is of critical importance—pushing and driving air equals vocal strain.

Unfortunately, pushing air during voicing is often so habitual that individuals do not even know they are doing it. Some singing qualities are more prone to pushing; pop/rock, belt, and opera are susceptible, especially when intensity increases at a higher vocal range. Shouting, screaming, and loud talking in general can elicit a push of air as well. Understanding what pushing feels like is the first important step to minimizing or eliminating it when speaking and singing.

Hold out /i/ at a comfortable pitch (not too high, not too low) and try to maintain the sound at the quietest and clearest tone you possibly can. Sense what your body must do to hold that note. Keep your tongue high with the sides of your tongue pushed up against your back molars, almost spreading those molars apart. The muscles of your soft palate and the back of your mouth (throat or pharynx) should be engaged, lifting up and spreading your soft palate and pharynx just like the onset of a yawn prior to the release into a full yawn. Raise your eyebrows and see if you can maintain the clear quiet tone. You should begin to feel a muscle pull in the back of your head where your skull meets your spine. Engage your back and shoulder muscles, pulling down on those muscles while spreading your chest muscles out away from midline. You should be working hard, but not bearing down. Take a breath as needed and then continue.

Put your mind's eye into the muscles and parts of your body mentioned so you can get a sense of what they are doing throughout the activity. You can stop holding out /i/ at this point. For contrast, you can do a negative practice exercise between open, anchored posturing and closed, tight posturing. Let your eyebrows down and scowl; scrunch your eyebrows down and pull your shoulders in towards the midline of your body as if you are about to hug yourself. Your stomach muscles may also engage. Feel how closed your posture is now in this position. This posturing is the extreme opposite of the open, anchored posturing you were performing before. Return to the posture your began with, eyebrows up, soft palate and pharynx lifted up and spread, tongue high and spread against your molars, and your back and chest muscles down and spread out. Go back and forth from one posture to the other. The open, anchored posture is what you aim for during speaking and singing. Any muscle contraction that pulls your body close to midline in the closed posture falls short of the ideal.

Now, let us focus on a negative practice exercise between pushing air and increasing pressure, and balancing airflow and pressure—your goal being the latter. Go back to holding out /i/ in the quietest and clearest tone that you can. Make sure your posture is open and anchored. When you can hold out the note consistently while staying open and anchored, you are balancing airflow and pressure. When you are ready, blow the air harder out as you hold out /i/. You should feel more airflow at the level of your vocal folds, your voice may become breathier, and your anchors may fall as your stomach muscles push the air out. This feeling is what pushing or strain feels like. Obviously, this example is an exaggeration of pushing. The idea of this exercise, though, is for you to feel what pushing feels like. Go back and forth between pushing and balancing airflow and pressure. Again, focus your mind's eye on what your body does during both practices.

This clear quiet tone, the preferred tone, is produced by an almost equal proportion of open phase to closed phase vocal fold vibration. The thyroarytenoid muscle is tensed with antagonistic contraction of the cricothyroid muscle (remember the intrinsic laryngeal muscles from Chapter 2) so that the vocal fold cover stays relatively tense and the mucosal wave maintains a small amplitude of vibration. This is called the thin True Vocal Folds: Body Cover (TVFBC) condition (Klimek, Obert, & Steinhauer, 2005; Story & Titze, 1994).

There are four primary TVFBC conditions: thin (clear and quiet, "head voice"), stiff (audible airflow and quiet, "breathy"), thick (clear and louder, "chest voice"), and slack (irregular vibratory pattern, "glottal fry"). Manipulating the proportion of the closed phase of vibration and changing the amplitude of vibration help to create the different TVFBC conditions. You have already attempted thin TVFBC. While in thin TVFBC, you can transition to stiff TVFBC by releasing interarytenoid and lateral cricoarytenoid muscle contraction slightly, moving the vocal processes of the arytenoids to a more abducted position. In this position the vocal folds stay primarily in an open phase of vibration with constant airflow throughout vibration. If you maintain your open, anchored posture the airflow in stiff TVFBC will be slightly audible.

Controlling the muscles of the larynx is difficult until you have learned the motor skill. An implicit, facilitator (auditory model) for stiff TVFBC is hooting like an owl, "hoo hoo," drawing the breathy, airy /h/ sound into the "oo" vowel. The sound should be similar to the sound you hear when blowing air across the top of a glass soda bottle. Remember, though, to maintain balanced airflow so that you do not push air out during your stiff TVFBC production.

Stiff TVFBC should be quiet like thin TVFBC. A higher airflow, stiff TVFBC is often louder because of its larger amplitude of vibration. Many of you will notice audible air even when attempting to do thin TVFBC. Throughout training, you will learn ways to achieve an equal open and closed phase of vibration to produce a clearer, thin TVFBC tone and, in that way, distinguish thin from stiff.

Remember that to produce a louder sound, you have to increase the closed phase proportion of vocal fold vibration compared to the open phase and increase the vocal folds' amplitude of vibration. Often, how you onset the sound will dictate how much of the vibratory cycle stays either closed or open, as well as the magnitude of vibration. If you want to learn to increase the closed phase of vibration, you should onset the sound starting in a closed, vocal fold position (not a bearing down, closed position). Try this exercise. Lightly hold your breath, stop the flow of air at the level of your vocal folds, and increase subglottal pressure. Open and release the air without voicing. The sound should be similar to the "ah" you make after you take a big sip of soda on a hot day. When you make this sound, you are closing your vocal folds and releasing air. Produce several quick repetitions of this sound and feel your vocal folds close and open, close and open. This onset is called glottal onset (Klimek et al., 2005), sometimes also called hard glottal attack or glottal attack.

The term hard glottal attack can connote an increase in effort or insinuate a need to bear down. This term also has a negative connotation in the speech-language pathology world—many feel the need to "reduce" hard glottal attacks in voice and speech therapy. The term, glottal onset, does not carry that negative meaning. This type of onset becomes a way to facilitate a thick TVFBC. Now, try producing the sound /i/ with a glottal onset. Close your vocal folds, release them, say /i/, and hold /i/ for three seconds. Say /i/ three times in a row in thick TVFBC. Your /i/ should sound louder than your thin TVFBC /i/, but not loud as though you were yelling or calling "Hey!" to a friend. Remember your goal for thick TVFBC is a clear, loud tone; make sure you are not pushing air to get the sound or increasing your loudness to a yell or a scream.

Slack TVFBC is the last of TVFBC conditions to review. Most people know the associated quality to this TVFBC condition as, glottal fry, fry, or creak. When producing slack TVFBC, the cover of the vocal folds is lax with decreased contraction of thyroarytenoid and cricothyroid muscles. The vibratory pattern is irregular with no clear fundamental frequency or harmonics. All of these TVFBC conditions can be distinguished from one another on a narrowband spectrogram (Figure 4–2). You can download free spectrogram software from the Internet (e.g., Praat and Spek) or purchase real-time spectrogram analysis from other sources so that you can practice. You will want to practice all of the TVFBC conditions on different vowels, in speech, and at different pitches. We will talk about pitch later in this section.

Another physiological change you can make to your vocal anatomy is called epilaryngeal narrowing, aryepligiottic (AES) narrow, or the inverted megaphone. This change will produce a louder voice with less effort and no push or strain (Klimek et al., 2005; Smith, Finnegan, & Karnell, 2004; Titze, Bergan, Hunter, & Story, 2003; Titze & Story, 1997). This vocal manipulation is discussed in

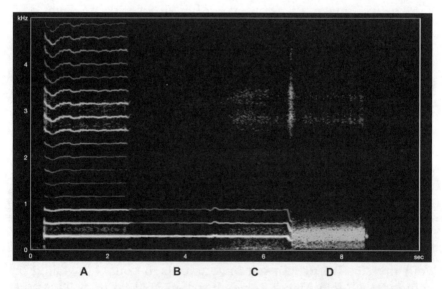

*Figure 4-2.* A narrowband spectrogram of the four True Vocal Folds: Body Cover (TVFBC) condition. **A.** Thick TVFBC characterized by bright harmonics, indicating higher intensity. **B.** Thin TVFBC characterized by lighter or absent harmonics, indicating decreased intensity, and minimal interharmonic noise. **C.** Stiff TVFBC characterized by lighter harmonics and increased interharmonic noise. **D.** Slack TVFBC characterized by absent harmonic lines and vertical striations, indicating inconsistent vibratory pattern.

Chapter 2. You can practice performing AES narrow on a spectrogram or power spectrum. What you are looking for when practicing is the presence of an increase in amplitude at a resonance peak between 2800 and 4300 Hz (Figure 4–3). AES narrow can be very

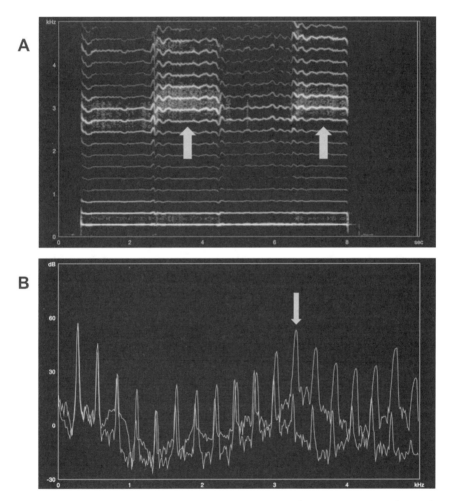

***Figure 4–3.*** **A.** A narrowband spectrogram showing AES wide and narrow. Arrows indicate portions of the spectrogram measuring AES narrow, characterized by a bright formant band between 2800 and 4300 Hz. **B.** A power spectrum contrasting AES wide and narrow. The bottom line tracks the spectral energy of wide AES, the top narrow AES. The arrow indicates the peak in spectral energy characteristic of AES narrow.

effective in increasing loudness during speaking and singing. It is also very effective in facilitating vocal fold closure in individuals with voice disorders (Lombard & Steinhauer, 2007; Lott, 2014).

Broadway belters, opera singers, and pop/rock singers, as well as drill sergeants, coaches, and theater actors use a combination of several vocal manipulations to produce a loud voice. To reduce push or strain, training the open, anchored posture mentioned above is of vital importance. There is also another vocal manipulation that facilitates a thicker thick TVFBC condition that further increases the closed proportion of the vibratory cycle as well as the amplitude of vibration. Estill Voicing Training calls this manipulation, cricoid tilt (Klimek et al., 2005), the inversion of the arytenoid cartilages anteriorly toward the thyroid notch. Although apparent on a spectrogram, as well as through flexible videostroboscopy, more research is needed on what is responsible for this manipulation. An implicit, auditory model for cricoid tilt is calling out to a friend who is at a distance: "Hey Johnny!" Some instructors teach cricoid tilt with the word "Aye" because you can have the student begin voicing with a glottal onset.

Try this exercise. Exhale quickly as if you are blowing out a match. Remember that this type of exhale gets you quickly to REL. Close your vocal folds to produce a glottal onset. Throw your hands out in the air to the sides of your body and tilt your head back. At the same time say "Aye!" loudly as you release your glottal onset. Your posture should be open and anchored, and you should feel almost a freeing sensation as you produce the sound. Repeat this exercise with "Aye!" as your facilitator (beginning sound) while counting by twos: Exhale as if blowing out a match, glottal onset, throw your head and hands back as you say, "Aye! One . . . two." Repeat with "Aye! Three . . . four." Make sure you maintain an open, anchored posture and that you do not push air. Again, work your way up to speaking longer phrases and singing scales, if applicable.

These exercises may seem easy to do at your comfortable pitch. The tricky part comes when maintaining the balance of air and pressure as you change pitch. For those who are uncertain what it means to change pitch, let us review the sirening exercise from Chapter 2. In this exercise, you want to make the sound of a siren, ambulance, or fire truck. Sometimes this exercise is called "pitch glides" (Stemple, Glaze, & Klaban, 2010). Sing the word "sing" at a comfortable pitch; hold out the "ng" sound. Make a siren sound, gliding all the way up to your highest pitch or tone (this will sound similar to a very high note or imitating a child's voice). You do not have to siren higher than what is comfortable to you. When you have reached the height of your siren, glide down past your starting pitch all the way to the lowest tone you can produce (this pitch will be similar to a very low note or imitating a male voice for females). Practice sirening up to your highest pitch and then all the way down to your lowest pitch. You can practice changing pitch on a narrowband spectrogram. Look for the very first line (fundamental frequency) to move up as you raise your pitch and move down as you lower your pitch (Figure 4–4).

You will want to practice your siren with a thin TVFBC condition. Do not get louder as you increase pitch. Take care not to push air as you increase your pitch. You can anchor and open more by raising your eyebrows as you go up in pitch; keep your eyebrows up while you siren to your low notes as well. Do not push air. If you have trouble maintaining an open, anchored posture while sirening, you can siren while performing a lip trill. The sound will no longer be "ng" but will sound more like /m/. As you practice

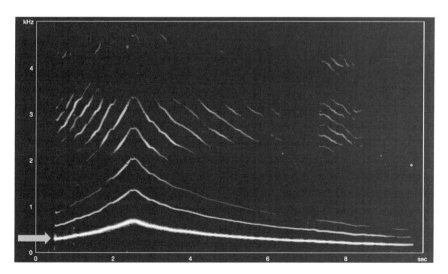

*Figure 4–4.* Narrowband spectrogram of a siren. The arrow indicates the fundamental frequency increasing and decreasing as pitch changes.

this exercise, you will gain more and more vocal flexibility with changing pitch.

### Speaking and Singing Exercises for Pitch and Loudness

Let us look back at the P-L Chart from Figure 4–1. The P-L Chart illustrates the continuum of pitch and intensity. If you place your index finger in the lower left corner, you are instructing your voice to emit a low pitch (low tone on your siren) and low loudness (quiet, clear) sound. Try it, using a rote recitation like the ABCs. If successful, you are taking your voice to the lowest audible intensity (smallest amplitude of vibration) and the least number of cycles per second your vocal folds can vibrate. If you proceed to a whisper, you are continuing to exhale without bringing your vocal folds together to vibrate. Do not whisper during this exercise; keep voicing.

Continue ABC-ing as you slide your finger up the left side of the chart, telling yourself to increase pitch while keeping loudness low. At the upper left corner, you are displaying your highest frequency along with your lowest loudness. That is very quiet but high-pitched sound. If you are not used to this sort of exercise, you will require practice to control pitch and loudness independently.

Now proceed back down the P-L chart to low pitch and low loudness, then move along the bottom to low pitch and high loudness. Perform the exercise you did with cricoid tilt to achieve a louder voice. You will hear your voice get louder without the extra effort. You can also narrow your AES to get a louder voice. Finally, work your way up the right side. Eventually, you will reach your voice's upper limit in frequency and intensity, as high-pitched and loud as you can get. Some voice teachers call this part of the exercise "taking your chest voice to higher pitches." Because the vocal folds do not like to be stretched to their limit to produce a high pitch and then be asked to vibrate at a large amplitude of vibration, you may find yourself switching to a thin or stiff TVFBC condition to sound more like a falsetto quality or "head" voice. If you are throwing yourself into it, you may experience strain at this point, not to mention acute embarrassment if you did not take the precaution of isolating yourself from the ears of the people now listening as you screech the ABCs. After all, you are literally talking "at the top of your voice."

Do not give up on this exercise. You will want to slowly move up in pitch in small steps while maintaining a high intensity. Keep open and anchored. Exhale quickly to REL (like blowing out a match) and say "A, B, C." Raise your pitch slightly and stay loud as you repeat: Exhale quickly to REL and say "D, E, F." Keep moving up in pitch as you move through the alphabet.

If you do this alone, you may wish to record your voice and play it back. If you got as loud and high as you thought you did, you probably have reasonably good vocal awareness. If you thought you were louder than you sound on playback, your vocal awareness may be in question. It is risky to draw conclusions without a voice professional's help, but you will almost certainly find the exercise interesting and enlightening.

If you are a singer you can go through the P-L Chart with some slight modifications. Use a five-note scale starting at a comfortable pitch and stay in thin TVFBC. Count up the scale "1, 2, 3, 4, 5" and then back down "4, 3, 2, 1." Do not get louder on the way up the scale. Move up by half notes to the next scale. Go as high as you can go and work on keeping an open, anchored posture on the way up as well as the way back down for each scale. Sometimes AES narrow will help maintain a thin TVFBC throughout the exercise. Your low notes are as important as your high notes. Maintain your posturing—high tongue, high palate, wide pharynx, and anchors as you move through your scales. Once you have mastered this exercise, you can try it with thick TVFBC and even a belt quality (cricoid tilt). Remember all the things you have learned: Take a small inhale; keep an open, anchored posture; do not bear down; and do not push air.

As you improve your vocal range, you will attain access to greater vocal flexibility and increase your ability to say what you want to say in the way you want to say it. Although the vast majority of your utterances will locate well inside your P-L chart, it is certainly a comfort to know that your range is considerably greater than you thought. Couple this vocal competency with correct prosodic elements and your communication arsenal swells.

As you master the prosodic paraverbals, it is equally crucial to focus on vocal quality. The effective voice is strong, consistent, clear, and steady. It is free from breathiness, roughness, hoarseness, weakness, and strain. All these vocal characteristics will either enhance or detract from what you intend to transmit, so they too can be seen as paraverbals. Although a clear, strong voice may be viewed as authoritative, a weak, wobbly voice may be construed as unreliable, and a dry, creaky voice as tired, dismissive, or not serious. More detailed discussions of vocal quality occur in later chapters that address the specific intentions of communication.

## The Other Senses and Semantic Enrichment

There are myriad other sounds you make that are not exactly words or inflections. Such utterances, which often have precise meanings, can be called paraverbals because they are not composed of words, even though they may perform as commendably as any word in the dictionary. Here are some examples: "uh-huh," "uh-uh," "hm," "hunh" "aw," *whistle*, "yaay" "whew."

There are other sounds that are not vocal that serve as paraverbals. Context matters. Clapping, when done by an audience, signifies approval and delight. When your fifth-grade teacher clapped, it meant she was disgruntled with the unruliness of the class and insisted that you better quiet down posthaste. The sound of fingers strumming on a desktop can indicate impatience. Snapping those same fingers is a way of saying, "Just like that!" These paraverbals, along with other gestures, may well serve more than just a communicating function. They may help retention and learning, perhaps by reinforcing the verbal content (Cook, Mitchell, & Goldin-Meadow, 2008).

In short, the ears conduct huge amounts of meaning from many sources. Words are only the beginning. In fact, ears are only the beginning.

For the hearing and sighted, the other senses provide an amazing array of paraverbals that can enable you to hone and embellish your meaning, all that you intend to transmit. Some of these meaningful symbols likely preceded the development of voice (Allwood, 2002). You may not think of the sense of smell as a source of paraverbals, but people use perfumes and aftershaves to transmit, among other things, a desire for social acceptance; it is almost certain that the sweat glands of distant ancestors provided an inexpensive scented lotion that sent all the right signals—once upon a time. And that is just one of many examples (Theune, Heylen, & Nijholt, 2005).

In our culture it is safe to say that, after sound, it is the visual that provides the richest and most varied source of paraverbals. As if to emphasize the fact, when you speak face to face (note the phrase) to others, what you notice most immediately are their eyes, which may be innocent, shifty, shady, smitten, dewy, doey, or dry-eyed. When it comes to transmitting your innermost thoughts, the eyes have it (Figure 4–5). They are the window of the soul. When you are fascinated, they burn with interest; when not, they just glaze over. You use them to stare in amazement or barely register a passing glance. They may look up to you with respect or down on you with something less. A jaundiced eye, perhaps, or a probing eye, or, if worse comes to worst, the evil eye.

**Figure 4–5.** The eyes have it. Steady, energetic eye contact is, in mainstream U.S. culture, a key indicator of attention.

When asked to identify the most obvious way to indicate that a person is listening to another person, people universally agree that eye contact does it best (see Figure 4–5). In fact, eye contact seems to be anticipated of a listener in mainstream U.S. culture. There is surprisingly little empirical research on eye contact (Turkstra, 2005), but you can test this proposition by looking away when someone is speaking to you. The speaker will soon exhibit signs of uneasiness and will probably ask whether you are maintaining interest. The listener's eye contact is expected to be fairly constant. The speaker is allowed to establish more intermittent eye contact, and the expectations shift when the roles shift.

These expectations are cultural, not biologically based. In some cultures the steady eye contact favored in the United States is considered incorrect, even impolite. Among many mammalian species, eye contact is a sign of dominance or aggression, far from a friendly indicator of attentiveness (Hinde & Rowell, 1962). In all cultures the eyes send powerful paraverbal messages. If you plan to spend a lot of time interacting in mainstream U.S. culture, then it is a good idea to get comfortable with establishing eye contact with your neighbor.

In any population, shyness or some other habit of aversion will discourage a segment of people from making steady eye contact, even in one-to-one conversations. They will look down or away, or their eyes will dart and shift. Everyone knows how shifty-eyed people are thought of, so you should find a way to be comfortable looking into the eyes of another. If you suffer this aversion, practice making eye contact with people you know. Then practice with strangers in safe situations: in restaurants with a waiter, on planes with a passenger, at the checkout counter with a cashier.

This advice may seem silly, but look in a mirror. Put an interested expression on your face, become aware of what that expression feels like when you make it, and learn to use it when listening.

Along with eye contact, other movements can create useful paraverbals. There is a world of gestures available to enhance meaning. Good listeners use head nods and a pleasant smile to invite the speaker to continue. Noted researcher Allwood (2002) has written extensively about what are called paraverbals and how they serve to enhance and even create meaning in a communication exchange.

After the face, the hands are most attended to by those with whom you are communicating (Figure 4–6). Individuals who are deaf express the full lexicon of verbals with hand gestures; for the hearing, gestures contain mostly paraverbals. There are exceptions. If I see you down the street and wave, I am saying, "Hi." If a policeman raises his hand to me as my car approaches, I will receive the message, "Stop!" It could be argued that these are verbals, full gesticular messages.

For the most part, though, the hands are supporting players in the communication process. They enhance meaning, reinforce

***Figure 4–6.*** Putting it all together. An open, smiling face and comfortable, palm-up hand gestures display an attitude that creates a positive connection.

it, clarify it. There are a number of useful guidelines, derived from our Presentation Practicum, to keep in mind if you want to use your hands effectively as you transmit.

- The hands carry much meaning. If you employ them dysfunctionally, they will detract from your message and may actually cause confusion. Avoid random hand movements, as your listener will try to "interpret" them and, of course, create muddle rather than clarity.
- Gestures should be natural and comfortable (see Figure 4–6). Everyone has a gestural style. Use your own style, not someone else's.
- Frequency of gestures depends mainly on your style and, perhaps, your socialization and cultural background. Some people simply gesture more than others. It is useful, however, to learn to use gestures more effectively.
- All hand motions are likely to be viewed as gestures, so there should be a point to each motion. Avoid mannerisms like hands in pockets, behind back, crossed in front. These mannerisms convey no messages and serve only to distract your audience.
- A palm down or pushing gesture is off-putting. It says, "Be quiet," "No way," or "Hurry up and finish." Forms of the pushing gesture include pointing, the karate chop move, or the wrist wriggle. Usually, the hand(s) will start close to the body and move out.
- A palm up or pulling gesture is welcoming. It says, "Let me hear more" or "Come here." The hands assume an embracing motion and usually start away from the body and move in.
- Ninety percent of all gestures should take place close to your body between your waistline and shoulders: This is the effectiveness zone or effective zone of gestures. Gestures placed too low can signify a lack of assertiveness (Figure 4–7); gestures that are too high impede the receiver's view of the face.

Accompanying your gestures is your bearing: your posture and positioning. The decision to sit or stand sends a message. Assuming a posture that is straight, slouchy, tense, relaxed, or in

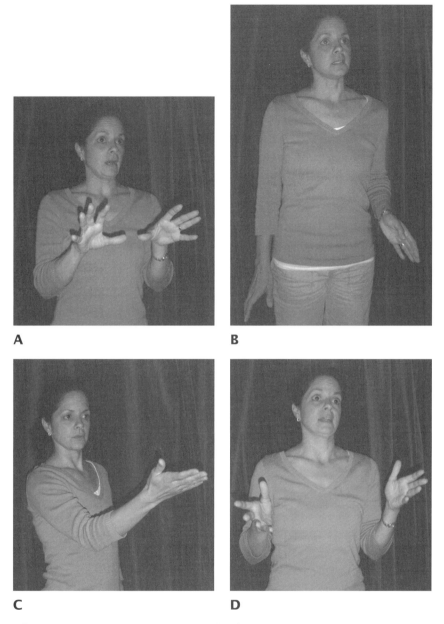

A        B

C        D

*Figure 4–7.* Hand talk. For the deaf, hand gestures contain the entire lexicon of language. For the hearing, hand movements are used mainly as paraverbals. This series shows some different effects created by changes in gesture. **A.** Although hands are in the effectiveness zone, the palm-down mode is disconnecting. **B.** Low gestures, as shown here, are less assertive. **C–D.** Higher, palm-up gestures are more welcoming.

perpetual motion will convey distinct emotional tones. Arthur, a Ph.D. professor at a renowned business college, was constantly receiving feedback from students that he seemed to lack authority; they were unsure he knew what he was talking about. The presentation coach who worked with him noticed at once that, although his voice was strong and authoritative, his posture was variable. He typically stepped back when asked a question. As he spoke he fidgeted, shifting from foot to foot. He was coached to stand straight but relaxed, to use fewer but more definite hand gestures, and reduce the amount of pacing. Arthur's students' perceptions of him improved markedly after a very short period of time. He needed almost no help with voice improvement.

Spatial positioning refers to your reference point, where you are in reference to the other(s). There are three basic positions, called the three Cs: confronting, collaborating, and cozying (Figure 4–8).

The confronting position is head to head, a position where you can reach across and easily grasp the other's throat if you so desire. Generally, this position is recommended if you wish to send a confrontive message: We are battling here and do not forget it. Sometimes, for example in voice therapy, the confronting position is ideal. The collaborating position is diagonally opposite (catty-corner) and is the position most likely to reinforce the notion that two adults are having a discussion, problem-solving, or sharing

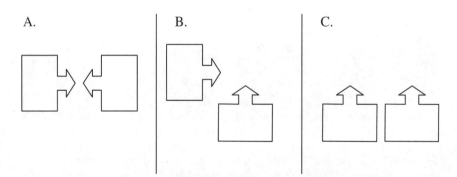

**Figure 4–8.** Three Cs of positioning. **A.** Confronting. Head-to-head positioning indicates a more aggressive posture. **B.** Collaborating. A diagonally opposite, catty-corner arrangement indicates a dialogue among equals. **C.** Cozying. The side-by-side position creates a more intimate posture.

ideas. It is a position of mutual respect. The cozying position is side by side and is recommended for two people on a date and not much else. "Cozying" sounds nice and comfy but it is often anything but.

As you can tell, there is a great deal to learn about verbals and paraverbals, the universe of symbols by which we hurl our intended meanings across to one another. Knowing less than you could learn about this universe amounts to semantic impoverishment, a willful reduction in the horsepower available to you as a communicator (Allwood, 2002). It is as if you decided to eliminate half your vocabulary, to just not use those words.

It is illogical even to consider such a strategy. Yet that is what you do if you decide not to avail yourself of the means to improve what your voice and body can do in the communication effort. That is what you do if you fail to make a serious study of the wealth of paraverbals our culture has accumulated. This kind of self-improvement is a lifetime pursuit, to be sure, but it is one with an enormous payoff. You are increasingly better able to get yourself across to others and better able to take in what they are trying to get across to you.

## Review of Key Ideas

- Verbals are the words we use in speech and writing.
- Paraverbals include the voice tone, gestures, and facial expressions that accompany the words and enhance meaning. Instead of the term nonverbals, paraverbals is used to connote that words are there in the transmission, but that, along with the words, there are other sensory realities that communicators call upon to enhance meaning.
- Syntax regulates language, structures it, and molds it into a form that enables communication.
- The basic component of language is the morpheme, the smallest unit of meaning. Morphemes are made up of linguistically distinctive sound units called phonemes. Lexemes are units roughly equivalent to what we call words, which can name a thing or concept, denote action, or describe attributes.

- A sentence expresses a thought that contains a subject (what the sentence is about) and a predicate (what the sentence has to say about the subject).
- A paragraph is a relatively short, tightly connected series of thoughts comprising one intelligible idea.
- Beyond the paragraph there is the essay. An essay contains a thesis, the intended message each time we speak (or write).
- The paraverbals most closely associated with the spoken words are intonation and inflection. When I recite a sentence I do so with inflection, utilizing variations in pitch and intensity to make my meaning clearer. Consider the sentence: "I didn't say you stole the pickles." Place the main stress on each word in that sentence and the sentence actually takes on seven quite different connotations.
- Changing pitch and loudness at will is a basic language skill. The P-L Chart is designed to promote vocal awareness and improve basic ability to distinguish pitch and loudness in the voice. With professional assistance and coaching participants learn effective posture and techniques to expand their vocal range with minimal effort or strain to their voices.
- As you master the prosodic paraverbals, it is equally crucial to focus on vocal quality. The effective voice is strong, consistent, clear, and steady. It is free from breathiness, roughness, hoarseness, weakness, and strain.
- The following guidelines are vital to producing an effective voice: Take a small inhale; keep an open, anchored posture; do not bear down; and do not push air.
- Other utterances that often have precise meanings, like "uh-huh," "uh-uh," "hunh," "eh" can be called paraverbals.
- In our culture, after sound, it is the visual that provides the richest source of paraverbals. The most obvious way to indicate that a person is listening is through eye contact.
- After the face, the hands are most attended to by those with whom you are communicating. Tips for effective gestures appeared earlier in this chapter.
- Use good posture and avoid pacing when communicating.
- Be mindful of spatial positioning, which refers to where you are in reference to the other(s). The three basic positions

are confronting, collaborating, and cozying. The collaborating position is diagonally opposite and is the position most likely to reinforce the notion that two adults are having a discussion, problem-solving, or sharing ideas. It is a position of mutual respect.

## References

Allwood, J. (2002). Bodily communication dimensions of expression and content. In B. Granström, D. House, & I. Karlsson (Eds.) *Multimodality in language and speech systems* (pp. 7–25). Dordrecht, The Netherlands: Kluwer Academic.

Cook, S. W., Mitchell, Z., & Goldin-Meadow, S. (2008). Gesturing makes learning last. *Cognition, 106*(2), 1047–1058.

Grandin, T. (2006). *Thinking in pictures: My life with autism.* New York, NY: Vintage Books.

Hinde, R. A., & Rowell, T. E. (1962). Communication by posture and facial expression in the rhesus monkey. *Proceeding of the Zoological Society of London, 138*(1), 1–21.

Klimek, M. M., Obert, K., & Steinhauer, K. (2005). *Estill voice training system level one: Compulsory figures for voice control.* Pittsburgh, PA: Estill Voice Training System International.

Lombard, L. E., & Steinhauer, K. M. (2007). A novel treatment for hypophonic voice: Twang therapy. *Journal of Voice, 21*(3), 294–299.

Lott, J. (2014). The use of the twang technique in voice therapy. *Perspectives on Voice and Voice Disorders, 24*(3), 119–123.

Pinker, S. (2000). *The language instinct: How the mind creates language.* New York, NY: Harper Perennial Modern Classics.

Smith, C. G., Finnegan, E. M., & Karnell, M. P. (2004). Resonant voice: Spectral and nasendoscopic analysis. *Journal of Voice, 19*(4), 607–622.

Stemple, J. C., Glaze, L., & Klaban, B. (2010). *Clinical voice pathology: Theory and management* (4th ed.). San Diego, CA: Plural.

Story, B. H., & Titze, I. R. (1994). Voice simulation with a body-cover model of the vocal folds. *Journal of the Acoustical Society of America, 97*(2), 1249–1260.

Theune, M., Heylen, D., & Nijholt, A. (2005). Generating embodied information presentations. In O. Stock & M. Zancanaro (Eds.), *Multimodal intelligent information presentation* (pp. 47–70). Berlin, Germany: Springer.

Titze, I. R., Bergan, C. C., Hunter, E. J., & Story, B. H. (2003). Source and filter adjustments affecting the perception of the vocal qualities twang and yawn. *Logopedics Phoniatrics Vocology, 28*(4), 147–155.

Titze, I. R., & Story, B. H. (1997). Acoustic interactions of the voice source with the lower vocal tract. *Journal of the Acoustical Society of America, 101*(4), 2234–2243.

Turkstra, L. S. (2005). Looking while listening and speaking: Eye-to-face gaze in adolescents with and without traumatic brain injury. *Journal of Speech, Language, and Hearing Research, 48*(6), 1429–1441.

Whorf, B. (1956). *Language, thought, and reality*. Cambridge, MA: MIT Press.

*Chapter 5*

# The Point of It All

*The comfort and advantage of society not being to be had without communication of thoughts, it was necessary that man should find out some external sensible signs, whereof those invisible ideas, which his thoughts are made up of, might be made known to others. For this purpose nothing was so fit, either for plenty or quickness, as those articulate sounds, which with so much ease and variety he found himself able to make.*

—John Locke, Philosopher

## The Voice in Action

It is not as if our voice is unimportant to us. More than 2300 years ago, Aristotle put speech on a pedestal when he defined "rhetoric" as "the faculty of observing in any given case the available means of [vocal] persuasion" (Honeycutt, 2011). Persuasion is the art of the rhetorician, whom we today would call an orator or speaker. Rhetoric, then, is the voice in use to persuade others. The great philosopher saw three divisions of persuasiveness used by speakers to sway their audience.

The first is *ethos* or credibility, the moral authority of the voice to convey the good character of the speaker. One of the most famous American speeches of all time, Dr. Martin Luther King Jr.'s "I Have a Dream," is generally agreed to carry this moral authority. When we discuss credibility in a later chapter, this moral dimension will be more fully explored.

The second rhetorical division is *pathos*, the speaker's power to stir the emotions. A speech that stirs, rouses, and grips its audience employs pathos. Applications of this concept appear in the chapter, "Moving Them." The third division is *logos*, the logic and sound argumentation that convinces the mind that what is said is true because it is rational. The logos of Lincoln's immortal two-minute speech, the "Gettysburg Address," is argued more heartily today than in its own time. The chapter on persuasion discusses this division of rhetoric.

The ancient Greeks and Romans valued rhetoric, the persuasive use of the voice, and honored its best exponents. Three hundred years after Aristotle, the Roman orator Cicero was justly noted for the use of his commanding voice before the Senate and elsewhere. His surviving speeches remain a model of classical Latin, as any third year Latin student can (not always happily) attest. Our best orators always leave behind a linguistic trail of memorable clippings, from "I have a dream . . . " to " . . . that government of the people, by the people, for the people, shall not perish from the earth."

If rhetoric is the voice in use to persuade, song uses the voice to bring music to our ears. The application of the voice to song is likely as ancient as its use in speech, perhaps more so. Our ancestors likely mimicked the melodies of the animals they heard. It is probable that the more talented individuals eventually achieved notice for their ability to raise their voices in song. Voice as music became entertainment.

Centuries later, when Thomas Edison presented his phonograph (a combination of the words "telephone" and "telegraph," the two inventions that inspired it) to the world in 1877, it initially did not sell well. Its presence as a mainstay of entertainment in every home that could afford it was only ensured after the great Italian tenor Enrico Caruso cut his remarkable voice into the rotating disk in the early 1900s. Great singing was something people wanted to hear, and the universal hunger for it has never abated.

The enduring popularity of Broadway musicals, TV shows like "The Voice" and "America's Got Talent," and use of the term rock star to denote anyone who rises to great prominence—all these phenomena demonstrate the overwhelming allure of the human voice in song. The study of the singing voice is centuries old; the advent of voice science has unlocked a tremendous and growing deposit of data about the voice as a musical agent.

One branch of science, linguistics, connects voice not with song but with meaningful utterances. Linguistics embodies two major divisions. The first involves the study of how the elements of language play together to create the miracle of communication in voice, sign, and writing. This first division examines grammar, syntax, and semantics: the things we voice or sign and how they become language. The second division explores the sounds themselves: how they are made, combined, and received. Linguistics studies the foundations, structures, and uses of language. You might say that linguistics covers most of the reasons the voice is of interest to us. All those reasons involve the voice in the act of communication.

## Communication and the Missed Connection

In his presentation skills workshops, Lonnie uses a typical podium to illustrate the "most important aspect" of presenting. Standing behind the lectern, all but his head and shoulders are obscured by the big wooden carton looming between him and his listeners.

Lonnie looks over the podium out at the group. "Does this thing connect me to you or disconnect me?" There is no hesitation in the response. It disconnects. It creates distance. It puts the speaker and the audience on two sides of an obvious divide.

Lonnie believes that those large obtrusive lecterns are made to create separation, to set the speaker apart from the audience. They put us in mind of the church pulpit placed far above and far away from the congregation, an actual wall between preacher and people. Perhaps this design is intended to confer authority upon the speaker, make the speaker special, someone apart.

The problem is that this divider exacts a price for creating specialness. Visually and logically the special person does not identify with the audience; the audience is deliberately separated, pushed away, literally lowered. Separation is reinforced by directionality. As the orator looks down at the listeners, they become acutely aware that they are being spoken to. The messages flow from orator to audience, and that's it—one direction only. This form of directionality can only enhance the sense of separateness.

Stepping behind a podium is not the only way to defeat your purpose when you attempt to make the communication connection.

Medical researchers looked at communication failure in the operating room and identified four ways people involved in surgery failed to connect: occasion, content, audience, and purpose failures (Lingard et al., 2004). This study reported that 30% of the observed attempts to communicate failed in one way or another and, of that 30%, 34% resulted in outcomes that jeopardized the patient.

In the study, almost half the missed connections happened because data was asked for or delivered too late to be useful. These missed connections are called *occasion failures*. An example would be a surgeon asking if anesthesia had been administered one hour into the operation. A seemingly great question to ask, except that one hour into the surgery is too late for the inquiry to nudge the anesthesiologist or double check that anesthesia had been given. It may seem unlikely that such a question would be asked well into a surgery, but this was a real example observed during the study. Pretty much the only response is either "Yes" or "OMG"; neither is very helpful.

Effective communication is timely communication. When the marriage official tells you to speak now or forever hold your peace, the official is indicating that a post-ceremony objection is useless. Cari instructs future speech-language pathologists about the need for effective communication in the clinical setting and she is acutely aware of the importance of timing. When students learn about a topic in class, it is most beneficial for them to have an immediate opportunity to trial the skills with a client in the clinic. Occasion failure can rear its ugly head if too much time elapses between learning the skill and practicing it in a real-world setting.

The reverse can happen as well. Students are encouraged to discuss challenges they experience in clinic during the next class while the event is fresh in their minds. Exploring a topic after a related experience can be illuminating. Students have the opportunity to explain what they tried and how well it worked. The instructor and classmates discuss and give advice for improvement in the future. If the class is held a month or so after the experience, the chances of occasion failure are greatly heightened.

*Content failures* are another type of missed connection. In this failure type the information given is either insufficient or wrong. An example is an anesthesiologist asking a nurse or medical technician if an ICU bed is available and the other replying that "we

don't really need an ICU bed" and "there probably isn't one ready."
Asking about the availability of a bed infers that the need for an
ICU bed was already established. The information provided by
the nurse or medical technician is insufficient to make a quality
decision until something more definite is determined. A second,
less frequent example of a content failure is wrong information, as
happens when the nurse says that an ICU room is available, but
the nurse's statement turns out to be untrue.

You are less likely to miss the connection if you know what
information is required for you to proceed. If you are the one
supplying the information, you need to know what information
must be given or know who to ask for it. It is unfortunate for you
when communication is untimely, either too early or too late. It
is downright frustrating when the communication is given at precisely the right moment, but the information is wrong or misleading. A good way to forestall this failure is to double check that the
information given is on point and then make sure the message is
accurate and complete.

The third type of missed connection happens when not all the
right people are in on the conversation. This is an *audience failure.*
Let us go back to the operating room. An audience failure can happen if the nurse and the anesthesiologist discuss how to position
a patient prior to the arrival of the surgeon. The surgeon has the
last word on patient positioning; his absence probably made their
whole discussion irrelevant or, at best, inefficient.

Lonnie has found audience failure to be very common at business meetings and school faculty meetings. Lengthy conversations
are held while a key party is missing. Much time can be wasted
when everything has to be repeated once that key player arrives.
If someone in the group says, "Well, we can't do anything about
this without Max" or "Max needs to be filled in on all these points,"
you may well be in the throes of an audience failure. Waiting for all
key players to be in attendance before continuing a conversation or
meeting will minimize the risk of this type of missed connection.

The fourth type of missed connection is a *purpose failure,*
where the objective of the communication is muddled, inappropriate, or simply not achieved. Imagine you are at an airport. You must
catch a connecting flight and you do not have much time. You
approach an airline official to ask at what terminal and gate you
need to be to get to your connecting flight. The official begins talk-

ing about the fact that your airline used to have all its connecting flights in Terminal A, but then the airport added Terminal D. Yes, you are getting information but not information that achieves your purpose. You still do not know where your next plane is parked. Just having a discussion does not guarantee that the objective of the discussion is attained.

Researchers have noticed that purpose failures and content failures are similar. You could read the airport example above as a failure to give correct or complete information, but you could easily see it as a failure to achieve the purpose. Identifying the most suitable label for the failure is less important than taking effective steps to assure that the failure does not occur. One way to thwart purpose failure is to keep your eye on the information you need and insist that the other person supply that information.

These four categories of missed connections give you some idea how humans fail to communicate effectively. Sometimes we are too late—or too early—with our message or our request. Other times we receive insufficient or just plain incorrect information. A key player may be missing from the discussion, or the discussion might be unsuccessful in meeting its objective. Whatever the failure—occasion, content, audience, or purpose—the result is detachment when there should be engagement, separateness when there should be connection.

In the scenario below see if you can detect each of the four missed connections and assess how effectively the connection is re-established. Instead of an operating theater, this conversation takes place at a marketing team meeting. The participants are: Norabelle, the VP of marketing and sales; Vic, the financial manager; Ranee, the product manager; and Naomi, head of human capital management. They are discussing the rollout of a new product.

Norabelle: OK, I received an email from corporate: "The XM11 is due to be ready for delivery to our stores in exactly one month."

Ranee: That's four weeks.

Vic: No, it's one month, Ranee. Today is October 7; rollout is November 7. That's four weeks and three days.

Ranee: How do you know that? Does the email clarify this, Norabelle?

Norabelle: No.

Vic: We should discuss it, then. Three days makes a difference for my financial planning.

Naomi: I think a month is meant to be four weeks. That's the way I always interpret it.

Vic: No, it's most likely a month, from one date to the same date the next month.

Norabelle: OK, let's be conservative and say it's four weeks. OK? OK, four weeks it is. Our next issue is human capital requirements. How many work hours do we need to divert to get ready for the rollout?

Naomi: I've run some preliminary numbers. We need about five full time equivalences for the next four weeks.

Vic: I can spare four. We're in a lull this time of year.

Ranee: That's good. I can spare Angela, our supply chain supervisor.

Norabelle: Then our problem is solved. That's five!

Naomi: Not quite, Norabelle. You're giving me four accountants and a supply chain person. I need two marketing people, a sales rep, and accountant, and a supply chain person.

Norabelle: Oops. [Discussion yields the right mix.]

Vic: Now, how much money do we need up front? This rollout was not in the budget. We didn't even know about it until a few weeks ago.

Norabelle: Corporate estimates $76,000.

Vic: Based on what?

Norabelle: I don't know. We'll just have to live with that.

Vic: But I'm tight right now. Do I just print money?

Norabelle: Just relax, Vic. I'll get you a breakdown in two weeks.

Vic: That's half the time we have. Managers need more notice to adjust for the shortfall.

Norabelle: No sweat, Vic. You'll handle it. Now, I'm going to need a project head to lead this effort.

Ranee: I'm happy to do it. What are my goals and objectives?

Norabelle: Simple. Make sure the product is rolled out in four weeks.

Ranee: Well, yes, but what does that even mean?

Norabelle: It means roll the product out in four weeks. If there are no more questions, the meeting is adjourned.

Was Norabelle's meeting successful? Were the essential communication connections made? Go back over the scenario and see if you can pinpoint missed connections. See if you can identify the types of failures and whether or not the failure was addressed. You can try this on your own. In the next few paragraphs the scenario is analyzed for communication failures.

The first potential failure is an occasion failure. Norabelle is not clear on how much time is available to prepare for the rollout. It could be four weeks or four weeks and three days. No big deal, you might say, except that Vic, the financial manager, says it is a big deal. Good for Vic. He identifies the occasion failure and seeks clarification.

Is the matter cleared up? No, it is not. Norabelle dismisses Vic's concern. The occasion failure turns into a purpose (or possibly content) failure, as Norabelle decrees that the email will be interpreted to mean that a month is four weeks. Vic has just been deprived of three days prep time, which, in reality, might be available to him.

Next, human capital manager Naomi asks for five people to work on the planning. Norabelle solicits five people and declares the problem solved. "Wait!" Naomi says. "We don't need just five people. We need five people with various levels of expertise and competence." In this case, Norabelle and the team address the misconnection and repair the failure.

On the question of budget, Norabelle is clearly committing a content failure. She has some information on the total budgetary allotment, but Vic needs specifics. An audience failure may also have occurred, because someone from corporate is probably needed to interpret the numbers. Someone with authority to change the budget might also be useful. As it is, Vic is left with a poor understanding of his financial constraints and allowances.

Examples of communication failures can point to a way of clarifying what it means to be an effective communicator. You will be exploring effective communication in great detail throughout this book. At this point, you want to get a feel for what a missed connection is like. The next section looks at connection and meaning.

## Communication as an Act of Connection Through Meaning

If this book is about anything, it is about reversing the separateness you encountered in the Norabelle scenario and creating a unique kind of human connection. Connection in this usage is defined as the linking of two or more people. Two people can be linked in infinite ways but we are discussing a specific kind of connection: one that requires work, the kind of work that results in common meaning and avoids the missed connections of communication failure. Through that act of communicating (a word that actually means "making common"), we achieve that particular connection.

To attain a connection through meaning you need to grasp what meaning means. If that sounds circular, it is. After all, writing these paragraphs is an act of communication, connection through meaning. Ask yourself this: When you say, "Here's what I mean," what do you mean? Okay, before the word loses all meaning, let us get to it.

Meaning can be defined as "intending to communicate." To mean is to have the intention to get a thought across to another. Before a thought is intended to be sent across to someone else, it is not yet meaning; it is a thought. It is not meant, at least not yet. Meaning, then, is a thought on a mission, a thought in transit, a thought on the wing. It is a thought placed in packaging suitable for delivery.

When that packaged thought is sent successfully, the recipient can always say with conviction, "I got what you meant." To connect through meaning is to find a way to ensure that the thought in me gets across to you in the same form as it exists in me. If I say, "Duck!" and you lower your head thereby avoiding an oncoming Frisbee, I smile knowing I have made the connection. If I say, "Duck!" and, head held aloft, you listen for an expected quack, thereby experiencing an unexpected thwack from the aforementioned Frisbee, what we have here is a failure to communicate.

What meaning does is bring two or more people together, connecting them in a singular way. That connection is a thought that, through their mutual effort (communication), they make common or share. Or, at the least, the connection is a thought that one party imparts and the other receives. That thought may be a sliver of trivial data, a universal verity, an impulse to act, a bald-faced lie, or the incitement of an emotion. If it is something I can communicate to you, it is on the list.

When I give voice to a thought, when I send it across to you, it does not embark unaccompanied. Traveling with the thought always, inexorably, is an honor guard consisting of me. I do not say, "This thought wants to communicate with you." I say, "I want to communicate with you." When I make the connection through meaning, then, I reveal not only the thought but also myself or at least something of myself. When Aristotle spoke of ethos as a mode of rhetorical persuasion, he held that the voice carried nothing less than the character of the speaker. Part of my message, therefore, is always my self.

## Modes of Connection: Using the Five Senses

Connection, of course, implies at least two terminals, two endpoints, which are often designated as transmitter and receiver. Those two terms are helpful, but a bit misleading. In the real world communication consists of the transmission and reception of thoughts and feelings, a simultaneous interactive relay. The flow always moves both ways at once. That fact helps to clarify the flaw in the orator-listener model of communication often perceived as unidirectional.

The interpersonal project is nothing less than a meeting of minds and hearts across whatever the gulf that divides one person from another. The word *project* is itself illustrative of the act of connection. Project literally means the act of throwing forth. That is what you do when you transmit. You throw your intended message forth into the world, specifically at another person (or persons). The reason you can do this is that you have launch capabilities, mechanisms that allow you physically to send thoughts from within you into the air about your listener. These mechanisms include the expressions on your face, the gestures of your hands, and, to be sure, the sounds of your voice.

Fortunately, your intended receivers have complementary mechanisms suitable for receiving these messages. The eye can see the faces and the gestures; ears can hear the vocal utterances. The sense of touch may also be employed as your communication partner receives your handshake, takes a friendly elbow to the ribs, or marvels at the tactile gesticulation of deaf-blind manual language. The seeing eye, the listening ear, the touching hand are the receptors that complete the connection. Like voice and gesture, they too can be honed, exercised, and improved to enhance the interpersonal project.

## Ways to Mean: The Kinds of Connection

There are five primary intentions of communication, the reasons you make connections when communicating. They are: information, small talk, self-affirmation, persuasion, and emotion or feeling. We call these The 5 Intentions of Communication. We will discuss each intention in detail in subsequent chapters.

Along with The 5 Intentions, which are the reasons we connect through communication, there are four *types* of connection, the ways we connect, the kinds of content in a given item of communication. These are the fundamental ways in which you establish common meaning with another, and any of these types can be found in all five intentions. Understanding these types of connections and utilizing them appropriately make missed connections less likely. These four are (1) facts or data; (2) arguments or logic; (3) loyalties or kinship; (4) narratives or stories (Table 5–1).

You can connect with another by transmitting or receiving facts or data. Even though this mode of connection is found in all

**Table 5-1.** Four Ways to Establish Common Meaning

| 1. Facts or Data | Instruct, update, and inform about what is occurring or has occurred |
|---|---|
| 2. Arguments or Logic | Reach agreement on a conclusion supported by facts or analysis |
| 3. Loyalties or Kinship | Maintain allegiance to a person, principle, or an ideal |
| 4. Narratives or Stories | Depict a sequence of linked events |

five intentions, it aligns with the informational intention, which will be addressed in a later chapter. The motivation to connect in this way stems from a desire to know or to impart knowledge.

A fact is a statement denoting something that has really occurred or is really the case. We impart facts to instruct, to update, and to let the other know what is going on. Research, scientific experimentation, yields verifiable forms of data. You make less rigorously researched statements of fact constantly on a daily basis. Less edifying talk, like gossip, falls into this fact category, too. These statements purport to be true but, obviously, some of the assertions might not stand up to careful scrutiny. For our purposes, that possibility does not put the statements into a different category. They are still fact-data kinds of statements.

The second type of communication connection is logic or argument. These bits of communication start with facts but then muster those facts to support a conclusion. This type of connection often links with the persuasive intention discussed in a later chapter. That chapter also delves into the way logic is employed in argument.

Argument is a specific and common use of communication, communication designed to show that a conclusion follows from previously ascertained facts. Argument does not merely say, "This is true." Argument contends, "This is true because . . . " You are proposing an argument if you say, "A bird in the hand is worth two in the bush because you have the bird in the hand but the birds in the bush will fly away as soon as you approach them."

Argument can be expressed much more assertively than that. You can issue a simple command: "Get me a glass of water." or "Stay away from me." More polite phraseology, using "please" or "may

I," changes the tone but not the kind of connection. These orders or commands are argument because a logic is implied. "Get me a glass of water or I shall be thirsty." "Stay away from me or I will damage you." The logic is always there in these statements, even if that logic is never expressed aloud.

The third connection takes you from what is to what ought to be. It moves from statements about what is true to statements about what is right. An archaic word, fealty, is called into service to specify what is being discussed here. Fealty means keeping faith, maintaining your allegiance to a person, a principle, or an ideal.

A fealty statement can be a personal testimony. If so, it often takes the form of an I-statement, a statement about the self. "I would never do that." "I think that's the correct thing to do." Such statements announce your fidelity to a certain concept of right and wrong.

Fealty can also be expressed in terms of a principle. "Theft is wrong," displays fealty, as does, "don't steal," or the familiar, "Thou shalt not steal." All statements of morality or correct behavior fall into this category. An ideal can evoke fealty. The entire Pledge of Allegiance is a statement of fealty to the ideals represented by the flag of the United States.

Loyalty to a person or persons is fealty, too. Family members express such loyalty when they say that they will "always be there" for the loved one. The motto of Boys' Town, "He ain't heavy, Father, he's my brother," is a fealty statement which interestingly seems counterfactual, since the boy making the claim is hoisting a child almost as big as he is. In earlier times, knights pledged loyalty to the king (the word "fealty" literally fits in that instance).

The fourth way of connecting is through story. Story is a narrative depicting an event or a sequence of linked events. A story can be true or documentary. A story can be made up or imagined. Imagined stories might begin, "Once upon a time . . . " Documentary stories are more likely to begin, "In September 1943 . . . "

Story is an ancient form of connection, as can be seen in cave art produced possibly as long ago as 30,000 years. Children are adroit storytellers, always ready to reveal "what happened" and often in vivid and colorful language. Their storytelling improves their language skills and their confidence, especially in front of others (Hayes, 1989).

We use story for many purposes. This book recounts dozens of stories, like the Norabelle scenario above, to illustrate various points. Stories are used to prove a point as well. "Let me tell you what happened to the last person who tried to ski down that slope." Sometimes we tell a story to entertain or reinforce notions of right and wrong, smart and dumb, knowledgeable and ignorant. Stories populate all five intentions; they add depth and richness to the conversation.

Story is perhaps the most human of connections because it depicts us involved in our world and asks the listener to experience a reality as we are experiencing it. It can be the shortest of short stories: "I once ate at that restaurant and paid the consequences for a week afterwards." It can be as long as *The Hunger Games* trilogy or longer.

A story can be funny, scary, historical, fantastical, simple, or complex. It can be about people, chimpanzees, space aliens, or glaciers—pretty much anyone or anything. As long as it contains a narrative, an event of some kind, it is story.

Fact, argument, fealty, and story, these are the ways you connect with another. When your efforts hit the mark, the result of that connection is a shared understanding or common meaning. That sharing warrants discussion.

## Common Meaning: A Successful Connection

Connection, as we have said, finds a way to ensure that the thought in you gets across to your communication partner in the same form as it exists in you. We have called this "connection through meaning." When it happens, you and the receiver have established common meaning. What you intended to say has been received by your partner as you intended it. Communication is the creation of common meaning. It is intentional, not accidental. Transmitter and receiver both participate energetically in the creative act; both forge the meaning that is shared.

As Malle and Knobe (1997) describe intentionality, it is a complex notion. An action is considered intentional if the person doing the intending had a desire for something to happen, a conviction that the action would cause the thing to happen, an intention to perform the action, the ability to perform the action, and awareness that the person was, in fact, doing what the person intended when performing the action.

Although there is abundant evidence that communication is intentional (Levinson, 1983), the notion that all communication is intentional is not without controversy. There are those who firmly believe that poets and artists transmit messages they never thought of as long as their observer or listener claims to receive it. Our definition of communication simply contends something different. Our definition restricts the notion of communication to an intentional connection through meaning. In fact, "intentional connection through meaning" is redundant because meaning, as we have stated, refers to that which a transmitter intends to transmit.

From the point of view of the receiver, of course, meaning is the successful retrieval of what the transmitter intended to transmit. To achieve this success, a receiver must be ready to hear and understand; that readiness is contingent upon a few fundamental capacities and motivations.

Readiness to hear requires first that the receiver comprehend the language of the transmitter, be it English, ASL, Hindi, or any other language. It is also important that the receiver share some context with the transmitter. If I am spinning for you an esoteric hypothesis in higher-level quantum physics, good luck if you have no physics background! You and I may both be speaking English, but you do not speak Quantum. The connection will fail; we will not achieve common meaning. This ability of a listener to grasp precisely what a sender intends to transmit is, according to psychologists Krauss and Morsella (2000), "truly remarkable," given the number of possible meanings in even the simplest sentence.

Along with a common linguistic context, you also need sensory capacities—hearing if being spoken to, sight if someone is signing, touch if using Braille. Furthermore, you must be motivated to listen to transmitters; you must want to get their message. You must be able and willing to invest the time, energy, and focus necessary to make the connection. You must have some level of commitment to getting my message.

The other side of the connection is the actor, the one performing the role of transmitter. As sender, the transmitter must also have certain skills, knowledge, abilities, and motivations, starting with the obvious linguistic competence. The speaker may span the skill gamut from serviceable to eloquent, but some level of ability must be present so that the meaning can be packaged or formulated, made suitable for delivery to the listener.

If using audible speech, your vocal mechanism must be in working order and that encompasses a lot of functioning parts as we saw so clearly in Chapter 2. Giving voice is many things, but it is always and definitively a physical act. The sound of your voice, its intonation—melody, or lack thereof—its pitch, and loudness are all meaningful factors in communication. In the United States, a drop in pitch to a major key at the end of a phrase denotes that a statement is being made. A rise in pitch to a major key at the end of a phrase insinuates that you are asking a question. If you intend to make a statement but you raise your pitch at the end of the phrase, you can imagine the confusion your listener may feel. You may be perceived as either unsure or unconfident.

A gravelly, slack voice may indicate tiredness or a relaxed state. A person with a clear, loud voice may be perceived as boisterous or confident. The voice carries a lot of meaning during communication, whether intended or not. Speakers must be cognizant of the impact their voices have when communicating. Listeners should also be aware that the voice may influence the perception of an individual's emotional state, character, maturity, or intelligence.

As stated above, meaning also implies intention, the motivation to send a thought to another. To communicate, I must want to communicate. There is work to be done, a package of meaning to be built, a connection to be made. Success in this effort is no accident.

The results of all the talents, skills, and motivations of transmitter and receiver are twin packages of meaning, as close to identical twins as possible. In speech science this process is seen as a production-perception cycle. On the production side is the package in the speaker that is wrapped up and sent to you. On the speech perception side is the package that winds up in you, the one you unwrap and figure out. And there, at long last, emerges the ultimate achievement that is the communication process, the whole point of connection.

*Understanding.*

## Review of Key Ideas

■ Rhetoric is the voice in use to persuade others. The three divisions of persuasiveness are ethos, pathos, and logos.

- The science of linguistics embodies two divisions: (1) how the elements of language play together to create communication in voice, sign, and writing; and (2) the sounds themselves, how they are made, combined, and received.
- The four missed connections or communication failures are (1) occasion failure when we are too late or too early with our message or our request; (2) content failure, when we receive insufficient or just plain incorrect information; (3) audience failure, when a key player is missing from the discussion; (4) purpose failure, when the discussion is unsuccessful in meeting its objective.
- Meaning can be defined as "intending to communicate." To mean is to have the intention to get a thought across to another. Meaning connects two people in a singular way. That connection is a thought that, through their mutual effort, two people make common or share. Part of my message, too, is always my self.
- Communication is the two-way transmission and reception of thoughts and feelings, a simultaneous interactive relay. The flow always moves both ways at once. Communication is the creation of common meaning.
- Transmission requires mechanisms that allow me to send thoughts physically from within me to another. These mechanisms include the expressions on my face, the gestures of my hands, and the sounds from my lips. Receivers have complementary mechanisms. The seeing eye, the listening ear, the touching hand are the receptors that complete the connection.
- There are four types of connection, the ways in which common meaning with another is established. These four are (1) facts or data; (2) arguments or logic; (3) loyalties or kinship; (4) narratives or stories.
- Readiness to hear presupposes that the receiver understands the language of the transmitter, shares a common linguistic context with the transmitter, possesses sensory capacities to receive the message, and has the motivation to listen.
- The sender must have linguistic competence (if speaking), a vocal mechanism in working order, and the intention to send a thought to another.

■ The desired results of all the talents, skills, and motivations of transmitter and receiver are identical twin packages of meaning, a speech production-perception cycle. What emerges is the ultimate achievement of the communication process: understanding.

# References

Hayes, David (1989). Children as storytellers. *Reading Horizons*, Winter, 139–146.
Honeycutt, L. (2011). *Aristotle's rhetoric*. Retrieved from http://rhetoric. eserver.org/aristotle/
Krauss, R. M., & Morsella, E. (2000). Conflict and communication. In M. Deutsch & P. Coleman (Eds.), *The handbook of constructive conflict resolution: Theory and practice* (pp. 131–143). San Francisco, CA: Jossey-Bass.
Levinson, S. C. (1983). *Pragmatics*. Cambridge, England: Cambridge University Press.
Lingard, L., Espin, S., Whyte, S., Regehr, G., Baker, G. R., Reznick, R., . . . Grober, E. (2004). Communication failures in the operating room: An observational classification of recurrent types and effects. *Quality & Safety in Health Care, 13*(5), 330–334.
Malle, B. F., & Knobe, J. (1997). The folk concept of intentionality. *Journal of Experimental Social Psychology, 33*(2), 101–121.

# SECTION II

## A Human Connection

# Chapter 6

# Why You Transmit: The 5 Intentions

*The greatest thing in family life is to take a hint when a hint is intended—and not to take a hint when a hint isn't intended.*

—Robert Frost

## Choosing Your Intention

Up to this point, you have explored the tools of direct communication, especially the voice and its role in the production of language for the hearing. You now know that communication is connection through meaning, the process of transferring a thought from one person to another. In fact, meaning can be defined as "intending to communicate," that is, to communicate something, a particular thought.

The rest of this book is dedicated to understanding these intentions and improving your ability to fulfill the intentions with the role of the voice sustaining a significant focus. The key question is: Why do you transmit? Why are you bothering another person with a request for his or her attention? Obviously, there are an infinite number of thoughts you could be sending off at a particular time. All those thoughts, however, can be grouped into categories, reasons you tap someone on the shoulder and begin speaking to that person. Some researchers have posited three categories of intentions, some four (Share, Jolls, & Thoman, 2002). In this book five categories are identified. They are called The 5 intentions.

It is entirely possible that some element of all five intentions is present in every transmission, and you will investigate that possibility as you proceed. Importantly, however, one these five intentions is usually front and center, predominant, in a single transmission. It is crucial for speakers to recognize which intention is foremost because that awareness clarifies for them just why they are speaking. It is equally important for listeners to discover which of these five intentions is predominant because that knowledge is necessary for listeners to decode the message with clarity and precision. In theater, actors need to decide their character's intention to deliver a line effectively. A slight deviation in intention could skew the audience's perception and leave them confused about the outcome of a scene.

The 5 Intentions are self-affirmation, small talk, information exchange, persuasion/direction, and feeling.

## Self-Affirmation

Whenever you open your mouth and speak to another, you are affirming yourself. You are making a claim on another person's attention, implicitly declaring that you and your message are worthy of that person's time and consideration. Self-affirmation is present in everything you say, every transmission you make. Sometimes, self-affirmation is not only there, it is the main reason you open your mouth to speak (Figure 6–1).

A not overly attractive form of self-affirmation is windbagging, saying whatever comes to mind just to let the listener know you exist. Researchers like Gollwitzer and Wicklund (1985) have discovered that speakers not only have a self-concept but that they will often go to great lengths to reconfirm that concept, especially if they believe that self-concept has been challenged or denied. Self-completion theory (Gollwitzer & Wicklund, 1985) implies that windbagging, as it were, may have a distinct purpose. This theory explicitly states that individuals will actively pursue an acknowledgement of an aspect of their self-concept that has been called into question. They will speak out in defense of their view of themselves.

Sometimes self-affirmation takes the form of self-promotion, singing one's own praises. When individuals feel they are being

**Figure 6–1.** Self-affirmation.

observed or judged, they use self-promotion to enhance others' opinion of them. If you are clever, you will not just brag. You might feign modesty: "I never thought I could do it, but . . . " Or you might discount the virtuosity of what you did: "Not that it was a big deal, but . . . " In any event, self-promotion is a way of asserting your value, skill, achievements, or genius. Promoting the other person can also be a form of self-promotion. You flatter others so they think more highly of you.

There is another species of self-affirmation that can be called classroom participation. This intention was evident during a teleconference in which consultant Ryan was a participant. He joined more than 50 consultants from all over the United States; the floor was open to questions throughout the call. One caller, Joplin Trylon, repeatedly raised his virtual hand with increasingly inane questions and comments. After the sixth or seventh incursion by Mr. Trylon, a bemused caller remarked that the man was compensating for not being called on in the third grade. Self-affirmation can take this form—a near compulsion to issue a comment or come up with a question just to be noticed.

These examples of self-affirmation may seem to spin this intention in a negative light, but rest assured that affirming self is everyone's primary intention at one time or another. Not all self-affirmation needs to be obnoxious. People often take notice of the boisterous self-affirmer, but you should also be on the look out for the quiet self-affirmer—the one whose very silence is an appeal for your attention. Other intentions are also present, but presenters are unquestionably affirming themselves when they sketch their biography at the beginning of a presentation. Protesters participate in self-affirmation when they proclaim their beliefs or values. Teachers all but say "I'm the one to be listened to" when they try to regain the attention of their errant class.

## Small Talk

Often implicated in self-affirmation, but wider in scope, small talk is a second reason to transmit. Small talk is chit-chat, banter about seemingly trivial matters (Figure 6–2). Even though self-affirmation

*Figure 6–2.* Small talk.

may take the form of small talk, there are many more occasions for small talk than for self-affirmation. Small talk almost always involves information, though the information is less important than the function of the small talk. In fact, small talk serves several useful functions in human discourse.

Relationship building, the first function of small talk, is one of the most frequent occasions for chatting. You can use small talk to become better acquainted with your listener. Managers use it to get to know their team members. Facilitators and professors use it to give workshop participants and students an opportunity to "say something about themselves" before the heavy duty topics make their appearance. Health care professionals use it to build comfort and rapport with their clients or patients. Icebreakers are a form of small talk. All these activities have a major "getting to know you" component.

Small talk can involve paraverbals, so it is not always talk. Allwood (2002) calls these types of paraverbals "tertiary props." A cup of coffee and donuts can enhance the moment and the message. An offer of a martini holds a different nuance. A seminar arranged in a U-shape speaks to a desire to forge relationships. Although these paraverbals may appear far from crucial, the first function of small talk, relationship building, may be quite important. Certain people under medical care, for instance, have been shown to benefit from the simple opportunity to talk about their experiences or their feelings (White, White & Russell, 2007; Hogg, Garratt, Shaw & Tagney, 2007). Small talk is not necessarily small time.

A second function of small talk is climate setting, which is often used to set the stage for another intention. A presenter who segues to a new phase of a presentation by involving the participants in an inconsequential task is setting the climate for fuller participation after a heavy dose of lecture. Health care providers seek to put a patient at ease prior to disclosing a significant diagnosis. When a manager says, "Take a seat, Mario, I have something to tell you," she is using a more brusque form of small talk to transmit that a serious matter is about to be broached.

A third use of small talk is relaxation. During lunch, I meet you in the cafeteria and for forty minutes we chat about nothing vital; we are just taking a break. Attending a concert is actually a stylized form of this type of small talk in which the functions of the communication are to entertain and be entertained (Share, Jolls, &

Thoman, 2002). It is odd to suggest that listening to a musical performance is engaging in small talk but that is exactly what is going on, at least with the communication process as we have defined it. As with any communicators, the performers' intention is to make a meaningful connection with the audience members.

## Information Exchange

Most people describe communication as information exchange (Figure 6–3), yet information is only one of five possible intentions of someone who is transmitting a message. Just because a transmission contains information—and a large proportion do—that fact by no means assures that your primary intention is to inform. Sometimes, however, information is indeed what you most want to convey.

Examples are not difficult to locate. The company controller delivers a quarterly financial statement to the board. The lieutenant gives a status report on field operations to the commander. The director outlines the first act of the play at a cast rehearsal. All these are instances when information exchange is likely the foremost intention of the speaker.

Conveying a point of view, an opinion, can also be informational if the belief is presented as someone's position with no

*Figure 6–3.* Information.

purpose of changing the opinions of the listener. You can tell your friend that you believe the pizza is delicious, your intention being only to let your friend know that this is your belief. If your friend disagrees, fine. You just happily enjoy your pizza. A professor can deliver results of a study to a group of colleagues and not care at all if their minds are changed about the topic. The professor's only wish is that they become aware of the results.

Comparisons of differing points of view are also informational exchanges. A newscaster may present candidates' opposing opinions on the same issue, but these opinions are presented precisely as information. The goal is only to inform the viewers of the candidates' opinions. As long as the newscaster has no desire to change anyone's mind, the intention is strictly informational.

## Persuasion/Direction

If you do want to change someone's mind or to change behavior, you have slipped into the fourth intention, persuasion/direction (Figure 6–4). The persuasive intention can be overt; you can come right out and state your wishes. Or the intention may be covert; you may keep hidden the fact that you want to create a change in your listener.

In either case your intention is to change how someone thinks about something. You may present a line of reasoning that your listener has not previously contemplated. You may also pose options not previously considered. Mike enjoys the political scene and has formed strong liberal-leaning positions. Every other Tuesday he meets for lunch with another avid political junkie, Sacha, has been known to slant conservative. Their conversations are lively and heated, each attempting to alert the other of the error of the other's way. Both grudgingly admit that their viewpoints have been substantively affected by these sharp encounters. Both happily admit that their intentions are very much of the persuasive variety.

Another kind of change that falls into this category is action. If you try to get others to behave differently than they otherwise would, you are intending to persuade/direct. If Mike wanted to sway Sacha's actions in the voting booth, he would not only have a change of mind in mind, he would be seeking to change her behavior. Less momentously, if you ask someone to pour you a

***Figure 6-4.*** Persuasion/direction.

cup of coffee, your intention is also persuasion/direction, as is the intention of the presenter who asks for a show of hands.

In every instance of persuasion/direction, the intention is to convince. You want to bring another person to the conviction to think a certain way, believe a certain way, or act a certain way. It is frequently the intention of choice of sales agents, preachers, politicians, managers, and parents. This intention uses tools of argument, authority, good will, or threat. It appeals to the mind and the will.

## Feeling

The fifth intention, feeling, appeals less to the mind and will than to the heart (Figure 6-5). Like persuasion/direction, this intention

**Figure 6–5.** Feeling.

seeks to create a change in us, but it is a change in the way others feel rather than the way others think or act.

You may seek to strengthen an emotion already felt. As a politician, you might be aware that your supporters feel comfortable with you, as though you are a member of their family or could be a good friend. Your stump speech may be designed to make your supporters even more comfortable with you by emphasizing family values, folksy ways, and warm regard for grandmothers and newborns. If your forte, however, is national security, you may have a stake in making your supporters feel more fearful about their safety and the safety of their family.

We discussed a theatrical performance as a form of small talk because entertainment has a connotation of relaxation, similar to pleasant banter. Many actors and directors will disagree, asserting that they have a definite feeling intention and sometimes that feeling intention is far from "relaxation." That's fine. If evoking an emotion is their intention and they evoke the emotion, they are successful communicators. They are the ones making the transmission.

You may also seek to enhance an existing emotion. This goal may appear to be more challenging, but it is generally easier than

extinguishing a feeling in someone. A politician with high negative ratings will attack those negatives with reasons why the voter
should not feel them. A goal of this book is to generate the feeling that taking care of and considering your voice is essential to
effective communication. If you also end up feeling a little fearful
about damaging your voice, that is likewise a good outcome. The
challenge is formidable, as is that of a used car sales person who
must squelch a feeling of insecurity in a shopper who has "heard
these cars break down as soon as they drive off the lot."

Admissions Officers (AOs) at urban campuses are in charge of
recruiting the freshman class to their institution of higher learning.
When discussing campus life with parents and high school seniors,
they are frequently confronted with some trepidation about safety
on a big city campus. A college's record on student safety may
be exemplary, and most are, but the fear factor in new prospects
must be addressed. The intention of the AO in these situations is to
douse the fear and make parents and students believe that safety
is of utmost importance.

Once expunged, fear can be replaced by a feeling of security.
If that politician can counter the negative feelings, she may then
be able to build new feelings of confidence or comfort. Advertisers too are in the business of creating a feeling. "Three out of four
dentists recommend this toothpaste" sounds like a dry recitation
of a fact, an informational intention. Hardly. While the ad contains
information, it is aimed entirely at feelings. The intention is to create emotions like comfort and trust with respect to the product.
That accompanying picture of the distinguished dental surgeon in
the white lab coat reinforces the message that all is well: The reader
of the ad is in very competent hands.

## Multiple Intentions

There are always multiple intentions in any transmission. They may
be going on at the same time. Of course, there is some feeling intention in every message you send. You want your communication
partners to be receptive to what you have to say no matter what
else you want of them, and receptivity is a feeling. If you want your
communication partners to accept your argument, you will choose

a persuasive intention. You may also want them to remember the premises of your argument, so you will choose an informational intention. You may incidentally transmit information and not care if they remember any of what you said. If your intention is to leave your listeners feeling kindly disposed toward your toothpaste, you could hardly be bothered if they forgot whether three out of four or four out of five dentists recommended it.

Sometimes one intention follows another. You may use small talk to set a climate and then move on to an informational presentation of facts you want to transmit to your audience. You then follow the presentation with a list of recommendations that you desire to persuade your audience to consider. What is important is that you know your intention during a given transmission. If you achieve that intention, you have been successful in your communication effort.

The following scenario has been constructed to portray every one of The 5 Intentions at least once. Read the scenario. See if you can detect the most probable intention of the speaker in each line of dialogue. Proposed answers will appear after the scenario.

Professor: Good morning, class. It's been raining pretty hard. Did any of you have trouble on the drive in?

Student A: I got caught in a big jam behind a car that stalled going through some high water.

Professor: Been there. Let's get to work. So, what was the assignment from last class?

Student B: We were to read the Smythe article and assess her case study of people with neurological anomalies.

Professor: Thank you. Did you think her conclusions were warranted?

Student B: Not according to the data she presented. The sample size was too small, and I had a real question about the supposed randomness of the sample. They were all from one school and female subjects seemed to predominate. What do you think, Professor?

Professor: I've been doing studies like these for more than 20 years. I did my PhD dissertation on a related topic, so I know quite a bit about this sort of research. Your objections are quite common. I personally think the studies have validity based on the sheer number of studies that have been done.

Student C: How do you do these studies without losing it? When I ask subjects the questions, they react strongly sometimes. It scares me.

Student D: They are paid to participate and they were all briefed on the nature of the questions. I ran a few dozen last semester. Some of the people were emotional, but nothing scary ever happened. I wouldn't worry.

Professor: This kind of research can be intimidating at first. Fear will subside as you run more and more of them.

Student D: What time do we begin tomorrow? And how many subjects will we run?

Professor: Ten in the morning. Fifteen are signed up. We'll end by 3.

Student D: Can we do 15 in that time? The average time per subject has been about a half-hour.

Professor: It should take about 20 minutes, based on previous studies, but if we do 10 to 12, I'll be happy. So, we'll meet in the lab tomorrow at 9:30.

Student A: Good. Are you going to the student-faculty coffee tonight, Professor?

Professor: I hope to, yes. Should be fun.

Student C: Yes, the last one was great.

Professor: OK, I'll see you there.

Below is the same scenario with suggested intentions in brackets.

Professor: Good morning, class. It's been raining pretty hard. Did any of you have trouble on the drive in?

Student A: I got caught in a big jam behind a car that stalled going through some high water. [Small talk]

Professor: Been there. Let's get to work. So, what was the assignment from last class?

Student B: We were to read the Smythe article and assess her case study of people with neurological anomalies. [Information]

Professor: Thank you. Did you think her conclusions were warranted?

Student B: Not according to the data she presented. The sample size was too small, and I had a real question about the supposed randomness of the sample. They were all from one school and female subjects seemed to predominate. What do you think, Professor? [Persuasion]

Professor: I've been doing studies like these for more than 20 years. I did my PhD dissertation on a related topic, so I know quite a bit about this sort of research. [Self-affirmation]

Your objections are quite common. I personally think the studies have validity based on the sheer number of studies that have been done. [Persuasion]

Student C: How do you do these studies without losing it? When I ask subjects the questions, they react strongly sometimes. It scares me.

Student D: They are paid to participate, and they were all briefed on the nature of the questions. I ran a few dozen last semester. Some of the people were emotional, but nothing scary ever happened. I wouldn't worry. [Emotion]

Professor: This kind of research can be intimidating at first. Fear will subside as you run more and more of them. [Emotion]

Student D: What time do we begin tomorrow? And how many subjects will we run?

Professor: Ten in the morning. Fifteen are signed up. We'll end by 3. [Information]

Student D: Can we do 15 in that time? The average time per subject has been about a half-hour. [Persuasion]

Professor: It should take about 20 minutes, based on previous studies, but if we do 10 to 12, I'll be happy. [Self-affirmation]

So, we'll meet in the lab tomorrow at 9:30. [Information/ persuasion]

Student A: Good. Are you going to the student-faculty coffee tonight, Professor?

Professor: I hope to, yes. Should be fun.

Student C: Yes, the last one was great.

Professor: OK, I'll see you there. [Small talk]

We will look in the following chapters at each of these five intentions. We will emphasize the ways in which voice, verbals, and paraverbals increase the odds that you will be successful in transmitting what you intend to transmit.

## Review of Key Ideas

- The key communication question is: Why do you transmit? Even though there are an infinite number of thoughts you could be sending off at a particular time, those thoughts can be grouped into categories, what we call The 5 Intentions.
- The 5 Intentions are self-affirmation, small talk, information exchange, persuasion/direction, and feeling.
- Self-affirmation includes windbagging, self-promotion, and classroom participation.
- Small talk is chit-chat, banter about seemingly trivial matters. Purposes of small talk include relationship building, climate setting, or relaxation.
- Information exchange is paramount when the content of a transmission must be remembered.

■ Persuasion/direction is the intention when the wish is to change someone's mind or to change behavior.
■ Feeling intention appeals to the emotional center. It seeks to create a change in the way someone feels rather than the way someone thinks or acts.
■ Multiple intentions can exist at the same time, or one intention may follow another in the same conversation.

## References

Allwood, J., 2002. Bodily communication dimensions of expression and content. In B. Granström, D. House, & I. Karlsson (Eds.), *Multimodality in language and speech systems* (pp. 7–26). Dordrecht, The Netherlands: Kluwer Academic.

Gollwitzer P. M., & Wicklund, R. A. (1985). Self-symbolizing and the neglect of others' perspectives. *Journal of Personality and Social Psychology, 48*(3), 702–715.

Hogg N. M., Garratt V., Shaw S. K., Tagney J., 2007. It has certainly been good just to talk: An interpretative phenomenological analysis of coping with myocardial infarction. *British Journal of Health Psychology, 12*(4), 651–662.

Share, J., Jolls, T., & Thomas, E. (2002). *Why we communicate: Three basic tasks.* Retrieved July 22, 2007, from http://www.medialit.org/reading_room/article702.html

White, C. P., White, M., Russell, C. S. (2007). Multiple sclerosis patients talking with healthcare providers about emotions. *Journal of Neuroscience Nursing, 39*(2), 89–101.

# *Chapter 7*

# Your Most Compelling Connection

*"My device," he continues, "is this: I give my word of honor most solemnly to myself to do or leave undone this or that. I am of course extremely cautious in the use of this expedient, but when once the word is give . . . I hold it to be perfectly irrevocable, whatever inconveniences I foresee likely to result. If I were capable of breaking my word after such mature consideration, I should lose all respect for myself—and what man of sense would not prefer death to such an alternative?"*

—William James, *The Energies of Man*

## Your Distinct Voice

The first of The 5 Intentions is self-affirmation—the claim that your message is important and worthy of another's time and consideration. Self-affirmation is embedded in your every utterance. When you think of the sound you make, you think of your voice. When you think of the sound others make, it is likewise their voice you bring to mind. Nowhere is your matchless self more intimately and powerfully realized than in your voice.

When you are seeking to get yourself across to others, you are usually referring to the message you are transmitting at that moment. In fact, along with your message, it really is your self that you are getting across. Aristotle's *Rhetoric*, an early, systemized look at persuasiveness, holds that there are three means of persuasion: *ethos, pathos,* and *logos. Logos* is logical argument. *Pathos* is an emotional appeal. *Ethos* is different; it is rooted in the character of the speaker, the speaker's reputation and trustworthiness (Aristotle, trans. 1984 by Roberts). The listener is persuaded because the speaker is a person of integrity. Aristotle's words are compelling, even two millennia after he wrote them:

> There are three things which inspire confidence in the orator's own character—the three, namely, that induce us to believe a thing apart from any proof of it: good sense, good moral character, and goodwill. False statements and bad advice are due to one or more of the following three causes. Men either form a false opinion through want of good sense; or they form a true opinion, but because of their moral badness do not say what they really think; or finally, they are both sensible and upright, but not well disposed to their hearers, and may fail in consequence to recommend what they know to be the best course. These are the only possible cases. It follows that anyone who is thought to have all three of these good qualities will inspire trust in his audience. The way to make ourselves thought to be sensible and morally good must be gathered from the analysis of goodness already given: The way to establish your own goodness is the same as the way to establish that of others. (*Aristotle, trans. 1984 by Roberts*)

"Establishing your goodness" and being seen as someone with "good sense" and "good will," as Aristotle views these matters, pretty much encompass the topic of this chapter. When you speak, especially when you try to convince another, your goodness, your character, counts.

When you say, "I cannot help it," there in the midst of your message is none other than yourself. The "I" that exists at that instant is being transmitted, and the listener perceives it. Signs might include the little tremor in your voice that tells your listener that you are nervous or the intonation of satisfaction that reflects your pride. Other aspects of your self are revealed in your phrasing, gestures, expressions, and body language. The deeper "I" is there, too, the one that points to your moral fiber.

Lonnie once consulted with a branch director—call him Thurston—at a computer sales company. A critical moment came in the director's work life. That moment is captured in the following scenario.

Thurston: Look, I had called a meeting of my managers to update them on the personnel cuts going on in the company.

Lonnie: Good idea.

Thurston: My objective was to calm them down. I mean, panic was brewing, and the people I was afraid of losing were my best performers. They could get jobs anywhere. What if they bolted? I had to settle things down.

Lonnie: What did you tell them?

Thurston: I said our branch was safe. We wouldn't get hit with a layoff, at least not this year.

Lonnie: Did you know that to be true?

Thurston: Management was pretty tight-lipped about it then. I was going by our branch performance, which was in the top 25%. I figured they probably wouldn't make cuts here.

Lonnie: Is that what you told your people, your managers?

Thurston: I just told them there'd be no layoffs at our branch.

Lonnie: And then . . . ?

Thurston: Then, two weeks later, I'm told to make a 10% force reduction in the branch. I called my managers back, told them about the cuts, that I was blindsided.

Lonnie: And?

Thurston: I could tell they didn't believe me. Started asking questions like "Didn't you have any idea at all two weeks ago?" and "Were you just trying to not rock the boat?" I told them I really thought there wouldn't be a layoff here.

Lonnie: Did they buy that?

Thurston: No. My systems manager said no one thinks that's true. Then the engineering manager chimes in and says, even if I thought there would be no layoffs, I was still giving them bad information. Now the place is in an uproar.

Lonnie:  You've been branch director for what . . . five months?

Thurston:  Closer to four.

Lonnie:  So they haven't had much of a chance to get to know you.

Thurston:  That's right and that really hurts.

Lonnie:  Yes, it does.

Thurston:  How can I get back in their good graces?

Lonnie:  It looks like your credibility has taken a big hit. And, really, they're still getting to know you.

Thurston:  I know.

What would you advise Thurston at this point? If you are pessimistic about his chances of getting back in his people's "good graces," you are not overreacting. First of all, he was simply wrong about the layoffs, a matter of vital interest to the associates. Second, he had a motive for ill will, the desire to keep things running smoothly, so he was suspected of not being entirely truthful. And finally, his character itself was called into question.

Thurston was in deep trouble. In the actual case history, Lonnie expressed doubt that Thurston could ever truly restore his credibility. He soon left the branch. The scenario teaches a number of important lessons. One you will want to explore is the need to be conscious of the self you are transmitting, especially when the stakes are high and people are listening to you carefully. You are always transmitting a self with your messages and you enter dangerous territory when you do not pay attention to the self you are conveying.

Matters change when you move from real life to the realm of theatrical performance. In the acting world sometimes the character you are portraying is not supposed to be credible. In that case, some of the concepts discussed in this chapter that you may not want to portray when your desire is to build credibility, may be things you will want to incorporate into your intention so that your character's lack of credibility is believable to your audience. *Othello's* supreme villain Iago is maybe the least credible character in all literature. If you ever get to portray him on stage, you would be wise to forget most of the advice in this chapter.

What voice will you choose for yourself? As a well-traveled management consultant, Lonnie has received many compliments during his eventful career. There is one compliment he prizes above them all. He once invited his best friend Gordon to sit in the audience during one of his open presentations. Once assured that admission was free, Gordon happily accepted. Lonnie was very pleased, since Gordon was a close confidant of many years—they lived near each other, raised their children together. They knew each other well.

Following a highly successful presentation, Lonnie strode through the audience seeking out Gordon who approached him with a smile and shook his hand. "Good job." Gordon then gazed right into his friend's eyes and said, "You know, you reminded me of someone up there."

Lonnie paused, waiting for the sarcastic jibe he knew was coming. Instead, Gordon went on. "You reminded me of Lonnie Barone."

Lonnie understood. Gordon was not kidding. He was making a powerful statement. The person he witnessed giving that presentation on that stage was the same person he knew as a fellow parent, neighbor, and friend. The voice Gordon heard may have been a little louder than normal, but it was unmistakably Lonnie's voice. Gordon was speaking to Lonnie's integrity, his resolve to be true to himself whatever his message, whatever his intention.

You send out many messages every day, but the most important message you send is you. As a leader, an employee, a salesperson, a speech-language pathologist, a professional—but more importantly, as a person—answer the call to be your true self and your best self. Let your own unique voice be a voice of integrity. No one can ask more of you.

Never ask less of yourself.

## Your Authentic Self

The self you want your listener to connect with is the real you, your authentic self. To realize this bond it is imperative that you secure a conscious connection between you and your authentic self. Otherwise, the core of your message, you self, is being transmitted unwittingly. At one level this unselfconsciousness is endearing. Nothing is sweeter than a two-year-old child interacting with complete abandon. You certainly detect a self and you may be enchanted by it; it is all the more appealing that the child has no awareness whatever that she is presenting a self.

Ideally, you as an adult will incorporate your authentic self seamlessly into your transmission with no affectation or pretense. That does not mean, however, that you are required to maintain a childlike innocence about the self that is being propelled toward your listeners. The employment of presentation skills presupposes that you have in mind a way you would like others to view you. There is nothing intrinsically deceptive about using presentation skills, as long as you use them to display and not mask who you are.

As you have seen, Aristotle got you started with his marvelous work on Rhetoric (*Aristotle, trans. 1984 by Roberts*). It is he who insisted that your character is an essential player in the effectiveness of your vocal transmissions. Aristotle noted three things that inspire others to have confidence in you and your message: (1) You have good sense or intelligence; (2) you possess strong moral character; and (3) others like you or, at least, have nothing against you.

First, you must have good sense; that means you must talk sense to your listeners. If you present poor arguments or give bad advice because you do not know what you are talking about, you are lacking good sense. Others have a right to question the value of a message from a person who is ignorant, illogical, or intellectually inadequate. In the scenario Thurston transmitted, at the very least, inadequate information to his associates. He was lacking "good sense" as Aristotle defines it. Thurston's advice to associates to go on as usual was based on the premise that there would be no layoff there.

The second confidence builder is that you are a good person. You do not lie to the people you are talking to or deliberately mislead them. It is interesting that Aristotle positions this characteristic after good sense. He seems to feel that, good person or not, if people lack good sense they should not open their mouths to begin with. Immorality, however, can cause you to say something other than what you know to be correct, thus subverting the whole point of communication. Thurston already faced the problem of not using good sense. His people also doubted his truthfulness; possibly, he was not being a good person, either.

The only other thing than can cause you to speak falsely or to give awful advice is that you lack goodwill. If you do not like a person or are not watching that person's back, as it were, you may be inclined to present the person with something other than what you know to be in the person's best interest. Thurston clearly had other interests beside those of his work force, and his employees certainly were aware of that conflict.

One of the premises of this book is, as the title indicates, that your voice is your business, your affair. You should develop and control the verbals and paraverbals you use to transmit clearly and precisely the message you intend. Your voice, however, is also the business of those with whom you connect through meaning, be they your employees or your family members. In truth, your voice is also other's business.

Like Thurston's associates, your communication partners have a stake in your character, your good sense, and your disposition toward them if you are seeking to inform them, convince them, or affect their feeling-state. When you choose to transmit to others they have a right not only to make clear what you mean to say—your intention—they are also right to probe your integrity, to clarify that the message emanates from a dependable source. Above all else, they will assure themselves of your credibility.


## Your Credible Self

How often have you begun a statement with the words, "You're not going to believe this but . . . "? It is as if you expect your listener to question you, to be suspicious that what you are saying is not the truth, the whole truth, and nothing but the truth. And there are a surprising number of these disclaimers:

You're going to think I'm lying . . .

No kidding . . .

No joke . . .

Really . . .

I want to be honest with you . . .

Let me be *perfectly* honest . . .

I'd like to speak frankly . . .

Frankly, my dear . . .

What is the origin of this insecurity? Why are these phrases used? Is your credibility really in such deep jeopardy?

Ryan, a reputable professor and excellent speaker, was addicted to disclaimers like these. Whenever he told a story, he would preface it with a statement like, "You're not going to believe this." One day, after a talk, a student in his class walked up to him and said, "You know, it never occurred to me to doubt your stories, until you said, 'You're not going to believe this.' Now you've got me wondering if you were telling the truth."

From that day on Ryan swore never to issue disclaimers again. He never wanted to cast doubt on his truthfulness. To deliberately undermine his own credibility, he knew, would devastate him as a speaker.

Credibility derives from the Latin for "able to be believed." It is the one quality that provides the foundation for all efforts at communication. With credibility you will not only be heard, not only be understood, but also be believed and believed in. If your communication connection is to make any sense at all, you need credibility; without it you are sending others messages that they will not believe.

Also, without credibility you cannot hope for trust or respect. According to one company survey of admired leaders, the most frequently mentioned characteristic of the superior leader is honesty (Kouzes & Posner, 1990). It was selected by 83% of respondents, far more frequently than the second highest-ranking characteristic, competence (67%). For executives a failure in credibility would seem to be the one unforgivable sin. Salespeople term credibility their greatest asset. Negotiators are reduced to second-guessing game players without credibility. And healthcare workers rely on credibility to get patients to adhere to their recommendations.

A story is told of a grizzled old labor leader, a tough, short-tempered fellow who typically won terrific contracts for his union.

He would pass from session to session astounding the young Ivy League lawyer who accompanied him. At one session the shrewd old leader entered a mahogany-draped board room garnished with the pin-striped suits of attorneys, executives, accountants, and professional negotiators. The labor king removed a well-chewed cigar from his mouth and said to the very important people in the very impressive board room: "I don't like the seating arrangement. Fix it." Then he left, tailed by the admiring young attorney, as the VIPs sat open-mouthed. Antics like this became almost commonplace as the youthful assistant watched the labor leader bob and weave, feint and attack, tough talk and sweet talk his way to really excellent contracts.

There was one day a strange turn of events. Into a room the old leader strode. He ignored the seating arrangement, ignored all the impressive-looking personnel and walked right up to the chief executive, dragged a chair beside him, and sewed up a fair, equitable agreement in record time.

The youthful lawyer chased his mentor to the elevator following the amazing exchange. In the elevator the young man confronted the gruff labor leader. "I don't understand. In all the negotiating sessions I've witnessed up to now, you have used every trick in the book. And now, this one time, you just stroll in and hammer out a contract with the CEO."

"Son," answered the labor leader. "Across that table was a man I've known and fought with for many years. He's tough. He's as mean tempered as I am. But he's honest, honest through and through. With him there just isn't any need for the dance."

The CEO was honest. He had credibility with the old labor leader. So there was no need for game-playing, colorfully characterized by the unionist as "the dance." That is one of the things credibility buys you: straight, simple, efficient communication—no second-guessing, no hidden agendae, no dancing around the point. That is the kind of communication you are after with your colleagues and clients, the kind of communication that gets results and wins trust.

It takes time to build credibility. And it takes effort. When credibility exists, it exists not in you but in the person with whom you are credible. Credibility is a perception of someone else about you. That is why it must be defined in the passive voice. Credibility is "being seen as someone who can be believed and believed in." With strong credibility a person can sustain a professional relationship in the most severe adversity. Without credibility, even in the best of times, that relationship is strained at its very core. Strong credibility, while difficult to build, is very resistant to erosion once established. On the other hand, once credibility is destroyed, it quite possibly will never be re-established.

Finally, credibility is the bedrock of all lasting and fruitful human relationships; it is the cornerstone of communication, teamwork, and mutual respect.

Credibility is a four-part perception that people have about you if you are credible. True, you may have trouble analyzing the abstraction "credibility"; words that end in "ity" often seem vague. Most people, though, are well aware of what it means to be credible.

When you think about a credible person, a real flesh and blood human being, the matter becomes specific and concrete. You can prove this fact to yourself by doing a little exercise. Bring to mind the most credible person you know. That is right, a real person, someone you are well acquainted with—the most credible person in your life.

Now, as you think of your most credible person, ask yourself some questions about your relationship with this person. First, is this person a good listener—does he or she listen well?

In credibility workshops Lonnie has delivered over the last 30 years, the great majority of people report that their most credible person is a good, even exceptional listener. There seems to be a close relationship between being a good listener and building credibility. There are a few possible reasons this is so. Good listeners are good data gatherers almost by definition. They tend to gain more knowledge than average. Because they listen to you, they are apt to understand you better than average. And good listeners tend to be secure, able to look at all sides of an issue without forming premature judgments. All these characteristics in turn foster credibility. The critical point is: Highly credible people are almost always very good listeners.

Another question you might ask about your most credible person is . . . why? Why does this person enjoy such high credibility with you? As you think about this you might be interested in how most others answer this question. See if these responses match your own.

People say that their most credible persons are credible for a number of reasons (Table 7–1). For one thing, they tell the truth.

**Table 7–1.** Credibility

| Why are they credible? | How do they make me feel? |
|---|---|
| They tell the truth. | Secure |
| They give sound advice. | Comfortable |
| They keep commitments. | Safe |
| Their track record is consistent. | Trusted |
| | Confident |

Also, they give sound advice. When they say something will happen, it does. They come through and keep their commitments. They have built a track record, and that record is one of competence and consistency.

Another question you might ask is: What emotions do you most frequently feel about your most credible person? Interestingly, this question may stop you for a moment. At first, some people cannot identify the emotions they might feel while dealing with their highly credible person. They eventually come up with feelings like comfort, security, trust, and confidence. Not exactly your wild and crazy emotions.

## What Credibility Is Not

Credibility, it seems, is quite a bit different from some other kinds of relationships in which the emotions are concerned. Take falling in love, for example. If you fall in passionate love, it is doubtful you will report that your emotions include comfort, security, and the like. People do not fall comfortably in love; they fall madly in love. Imagine a person falling madly in credibility with someone. I'm madly in credibility with you! It was credibility at first sight!

This is obviously silly. Credibility is unquestionably a different sort of relationship from passionate love. The source of this difference is pretty simple: Passionate love is an emotion-based relationship; credibility is a reason-based relationship. This fact does not mean that you cannot love someone whom you find very credible. Your most credible person may very well be someone you love deeply. What it means is that you can always give good, logical reasons why someone has credibility with you, whereas you may not be able to indicate precisely why you have fallen in love with someone.

While it is difficult to confuse credibility with passionate love, many people do confuse it with being personable, well liked, or sociable. It is quite possible to have excellent rapport with someone and fail to have any credibility at all. And although rapport is useful and positive in a relationship, it is not essential to credibility. You can have very strong credibility with someone but would not want to spend one more minute than necessary with that person.

Confusing credibility with rapport can cause anxiety and outright shock. A manager fails to win over a coworker, even though they clearly enjoy each other's company and spend long hours together. When questioned, the worker hesitantly admits that he went against the manager because he just did not believe the claims made by the manager. Likewise, a salesperson may lose a contract in spite of her most amicable relationship with the prospect. In the same way, a client unexpectedly fails to show up for therapy although he finds his therapist both friendly and sociable. In all these instances, while rapport is excellent, credibility is questionable.

Credibility is also different from authority. Managers, professors, and law enforcement officials may be tempted to confuse the fact of their organizational power or authority with credibility. They argue that the badge gives them credibility with people, whereas credibility in fact carries its own influence beyond that of formal authority.

Credibility is a function of the communication connection. It is built between one person and another. It is intrinsic to the relationship between the two people. If others have credibility with you, they believe certain things about your character, competence, experience, and knowledge. They learn these things about you as you relate to one another. Your authority is not something others learn about you: It is something they know about anyone that holds the same position as you within an organization. You may be obeyed because you have authority. Others may show you deference because you have authority. But you will never have credibility with others simply because you have authority.

Interestingly, while authority cannot give you credibility, credibility can give you a kind of authority. If you are credible on an issue, you will probably be perceived as "authoritative," having sound knowledge and competence in that area. This quality can cause people to follow you even when you have no formal authority at all. Salespeople typically earn respect from customers with absolutely no formal authority over the customers; while subordinates have been know to abandon ship on a manager with all the authority in the world—the manager simply lost credibility.

Intimidation, force, submission—none of these have a bearing on a person's credibility. Managers may have and be willing to exercise power over you, either organizational power or brute power, and you may do their bidding, but you will not necessarily have a shred of credibility with them. In fact, people who frequently use intimidation damage their credibility in the very act. If you perceive that others need to use force with you, you might logically wonder just why they need to do so. If they had credibility with you, intimidation would be superfluous in most cases, would it not?

Certainly, people who employ intimidation with others are frequently very doubtful of their credibility with those others. Credible bullies are few and far between, if ever there was one.

All three of the above practices—rapport, the use of authority, and intimidation—can bring about submissiveness, even if they do not engender credibility. If people are personable and popular, they may cause you to acquiesce to their wishes, perhaps because you do not perceive yourself as very personable or popular. You might submit to them because they have authority—maybe you have been brought up that way. And you might yield to their snarls and roars, because you are scared stiff. Credibility, however, never engenders submissiveness.

If you are submissive, there is an undertone of coercion. You are acting against your will. There is never coercion or the feeling of coercion if you go in the direction of others because they have credibility with you. You go because you believe them and believe in them.

Finally, you may be awestruck, enraptured, transported by others and their charisma, but they may also fail to have a shred of credibility with you. If others perform some spectacular stunt or feat, they might well engender in you a feeling of awe and wonder, but they will no more engender credibility in you than a showy display of fireworks would. Credibility is always built over time as a result of sustained contact between two people. Awe comes in a sudden flash and can leave just as suddenly. Credibility, once built, never leaves suddenly, except through some calamitous event.

Take the case of the empty suit: This is the person who transmits with flair, sparkling delivery, unimpeachable style. But no content. The words, once examined, add up to zero. It is a nice suit, but it is an empty suit.

Because of the wonderful feeling associated with awe, it is easy to confuse with credibility. Remember: Credibility always has a basis in reason and logic, is always built over time, and brings about a feeling often quite different from awe.

## Proxy Credibility

Credibility cannot be instantaneous. It requires a track record so that a person can make a judgment about you. Credibility is built over time. Early in any relationship—particularly with an employee, a student, a buyer, or a congregant—something needs to stand in for credibility while it is being built. The other person must be permitted to build that credible relationship with you. If the person slams the door in your face it is over, no matter what your qualifications are.

Proxy credibility is what stands in for credibility until credibility is developed. Proxy credibility is generated by any factor that creates a climate in which credibility can be built. There are at least three factors of this kind, what may be called the three Rs of proxy credibility. They are reputation, rumor, and rapport.

Reputation is your documented biography, the facts about your accomplishments and your character. These facts can be checked out, verified. They are, in effect, your credentials, your resume. If you are well regarded, well credentialed, or have a good record of performance, your reputation is enhanced, creating a favorable climate for building credibility for yourself, your company, your profession. When you read the authors' biographies at the beginning of this book, they may have propelled you into the text with a degree of confidence.

Like good reputation, good rumors about you can cause others to be more open toward you as they begin establishing credibility with you. Rumors are not verifiable in principle; two absolutely contradictory rumors about you can be circulating at the same time. Rumors about your organization or institution, its products or services, its record of achievement, also are circulating. If they are good, they will establish proxy credibility. If they are negative, the rumors could hurt.

Rapport is the third R of proxy credibility. Like credibility, and unlike reputation and rumor, rapport requires actual contact between you and the person with whom you are establishing credibility. Rapport begins as the real relationship begins, as you create your "meaning connection" with others. If others like you, enjoy your company, share common interests, feel comfortable with you, the path to credibility is smoothed.

Rapport always begins with first impressions, which have been discussed in a previous chapter. Good eye contact, a firm handshake, and a resonant vocal quality all contribute to a positive first impression. Individuals will rub each other the right way or the wrong way. First impressions are made swiftly and they last (Willis & Todorov, 2006). Much of the time, a first impression remains substantially the same throughout a relationship. You will hear people say, "She is not at all what I thought when I first met her," but that is relatively unusual. "Aha! Just as I figured" is much more likely.

So, fair or not, your colleagues, students, and clients will make swift judgments about you, and these judgments will be difficult to change. Your initial encounter with them is crucial in establishing proxy credibility. It is helpful to create a positive first impression. Social science writer Malcolm Gladwell (2005) in his book *Blink* has gathered a great deal of relevant research on the mechanism that generates first impressions. His provocative thesis is that an individual's "adaptive unconscious" renders snap judgments that are remarkably reliable if seasoned with the right measure of caution. Others are not foolish to give ample weight to their first impression of you.

If your first impression is upbeat, others will quickly develop rapport with you. If what people are saying about you is positive, people will be more inclined to think well of you. If you have a good reputation, people will be more willing to listen to what you have to say. By achieving these proxies—reputation, rumor, and rapport—others will give you the time and space to build credibility. Credibility itself is founded on four pillars. These pillars support development of your own credibility (Figure 7–1).

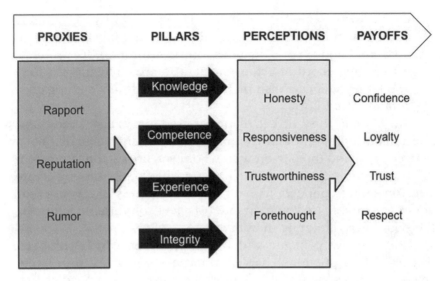

***Figure 7–1.*** The building blocks of credibility. Credibility begins with three proxies, items that indicate to others that you may be credible, that operate on your behalf as you build credibility. There are four pillars or qualities that constitute credibility. These create in others the four perceptions about personal characteristics, which deliver four payoffs in terms of how others respond to you.

## The Four Pillars of Credibility

There are four qualities that allow others to build credibility with you. If you are missing even one of them, you will lack an important tool in your efforts to become credible. First, there is knowledge. You know what you are talking about. You are an authority. You have done your homework. The alternative to having knowledge is faking it or professing ignorance. Neither strategy is a credibility builder. If you do not know the answer, however, your best strategy is simply to state that you do not know the answer.

The second quality is competence. You have the know-how you need. You are skilled at what you do. You deliver the goods because you can deliver the goods. The third quality is experience. You have been at it a while, long enough to develop a track record, long enough to develop knowledge and competence.

Experience is a conundrum for novices on the job. On your first day in a new position, you may lack experience. Does that mean you will lack credibility? Unless some other experience can substitute, the answer is yes; there may well be a credibility problem for a while. The new manager or professional must work extra hard to earn credibility.

There are two pieces of good news for the inexperienced person. First, everybody has their first day on the job, so you are not alone. Second, if you persevere, you will discover what millions before you have found: A lack of experience tends to go away with experience!

The fourth quality is integrity. Simply put, integrity means that what you project on the outside is what you truly are inside. What you promulgate is what you really believe. The person you portray is the person you are.

At root, integrity means wholeness. I am at one with myself. The alternative is hypocrisy, to fall into two, one inside person, one outside person. Duplicity is two-ness. Being two-faced is two-ness. So is talking out of both sides of your mouth, double-dealing, back-stabbing, and two-timing. Integrity is the process of pulling yourself together.

The credibility credo charts one path to integrity. It is not a simple formula and it is not all you need do to build credibility. But it is a crucial start. The credo has ten points.

- Tell the truth.
- Commit for self, not others.
- Do not make promises you cannot keep.
- Deliver when you say you will.
- Stay with your program.
- Be there when you are needed.
- Seek full understanding.
- Be empathetic.
- Stay in touch.
- Think before you speak or act.

If you have established the four pillars of credibility, others think four things about you. They think you are honest, responsive, trustworthy, and informed. Each of these perceptions merits a close examination.

## Perceptions of Credibility

The first perception of credibility is honesty, the quality most admired in leaders. If others have credibility with you, they think you are telling the truth. The quality of truthfulness is the core of credibility. The conviction others have that you are honest with them is the primary building block of credibility. They can never begin building credibility with you when they perceive that you are lying to them. Aristotle made this point long ago and it is still as valid as ever.

Remember: It is others' perception that you are honest which generates their credibility with you. If they think, or even suspect, that you are lying to them, credibility is tarnished whether or not you are knowingly telling an untruth.

If you are an inexperienced clinician or coach, you may innocently indicate to a client that a certain skill is easy to master. You will be surprised if the client returns indignant because she has discovered that the skill is more difficult to learn than anticipated. You may have simply made an error in judgment rather than lied, but chances are that the client will think you were misleading her. Such an unfortunate conclusion is even more likely in the early stages of a relationship. Your rationale may sound like an excuse to the client and only make matters worse.

Even so, the best way to build the perception of honesty is to be honest. Making a prediction about events over which you have minimal control is very risky. If the events turn out to be different from what you foretold, the cost may be enormous. Think of Thurston, who made a prediction about layoffs but expressed it as a decision, a decision he was not yet privy to that people above him were making. Of course, outright lying is extremely perilous if you wish to achieve any degree of credibility.

The second perception of credibility is responsiveness—the belief others have that you will come through for them. You give others the feeling that you have access to the resources needed to make things happen, namely that you have the intelligence, energy, and ability to carry it off.

You keep your promises. Responsiveness is built on honesty, but it goes beyond honesty. When a manager gets an employee a promised raise, when you deliver promised information before it is due, your credibility tends to increase. Thurston's team may have perceived that he promised them there would not be a layoff. His star would have shone more brightly had there been no workforce reduction. But there was. When Thurston pleaded that he thought he had the right information, he did not salvage the situation; his credibility deteriorated. The perception of unresponsiveness, literal irresponsibility, was deadly to his credibility.

The third perception of a credible person is consistency and reliability; in one word, trustworthiness. If others trust you, they will believe that they can depend on you. They will not expect you to change your tune from one day to the next because they know what to expect of you. An executive who is not reliable shows enthusiasm about a new project and infects the staff with excitement one day, but does not show the same enthusiasm when the plans are shown to the boss. Her credibility with her staff, who worked so hard on the project, will suffer because they will not trust her reactions from day to day.

Consistency and reliability do not equate to rigidity. Sometimes reliable simply means available, present. To responsiveness it adds the dimension of responsiveness over time, repeatedly, consistently. Changing the time of a scheduled appointment to accommodate an unforeseen circumstance is an example of responsiveness. Scheduling appointments so that changes are rare is an example of consistency and reliability.

Clinicians who adapt their lesson plans in reaction to their client's temperament on a particular day are being astutely present. Executives, on the other hand, who reshuffle organizations, reset priorities often, lose their tempers unexpectedly, will tend to tarnish credibility, as will a professor who claims a chapter in the text is critical and yet no question about it appears on the midterm. Consistency and reliability amount to the perception that the rug will not be pulled out.

The fourth perception, which is often the forgotten element of credibility, is forethought. What you say to others makes sense to them. You do not shoot from the hip. The things you say seem to have thought behind them and seem logical, based on sound suppositions, resilient to critical examination. You evince a command of the topic, the situation. What you assert aligns with the way things really are. You seem in touch. The perception of forethought is particularly important in dealing with long-term clients and relationships. Aristotle was right. They simply must believe that you know what you are talking about, that you have done your homework, and that you are informed.

This aspect of credibility is often overlooked and not identified when its lack erodes credibility. Failure in the perception of forethought may be due to a number of things. The speaker may have a proclivity to make off-the-cuff remarks. The speaker may simply be off base and out of contact with the real situation. The speaker may lack the expertise, knowledge, or smarts to make an intelligent comment on the issue. Whatever the cause, a lack of forethought will almost certainly damage credibility.

## Payoffs of Credibility

So if you have credibility, others think you are honest and that you tell the truth. They find you responsive; you keep promises and come through for them. They believe that you are consistent and reliable. And you give forethought to the things you say. What good are these perceptions? Why bother with them? They take work to build; they must be earned. The payoffs of credibility are the reason to bother. And the payoffs are confidence, loyalty, trust, and respect.

The perception of honesty generates confidence. Simply put, if others think you are telling you the truth, they will tend to have confidence in what you say. Confidence means you do not require being checked up on. If others have confidence in what you say, they do not need further verification beyond your word. This is a terrific payoff: The other person does not feel the need to check out what is said.

Having confidence in a therapist precludes second-guessing. The therapist says it and the matter is put to rest. There is no endless debate about what the therapist "really meant." Where confidence does not exist, however, the therapist's statement is the beginning of the matter, not the end of it. The perception of honesty means people believe you. Communication is clean, clear, and efficient. Messages are taken at face value, not analyzed and reprocessed. People listen for your content rather than for your motive. The question is: What did you say? The question is not: Why did you say that?

The second perception, responsiveness, generates loyalty. If others think you come through for them, they will come through for you. Responsiveness is actually a form of loyalty, the best form. If others perceive that you have that kind of loyalty, they will return it. This is not a loyalty born of obligation, not "organizational patriotism." This is reasoned loyalty, earned loyalty, loyalty rooted in legitimate self-interest. If credibility is strong, this loyalty has real staying power. Others will stay with you in a crisis. They will give you the right to make a claim on their loyalty when the going gets tough.

In the Capra movie *It's a Wonderful Life*, this kind of loyalty is epitomized by the townspeople when George Bailey, played by Jimmy Stewart, loses thousands of dollars he owes to the government. Poor as many of them are, the townspeople, even in the face of evidence that George may have been dishonest, contribute their life savings to help him out of his jam. They do this because George has always come through for them over the years. They were paying for his responsiveness with their loyalty.

If George Bailey had understood this feature of credibility, he would have comprehended his claim on his neighbors' loyalty, and he would never have contemplated suicide. Of course, it would have been a pretty dull movie, too. The angel Clarence, who had his own credibility problems with George, would not have been needed.

The third perception of credibility, the perception of consistency and reliability, generates trust. You are literally worthy of trust, trustworthy. If you make claims about a product and project a high level of enthusiasm about it, others are likely to respond with enthusiasm. They are secure in the conviction that you will not change course, reverse priorities, or lose enthusiasm precipitously.

Others trust you. They trust the course on which you have embarked with them. They do not fear sudden changes or unexpected priority shifts. There is a quality of constancy about their working relationship with you. Just as you will not pull the rug out from under them, neither will you leave them hanging. They know you will be there when you are needed. They have access to you; they can find you. They will not be scared off with mood changes or messages that you are too busy for them. Consistency is the quality most closely associated with trust (Covey, 2006).

Credibility, then, does not only mean that others believe what you say. They also believe that what you say today you will say tomorrow. This quality is not stubbornness, a refusal to change one's mind no matter what. It is really stability, a decision-making process that reaches conclusions sound enough that frequent changes of mind do not happen.

Forethought, the fourth perception, generates respect. Since others perceive that you give thought to the things you say and do, they respect you. Respect is really a sense of security. They feel secure that they know what you are doing and that you also know what you are doing.

Forethought also means that you understand enough about a topic to make intelligent statements on it. If you seem uninformed, lacking information you should have, you will make statements that appear irrelevant or off the mark, and you will lose the respect of others. Obviously, if they suspect that you are not in your right mind that too is a forethought problem. George Bailey made that calculation when Clarence claimed to be a heavenly being and George's lack of respect, initially, was quite evident.

In sum, having the qualities of knowledge, competence, experience, and integrity generate perceptions of honesty, responsiveness, consistency, reliability, and forethought that build confidence, loyalty, trust, and respect.

As authors of a book that combines presentation skill development with the applied science of voice, we, Cari and Lonnie, knew we were embarking on a project with few, if any, precedents. We are acutely aware of the challenge of building credibility with readers. Why should they believe that voice science and voice therapy are valuable to presenters with no clinical voice disorders? Why accept the notion that paraverbals like gestures, facial expressions, and clothing can be usefully combined with vocal techniques and insights to enhance the ability to communicate effectively?

Of course, we have attempted to establish proxy credibility with our credentials in both specialties (reputation) and with what we hope is an accessible, readable style (rapport), but that is only the beginning. We have been honest. We have taken great pains to make sure that every scientific claim is rooted in sound research and we have been scrupulously honest about the current limits of that research. We have been responsive with numerous practical recommendations that we know will work for readers when they try them out. We have maintained consistency throughout both in formatting and terminology. And we have given enormous forethought to every illustration, assuring relevance to a wide variety of professions, occupations, and situations.

If we have done the job and built credibility, we know readers will be confident when they quote us. They will express their loyalty by spreading the message we are advocating. They will trust our advice and use it. And they will take us seriously.

We will have earned our readers' respect.


## Review of Key Ideas

- Nowhere is my self more intimately and powerfully realized than in my voice. Self-affirmation is embedded in my every utterance. My voiceprint is unmistakable and is composed of elements that can be heard by others as well as elements that can be detected through spectrographic instrumentation.
- The self I want you to connect with is the real me, my authentic self. The employment of presentation skills presupposes that I have in mind a way I would like you to view me. There is nothing intrinsically deceptive about using presentation skills, as long as I use them to display and not mask who I am.
- Aristotle claimed that there are three things that inspire confidence in one's character. First, one must have good sense; that means I must talk sense to you. The second confidence builder is that I am a good person. The third thing is goodwill. A lack of goodwill can cause me to speak falsely or to give awful advice.
- Credibility derives from the Latin for "able to be believed." It undergirds all efforts at communication, teamwork, and mutual respect. It is the bedrock of all lasting and fruitful human relationships. It is the cornerstone of communication.
- It takes time to build credibility. And it takes effort. Credibility exists in the "passive voice dimension" because it cannot be defined in the active voice. Credibility is being seen as someone who can be believed and believed in.
- When credibility exists, it exists not in you but in the person with whom you are credible. Credibility is a perception

someone else has about you. Strong credibility, although difficult to build, is very resistant to erosion once established. On the other hand, once credibility is destroyed, it quite possibly will never be re-established.

■ Credibility is a reason-based, not an emotion-based, relationship. Being credible is not the same as being likeable. Credibility is different from formal authority. Intimidation, force, submission, awe have no bearing on a person's credibility.

■ Proxy credibility is generated by any factor that creates a climate in which credibility can be built. There are at least three factors of this kind, including what may be called the three Rs of proxy credibility. They are reputation, rumor, and rapport.

■ Credibility is a four-part perception that people have about me if I am credible. People believe I am honest, responsive, trustworthy, and informed.

■ There are four payoffs of credibility: confidence, loyalty, trust, and respect.

■ There are four qualities that allow me to build credibility with you, the four pillars of credibility. They are knowledge, competence, experience, and integrity. If I am missing even one of them I will lack an important tool in my efforts to become credible.

■ Integrity means that what I project on the outside is what I truly am inside. Integrity means wholeness. I am at one with myself. The alternative is hypocrisy, to fall into two, one inside person, one outside person.

■ The credibility credo charts one path to integrity. The credo has ten points.

# References

Aristotle. *Rhetoric*. Roberts, W. R. (Trans., 1984). Honeycutt, L. (Compiled, 2011). Retrieved from http://rhetoric.eserver.org/aristotle/

Covey, S. M. R. (2006). *The SPEED of trust: The one thing that changes everything*. New York, NY: Free Press.

Gladwell, M. (2005). *Blink*. New York, NY: Little Brown & Co.

Kouzes, J. M., & Posner, B. Z. (1990). *The leadership challenge.* San Francisco, CA: Jossey-Bass.

Willis, J. W., & Todorov, A. (2006). First impressions: Making up your mind after a 100-ms exposure to a face. *Psychological Science, 17*(7), 592–598.

# Chapter 8

# Establishing Yourself

*There is a voice inside of you*
*That whispers all day long,*
*"I feel this is right for me,*
*I know that this is wrong."*
*No teacher, preacher, parent, friend*
*Or wise man can decide*
*What's right for you—just listen to*
*The voice that speaks inside.*

—Shel Silverstein

*The hardest times for me were not when people challenged*
*what I said, but when I felt my voice was not heard.*

—Carol Gilligan

## Keys to Effectiveness in Self-Affirmation and Small Talk

This chapter considers two of The 5 Intentions, self-affirmation and small talk. To be sure, information is almost always being transmitted with both these intentions. The accompanying information, however, is secondary to the intention itself. That is why the information is often trivial. The very term "small talk" refers to the unimportance of the actual content, what is being said. The juxtaposition of small talk and self-affirmation provides us the opportunity to set the stage for effectiveness in presenting ourselves to others. We are able to examine the ways to set an appropriate climate, build meaningful relationships, and portray the self that is authentic and fully life-sized.

"Know thyself," said Socrates, but that is just the beginning. Most people boldy set forth a self with little or no thought as to what precisely the other person is going to perceive. You must not only know yourself, you must know the self you want to transmit to others. Then you need to know how to go about transmitting it. When Meryl Streep, as prima fashionista in *The Devil Wears Prada*, pairs her low-pitched, resonant, overly articulate voice with her anchored, structured paraverbals, she conveys to her terrorized employees an impeccable self that is perfectionist, demanding beyond reason, disdainful of lapses or excuses, and utterly in control of her world. The fact that most of us would cringe at the thought of portraying ourselves so negatively takes nothing from Streep's accomplishment for which she won a Golden Globe.

Classic movie actor Peter Lorre uses his nasal, accented voice, smarmy smile, and shifty eyes as he portrays shady characters, murderers, and all around creepy people. Many Hollywood stars and character actors become famous for their distinctive voices affirming a very distinctive self. As an actor you do need to know the self you want to portray and how to portray it effectively. Outside the acting world you need to present yourself, your actual self, in a way that others recognize. Wait around at the stage door and meet up with the actors after a Broadway show. You will get a sense of who these actors really are, their actual self. Actors like Meryl Streep, Tom Hanks, and Jennifer Lawrence portray themselves so well in public that their fans often associate them with themselves and not always the characters they play.

As we noted in Chapter 7, when you come upon someone who has never met you, you always deliver a first impression. First impressions, says the sage, are lasting impressions. Indeed, studies do show that others have a hard time scrubbing a first impression from their consciousness, even after they get to know people much better (Willis & Todorov, 2006).

First impressions are usually composed of both verbals and paraverbals, but paraverbals play a crucial role. Your actual words take a back seat. What others see when their eyes first fall upon you, what they hear in your initial voicings, these paraverbals create in others a set of perceptions and feelings about you. Willis and Todorov (2006), for example, found that facial features create definite impressions about traits like a person's attractiveness, likeability, and aggressiveness; those features require a mere 100 milliseconds to do their impressing!

When meeting people for the first time you may conclude that they "rubbed you the wrong way," "charmed you," "tickled you pink," "got off on the wrong foot." The metaphors point not to the content of the discourse but to the impact of their facial features, tone of voice, loudness, even possibly their touch. The resulting impression may be positive or negative, powerful or not especially memorable. In any transmission, it is your task to bring to conscious awareness the signals you will be sending to others when first you meet. Once aware, you can adjust the signals and make reasonably sure you are transmitting a suitable impression. As stated in the previous chapter on credibility: You want the self others first perceive to be a decent approximation of the self you intend to reveal.

In the previous chapter, we also stressed the importance of your first encounter with others and how important it is to begin building positive rapport at once. When people encounter you in person, the first thing they notice is your face. They will take note of things you can do nothing about: your complexion, apparent ethnicity, eye color, gender. They will also become aware of the look on your face and where your face is looking, and you can do a lot about these.

If you want to present yourself favorably in the initial meeting, look the other in the eye and smile. Say something like "Nice to meet you" or "Nice to see you again." The look on your face should match that sentiment. Make it clear you are taking a moment to be with them and greet them; be attentive and present to them.

In most cases shaking hands is a good idea. Step toward the one whose hand you are about to grasp. Extend your right hand and, when they extend theirs, clasp hands. Mainstream U.S. culture favors a handshake with a firm grip past the knuckles. While maintaining eye contact and a pleasant facial expression, actually shake the hand. Let go after about 2.5 seconds.

While you are busy creating a first impression with voice or other means, you are also setting a climate. As a result of your manner, small talk (or lack thereof), and content, listeners might feel relaxed, ill-at-ease, enthused, intimidated, or raring to go.

Everything that happens early in a discussion or presentation can contribute to how your audience feels about what is to come. A congenial climate is one that creates the emotions, the readiness, the energy that best suits the way in which you want your audience to listen, what you want your audience to retrieve and take with them from their encounter with you. Your voice tone, appearance, gestures, props, and audiovisuals all should mesh with your intended message; none should obstruct it.

The emotions stemming from a climate setting intention are not meant to be long lasting. In a later chapter we will discuss the feeling intention, which involves emotions you wish the receiver to retain during and after an interaction. Below are some tips on small talk and climate setting. These are tips Lonnie often gives to his MBA students who definitely want to make a favorable impression in job interviews and at formal and informal business gatherings. The suggestions have broad application.

- When you start small talk, ask about the other person. Adopt a listening posture. Say something like "Let me introduce myself; I'm Lonnie." and then "How was the traffic on the way in?" or "I'm here to get to know a few people in the field. How about you?"
- Keep it friendly. Avoid controversial topics or assumptions about their point of view.
- Maintain a calm demeanor; let them make their point without interruption.
- Ask open-ended questions that allow for elaboration instead of one word answers: "What were the research findings of your project?" rather than "Will you be presenting at the conference?"
- Express interest in what they are saying by encouraging them to talk: "That's new to me; please go on." or "What happened then?"
- Do not stay at the small talk stage too long if you have a reason for meeting. Once the friendly environment is established, move to the agenda.
- If you wish to circulate around a gathering, say, "I'm sure you'd like to meet a few people, so I'll let you go."
- When "crashing" a small group, say at a cocktail party, step into the group and listen carefully. Talk within the

first 15 seconds, picking up on what you are hearing. You might say, "Yes, I've run into that problem too." or "Really? That's interesting." or "How long have you been dealing with that?" If you do not speak up early, you will be perceived as a spectator.

## Putting It Into Your Voice and Putting Your Voice Into It

The lights dim and then go black. Nothing is visible, although you know the boxing ring is directly in front of you and its contents include two edgy fighters and a ring announcer. You nearly eject yourself from your seat as an open, anchored, resonant belting voice issues the exclamation, "Let's get ready to RUUUUUUUUUM-MMMBAAAAAAALLLL!" Michael Buffer, who made this tag line famous, has utilized his vocal mechanism to create an emotional climate. He wants you excited, on the edge of your seat, perhaps even a tad bloodthirsty. Sometimes unseen, he accomplishes the feat with only a microphone and a voice.

What vocal strategies abetted the ring announcer's cause? Increasing loudness, for sure. His pitch rising on each syllable contributed, as did the elongation of the syllables themselves. He raised his larynx to accentuate the higher frequencies of his voice, supported and anchored his body, and made his vocal folds into a thicker, thick TVFBC to produce the belt quality. The resulting crescendo, although stylized and probably anticipated by most of the audience, created a climate quite well suited to the impending experience of two boxers engaging in their craft—at least if you are a fan of boxing.

As discussed in Chapter 4, there are ways to achieve a loud voice—to project your voice, as it were. Doing so in the right way reduces the risk of vocal injury. Buffer has been able to maintain his booming voice for many years. Singers like Kristin Chenoweth, Adam Lambert, and Sutton Foster strut their belt voice from show to show, demonstrating longevity in their belt. On the other hand, some pop singers like Steven Tyler and Adele, as well as known belt speaker Rachael Ray, have endured vocal injury. Even though their careers did not take a hit, their voices have surely taken a beating.

Many voice teachers shy away from training the belt voice, stating that young singers should not learn to belt or that belting could ruin their singers' classical voice. Let us delve into the first caution: Young singers should not belt. The opposite is actually true: Childhood is when the belt voice should be fostered. The high-pitched, long-lasting wail of an infant's cry can be heard throughout a house with little or no resulting hoarseness. Infants have the innate ability to cry or "belt"; it is a survival mechanism for them—they are hungry, they are tired, they are uncomfortable. Children will do the same. If you model the correct belt production in song, they will innately mimic that sound. If you instill in them a fear of belt, they will begin to constrict, tighten, and shy away from that sound.

Constricting the false vocal folds and tightening the pharyngeal muscles creates backpressure again the vocal folds and will cause the vocal folds to vibrate inefficiently. Remember that a loud production has a longer closed phase proportion of vocal fold vibration, increased subglottal pressure (built up pressure below the vocal folds), and a larger mucosal wave (amplitude of vibration). If you do anything to the structures above the true vocal folds to drive the air back toward those free, flowing vocal folds, you could set up an environment for vocal injury. Also, if you take a big breath and add more air into the system, the vocal folds are required to valve that increase in air, and you can create an inefficient belting environment. The same problem exists if you drive or push air out to attempt a loud belt production.

So what can you do vocally to create the correct belt production (Klimek, Obert, & Steinhauer, 2005)? The number one rule is to take in as little air as possible. Often when teaching belt, Cari has students exhale quickly to REL (like blowing out a match) before they ever attempt the production: quick exhale, close the vocal folds in a ready position for a glottal onset, and release voicing on the word "Hey!" or "Aye!" with an open, anchored posture. Notice that students are not instructed to inhale during this exercise.

Anchors of the back and chest, as well as the pharynx and palate, are also very important to a correct belt production. Remember the open, anchored posture discussed in Chapter 4. Other important components to a correct belt are a higher laryngeal position (think of Kristin Chenoweth's voice in *Wicked*) and a higher tongue position; you want to keep all supraglottic structures up and out of the way of the vocal folds.

When first learning how to belt, maintaining a high laryngeal position is helpful. Determine where your larynx is positioned mostly during speaking and singing by placing your hand on your larynx when performing these tasks. You may already assume a higher laryngeal position during these vocal activities. Play around with character voices to help you determine where you hold your voice for speech or song. Imitating Kristin Chenoweth's voice (high laryngeal position) versus Idina Menzel (lower laryngeal position) in the musical *Wicked*, Sesame Street characters, Ernie (higher laryngeal position) versus Bert (lower laryngeal position), or Sponge Bob (higher laryngeal position) versus Patrick (lower laryngeal position) will give you a sense of what laryngeal position feels most comfortable to you. You may discover that somewhere in the middle of high and a low laryngeal position feels right to you.

To get a sense of laryngeal movement, place your fingers flat across your larynx and swallow. You will feel your larynx rise and then fall back to its resting position after the swallow. Try to engage your infrahyoids (muscles that lower your larynx) after you swallow to pull your larynx down. You want to train your extrinsic laryngeal muscles to generalize the different laryngeal positions you use when swallowing to vocal actions you use during speech and song. Try sustaining the /i/ "ee" sound on one pitch as you move your larynx from high laryngeal position to low. Then, hold the high laryngeal position when speaking and singing. You will assume this high position as you learn to belt. As you become more experienced at belting, you may make choices to lower your larynx to add nuance or character to the sound of your belt. But when first learning to belt, a high laryngeal position is ideal to reduce the chance of vocal injury.

When you get good at changing laryngeal position, practice keeping a high tongue position. Your tongue should be high in an /i/ "ee" position with the back of your tongue against the back part of your hard palate before your soft palate and the sides of your tongue spread against your back molars. While in this position, push the body of your tongue slightly forward along your palate toward your front teeth. Now sing /i/ at a comfortable pitch. Do not change pitch while you move your larynx from high to low position. You'll notice that there seems to be a pitch change; as you lower your laryngeal position, your voice will sound as though you lowered your pitch. In a high laryngeal position, your voice will sound as though you raised your pitch. If you perform this task on a real-time, wideband spectrogram, try to keep your fundamental frequency (the bottom line) constant as you change laryngeal position. You should notice the lines higher in the spectrogram moving up for higher laryngeal position and down for lower laryngeal position. In this example, you are changing your filter (your resonant frequencies) but not your fundamental frequency (the rate at which your vocal folds are vibrating) (Figure 8–1).

Other examples of this filter change are seen in instruments. The same frequency can be played on a violin and a double bass, but the smaller resonating cavity of the violin will resonate better with the higher frequencies (harmonics) coming from the string than the double bass. The same frequency will sound lower when played on the double bass because the resonating cavity is much larger. A slide whistle provides a similar example. Blow into the whistle and draw the stopper toward the end of the whistle; the whistle chamber will resonate lower frequencies better, making the sound lower because you made the whistle chamber longer. If you push the stopper in, the sound will be higher because the chamber is now smaller, resonating better with the higher frequencies. Imagine the stopper is your larynx and the whistle cavity is your vocal tract.

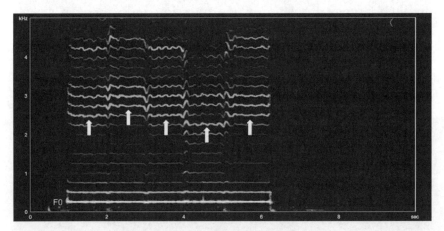

***Figure 8–1.*** Changes in laryngeal position on narrowband spectrogram. The arrows indicate format frequency changes beginning with a mid laryngeal position, moving to a high position, back to mid, then to low, and returning to mid.

Meryl Streep lowered her larynx in *The Devil Wears Prada* to accentuate those lower frequencies, making her sound authoritative and dramatic. When performing character voices of drama teachers most actors choose to include the low laryngeal position; think of Ms. Darbus from the *High School Musical* movies. Peter Lorre made a different choice. Instead of lowering his larynx, he raised his accentuating the higher frequencies which provided an almost shrill sound to put the audience on edge, making him sound like someone who is not to be trusted. We'll delve into feelings more in the Chapter 11, but accomplished actors often set the right climate with their choice of laryngeal position.

Another important ingredient to the belt recipe is narrow aryepiglottic sphincter (AES) or epilaryngeal narrowing. Narrowing the vocal tract may sound counterintuitive because you have been told not to constrict the supralaryngeal structures, but narrow AES is not the same as constriction. Remember that narrow AES creates a tube-within-a-tube effect. The length of the small tube from the vocal folds to the narrowed portion of the AES is the same length as your ear canal. Both the vocal tract and the ear canal will vibrate at a frequency at about 3500 Hz so, in effect, you make your listener's ears ring. Narrow AES also helps to create a thicker TVFBC without extra effort from the intrinsic laryngeal muscles. You will decide how much narrow AES to add to your belt sound depending on the sound you want to produce.

Directors may decide to have actors perform choral productions of songs from musicals like *Annie* and *Matilda the Musical* solely in twang quality without adding the other features of belt, especially a thicker TVFBC (longer proportion of closed phase of vocal fold vibration compared to open phase) because when all the singers sing in twang quality together, they sound loud like belt. Twang also minimizes the impact high subglottal pressure and high airflow may have on the vocal folds because twang is produced with a thin TVFBC rather than thick TVFBC like belt; the risk of pushing is lessened.

Instead of learning the proper technique for belt, many singers avoiding every learning how to belt. The second reason voice teachers do not often train belt is because they believe belt will ruin a singer's classical voice quality. The opposite is actually true. While classical, opera quality is one of the most difficult qualities to sing because of its shifts in TVFBC and primarily mid to lower laryngeal position, aspects of the belt quality enhance opera quality because belt is often a component of the classical, opera voice. Learning to belt will help to improve the classical, opera voice.

Achieving a fortissimo dynamic in opera, vocal performance requires components of the belt quality (higher laryngeal position and what is said to be cricoid tilt—a technique used to enhance the thickness of the vocal folds and increase the proportion of the closed phase of vibration) especially when increasing loudness (crescendo) up to higher notes in a singer's vocal range. It is classical voice's traditional lower laryngeal position and vibrato that draws the performer away from the classic belt sound. Head and neck as well as torso anchoring dominate for support, and balancing airflow and subglottic pressure so as not to push air is paramount in producing either belt or opera quality. When you learn how to belt, you are likely to acknowledge an almost freeing feeling different from the controlled feeling often experienced during opera, vocal performance.

As we age, many of us lose the ability to wail in a healthy way. Coaches lose their voices after yelling during intense games. Politicians exhibit hoarseness after weeks on the campaign trail and teachers cannot make it to the end of the day because their voices are just "too tired." There are ways to learn how to get back to your roots, to learn how to yell or belt again like an infant. Certainly, you could simply not yell or belt, but that is usually not realistic when your voice must reach the back of a large auditorium. Another tactic is to use amplification. FM systems have been shown to greatly enhance the learning environment of students (Rosenberg et al., 1999), while also taking added pressure off the vocal folds.

Amplification, though, is no substitute for good training. Performers and presenters singing or speaking with accompaniment or background noise have to be aware of their bodies. When you cannot hear yourself, you have the innate tendency to get louder, a tendency known as the Lombard Effect. You have to understand what your body feels like when it is pushing so that you can make vocal adjustments regardless of what you hear or cannot hear. Follow these simple steps to learning how to belt.

1. Quickly exhale as if you are blowing out a match. Do not inhale.
2. Throw back your head but do not over extend your neck.

3. Simultaneously throw out your arms, extending your chest up and out.
4. Anchor your torso and head and neck. Open and widen your pharynx, retracting your false vocal folds.
5. Say "Aye!" and hold for the sound for 3 seconds.
6. As you learn the feeling, add on. For example "Aye! One, Two." Increase to functional phrase, like "Aye! Adam, get the ball!" or use words or lines from a play or musical.
7. If you feel a tickle, scratch, or cough—recheck your body and your anchors.

As you see, putting voice into the communication effort is crucial to creating a desired climate. Recent studies are increasingly demonstrating that the brain responds in specific ways to different emotions in the voice; for instance, a happy voice as opposed to an angry voice (Johnstone, van Reekum, Oakes, & Davidson, 2006). While the face alone certainly transmits perceived traits, voice can reinforce or diminish those perceptions and can generate new perceptions (Zebrowitz-McArthur & Montepare, 2005).

While research in this area is limited, Lonnie's work in presentation coaching and Cari's in voice therapy has detected definite vocal patterns associated with specific audience responses and perceptions. A pleasant conversational tone will probably put your audience at ease (Hills, 2006). If you accelerate your rate of speech, run one sentence into another, begin spluttering as you try to catch up with yourself, you may be perceived as nervous, unsure, or pressed for time.

If your voice is low in pitch, your larynx lower, your speech slow and deliberate, you may be heard as authoritative or confident. If your tone is lively, your pitch and larynx raised a bit, your inflection intense, your audience might decide that you possess great conviction about your message. If you have all those qualities except that you remove the intensity, your audience may view you as much less emotional (Reissland, Shepherd, & Herrera, 2001), possibly as more sanguine than committed.

Your voice will always portray a person, a self. Joe, an engineer, once stood before an audience in a Presentation Practicum and delineated a subtle aspect of his applied science, which emerged, to those not inclined toward engineering, as wildly lacking in the power to fascinate. Lonnie, the presentation coach, noted to himself the low monotone voice lacking color and intensity. "Who is your audience?" he asked. "Engineers," Joe answered. The coach nodded.

"Joe, I want you to pretend your audience is your five-year-old nephew." Some prodding induced Joe to give the experiment a try. He reworked the same content into a package he felt suitable for transmission to his little nephew. The result was almost magical. Joe's voice lit up. There was a smile in every word as his inflection varied, intensity increased, tone lightened. Joe himself seemed more interested as he worked to secure the interest of an imaginary five-year-old boy.

Although in Joe's mind his audience had changed, his new audience had actually changed him. He was transformed from a dry, indifferent sort of fellow into an upbeat, enthusiastic, even creative, authority. It was remarkable. Would Joe actually use the exact voice he uses with his nephew during a presentation for engineers? Probably not, but the make-believe change in listener worked wonders for Joe. Aspects of that voice brought life to his presentations.

Sometimes, though, self re-creation is fraught with booby traps. The biggest single error made by those wanting to cultivate an improved self-image is the "false face." Joe could have come off as condescending or patronizing if his audience read his tone the wrong way. A candidate in two presidential debates could be deemed the winner of the first debate because he was smooth and a loser in the second because he was slick. Samantha, a trial attorney, could fall to the same fate if jurors evaluated her closings as stiff and formal, rather than confident and compassionate. Audiences want to experience a genuine person, not someone pretending to be.

Still, people strive to change aspects they perceive to be unattractive. Sometimes the stiff and formal persona can be ameliorated or informalized by the addition of a joke or a lighthearted story at the beginning of a presentation. Presenters in general are frequently given the advice to start with a joke to break the ice. This advice may have worked for Samantha. The trouble is, if she is a terrible joke teller, an early stab at humor may contaminate her entire closing argument. She may come across as not only phony but sly and insincere. If her remarks are not delivered in the right voice, if she retained a lawyerly stolidity in her vocal quality, the joke could be discerned as smug instead of sincere. On the upside, no one would be able to say she was too formal.

Joe, the engineer, when attempting an appeal to his little nephew, was completely genuine; this was how he really tries to talk to a five-year-old. For him the change worked. The point is that any alteration in your manner, your vocal habits, or your accustomed practices runs the risk of constructing the false face, presenting yourself as inauthentic or less than thoroughly trustworthy.

The students Lonnie currently coaches range in age from 24 to 29. They are first-year MBA students at a well-regarded Pennsylvania business school. Lonnie is their executive leadership coach, which means they meet one-on-one regularly during the academic year and figure out what they have and what they lack as future high achievers.

They are energetic, assiduous, articulate, and smart—those attributes are pretty much guaranteed by this university's acceptance standards. Their individual personalities are as varied as their diverse backgrounds. Some are quiet, some more animated. Others are serious, still others more lighthearted. Most seem to have parents who themselves are highly educated and prosperous, and those parental accomplishments constitute an ever-present factor in these students' aspirations.

They want to be more than just leaders; they want to be transformational leaders, the kind who inspire workforces, who imagine powerful change and take their organizations on a thrilling charge through uncharted terrain to that amazing new world of breathtaking innovation and higher definition than anyone ever conceived. Their notion of transformation extends to this world we all inhabit. A startling number of these high achievers see futures in which they build a legacy of betterment. One and all, however, feel that they require one capability: to project to others, peers, direct reports, and investors, that they possess these commanding qualities of leadership. Lonnie teaches them to use an open and anchored posture to project strength, as well as vocal techniques taken from qualities like belt, twang, and opera to enhance that strength. Through these strategies, the students begin to show command and authority.

Power and strength, however, are not the only qualities you may want in voice and demeanor. When Jorge Bergoglio was elected pope in 2013, he appeared on the balcony of St. Peter's Square to multitudes who were cheering and shouting. Here, in front of them, was arguably now one of the most powerful persons in the world.

What climate was he choosing to project with his appearance and voice? How did he choose to project it?

His attire was the first clue. He was dressed, as commentators noted at the time, in a very simple and unadorned version of papal garb. He immediately seemed to distance himself from signals of power and dominion. His demeanor was the second clue. He stood quietly for more than a minute, smiling, looking around, and waving at the assembled crowd. His first words to the people were the third clue. He asked them, before he gave his blessing, to pray for him. Then came a startling visual: The newly elevated pope bowed his head low to receive the people's prayers.

His voice and intonation matched the moment. It was a firm voice but calm, lacking any bombast or soaring inflection. He came off as the most humble person in the square. That first impression was one of humility, simplicity, kindness, and approachability. He demonstrated all of those characteristics by his attire, demeanor, words, and voice. Those qualities endure as the way most people still see this man several years later. That inaugural appearance was clearly authentic and genuine. No false face was presented to the world on that fateful day; he was affirming the self he intended through his "small talk."

While the false face is the biggest pitfall of a vocal makeover, other common missteps should not escape notice. A vocal improvement should not be introduced too soon. If you have been working to raise—or lower—your loudness or pitch, make sure the higher or lower frequency voice sounds natural before you incorporate it into your discourse. The same principle applies to you if you are involved in voice therapy and find yourself rehearsing a new skill or technique.

There are also invented problems. Frequently, adults enter the Presentation Practicum fully believing they have a voice that is "too this" or "lacking in that." These non-problems may have had their origins in feedback the participant claims to have received "all my life" or "a long time ago." Like the rest of us, her voice is intimately bound up in her self-image; it is a very personal possession. Many of her insecurities or the beliefs she thinks others have about her, especially the negative ones, often migrate to judgments about how much she loves or hates her voice.

Angelique, a young woman with a clear, deep, low larynx, resonant voice that oozed authority, said that she has often gotten the feedback that she talks like a man. As a result, she claimed a severe dislike for her voice. During the Presentation Practicum, after giving her presentation, her classmates unanimously expressed admiration and envy at a feminine voice that carried such strength, conviction, and command. Angelique's response to these sincere reports from her peers was that they were just being nice, that they did not want to embarrass her by telling the truth about her mannish voice.

Often just one negative comment can forever affect an individual's perception of his or her own voice. Cari frequently hears people report that they do not sing because their elementary music teacher told them to mouth the words and not sing during performances because their voice did not sound good. If only it took one workshop with positive responses to change Angelique and other's perceptions of their own voices. Remember that judgments made about the aesthetics of voice are really just individual perceptions. A voice that one person findings pleasing to the ear may not be pleasing to another. Be aware of these perceptions. Set out to change what you feel is worth changing and what you have control to change. Accept the rest. What you can then always be sure of is that there is at least one person in the room who likes your voice. If you portray a confident demeanor, audiences often overlook any potential faults.

You can own any number of misperceptions concerning your voice and your self. Here are some most commonly reported during the Presentation Practicum and therapy sessions. To be sure, there are cases when the perception is accurate and needs correcting, but the examples listed below arise with surprising frequency in situations where they are not correct.

- My voice is too deep, masculine (mostly heard from women).
- I talk too loudly.
- I sound conceited.
- My voice shakes.
- No one understands my accent.

Other perceptions you have about yourself can also be self-defeating, if you allow it. While you can change your attire to present yourself more effectively to a given audience, you have no way to change your gender, ethnicity, height, or weight (at least not today). Some matters you must turn over to your audience and simply let them contend with their own preconceptions and perceptions. Improve where you can and never be bothered by things you cannot change.

## The Showroom

The environment around you has an effect on a listener's judgments and feelings about you and the climate you seek to create. When you walk into a well-appointed automobile showroom, you are met with a number of calculated sensory impacts. The first is a kind of glowing quality. The vehicles clustered there are detailed and spiffed up to a preternatural luminosity; they look like large gems, glistening and inviting. If you draw near to one, the leather seats emit a luscious aroma you may associate with a new wallet. No coincidence: The leather in cars is artificially infused with that aroma. The place literally reeks of newness, richness, and freshness—all the possibilities of a gleaming future. It is in the aura of this joyous, colorful, expectant climate that you are to purchase your next car.

In the example of the pope's first appearance, the "showroom" was the magnificent St. Peter's Square where you would expect a display of princely power and authority. Pope Francis opted to send a counter message and sent it with astounding effectiveness. His choice indicates the flexibility and creativity with which you can approach the environment in which you find yourself.

When you speak, there is also about you a showroom of sorts. Sometimes you have control over the showroom and sometimes you do not. Lonnie remembers delivering the same seven-hour workshop twice at two very different sites. In Baltimore, Maryland, he delivered to a class of 25 in a spacious, well-ventilated room with chairs arranged in a U-shape. He had control of the lighting and his computer projection setup was superb, with a large easily viewable screen and a fully functioning remote to control the slides.

The next week in Augusta, Maine, a new group of 25 was squeezed into a tiny, dimly lit, airless room with tables and chairs arranged in rows, the slides projected onto painted cinder blocks. Lonnie was compressed, treelike, into one spot from which there was no hope of ambulation. The materials, slides, and design of the two sessions were the same, but these were two very different workshops. Lonnie found himself stuck with very few options in Augusta, whereas in Baltimore, he had many choices.

Where possible you should seize control of your "showroom" and assemble it to foster a climate conducive to your aims. Ask yourself several questions:

- Am I positioned appropriately with respect to my audience (even an audience of one)?
- Is the room or space suitable? Check size, amplification, lighting, ventilation, seating, audiovisual set-up, and décor. Certain specification can be addressed even before you arrive.
- What have I done to make this space foster the climate I desire?

## Completing the Connection

Of course, the most salient feature of your showroom is you. You are affirming yourself by the showroom you create, but people notice you as well, your demeanor, facial expression, gestures (Figure 8–2). All these aspects combine to create the total impression people receive. As your transmission proceeds, face and gesture will be an ally or foe to your voice but never a neutral party.

Early in her career, trial attorney Samantha came to realize that her expressive face was a powerful asset. The diminutive lawyer knew that standing at a distance in a courtroom diluted the impact she had on the jurors; therefore, prior to beginning her remarks, she would move rapidly to the jury box. Then she would take several seconds to scan the jury at close range, make eye contact, and establish an emotional connection with each juror. She might show anger in her voice and face if her opening remarks expressed outrage; she might show sadness if that emotion served her purpose. The effect she accomplished was often profound.

When Samantha approaches the jury box with haste, she is using a specific climate setting device: movement. That device actually constitutes a kind of small talk. A company vice president uses

A

B

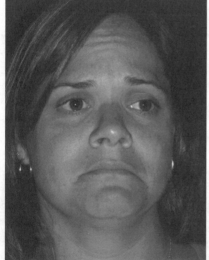

C

*Figure 8-2.* Facial expressions conveying a range of emotional states: happiness (**A**), surprise (**B**), sadness (**C**). Very few viewers would fail to identify the feelings expressed in this series.

movement as she steps from behind her huge oaken desk and escorts you to the cozy-looking corner nook where two padded chairs invite you to sit at a small round table. There the VP is dialing back the power messages and pumping up the informality. Sometimes movement is unavailable, as in Lonnie's situation in Maine, where the severely restrictive room conditions in Augusta made it virtually impossible for him to take a step. In instances like these, speakers must utilize whatever paraverbals are available to create a desired climate. Actors also use movement or lack of movement to portray different aspects of their character or intentions in a scene.

Your mode of dress also sends a message. Pope Francis' simple garb sent a strong signal of a man devoted to the less powerful in society. Lonnie once found himself in Maui, Hawaii, where he was about to deliver a keynote presentation. He walked into the beachfront conference room within earshot of the rhythmic surf. He was greeted by his client with a slow but unmistakable shake of the head. "Not here," the client said. "They'll think you're a realtor."

Lonnie had gone to the trouble of donning his three-piece suit, a major no-no in this setting before this audience. He began disrobing and was not halted until he had disposed of his coat, vest, and tie, and had rolled up his sleeves. He was fortunate. First of all, he had arrived early enough to be alerted of his sartorial faux pas. Secondly the correction involved the removal of excess clothing rather than the addition of a garment he had elected to leave behind. It is easier to take off a tie than find one you are not wearing!

A major part of dressing right is meeting the expectations of your audience. Your attire should be compatible with the audience, even an audience of one, because the one message that you send from the moment you step before your audience until you leave is the message sent by your wardrobe. If it is inappropriate, you will be sending that inappropriate message throughout your interaction.

When instructing participants in the Presentation Practicum about appropriate attire, Lonnie often hears these comments: "I'm not a conformist. I'll dress the way I like, not to please others. If they don't like it, too bad!" Lonnie rhetorically answers, "Too bad for whom? Your audience or you?" These participants' comments are similar to someone saying, "I'm not a conformist. In some cultures it is considered polite to burp loudly. If I feel a burp coming on during a presentation, I make sure to project it as long and as loud as I can!" That seems pretty ridiculous.

Dressing in a way that is compatible with your audience's expectations is not conformity; it is courtesy. It is resisting the urge to disadvantage yourself before you begin. It is just plain smart. You may ask yourself, "What should I wear?" The answer varies according to the situation. Maui is not Manhattan. The point is, you should ask the question, think about it, and arrive at a sensible conclusion. Here is the way to ask it, and remember: These considerations apply whether your audience consists of one or one hundred.

1. What attire would be acceptable to my audience given their customs, habits, and expectations?
2. What attire would present me in the best light—most agreeable, most professional—by my audience's standards?
3. What attire would permit my audience to concentrate on my message and not on what I am wearing?

If you wonder what you should not wear, then ask these questions.

1. What attire would offend my audience or make them think I do not care about them or their opinions?
2. What attire would be considered garish, racy, bizarre, or too straight-laced to my audience?
3. What attire would distract my audience and make it difficult for them to focus on what I am transmitting?

Beyond these questions, find out what style of clothes suits your size, gender, waistline, and complexion. Find out if there are any audience expectations springing from their local customs, practices, or culture. You may find this process fun; you may find it tedious. The point is, you are taking the time to send your audience a very important message: You respect them. And a well-selected wardrobe also tells your audience that you respect yourself.

Throughout the following chapters, audiovisuals will get some scrutiny. They too promote a particular climate. If you dim the lights to cinema darkness and then flash slides, your disembodied voice may pierce the gloom, but you are no longer the central transmitter. You have assigned that responsibility to the slides or the video. The audience is the equivalent of a crowd of moviegoers and something very different from interpersonal communication is occurring.

In some circumstances slides, whiteboards, flip charts, videos and the like serve as paraverbals supporting your presentation.

Their very presence sends a message and contributes to a climate. They say, at the very least, "Focus up here, and take note. What's happening here is important enough that I have gone to the trouble of preparing these AVs."

Beyond the climate setting established by the very existence of audiovisuals, the particular audiovisuals you select will reinforce certain intentions. A slide series with lots of wordy bullet items will engender a mood quite different from a sequence of graphs. A set of colorful photos will foster something else as well. If you avoid slides and use only a flip chart, you may reinforce intimacy; what is on a sheet is written (usually) just for this audience. It is in your handwriting, often written in real time during the presentation. Once used, the sheets are discarded.

Audiovisuals, then, can be more or less intimate, more or less impersonal. It is possible to rank them from most intimate to most impersonal (Figure 8–3).

Of course, the most intimate audiovisual is you. The term "interpersonal communication" implies a direct connection between two

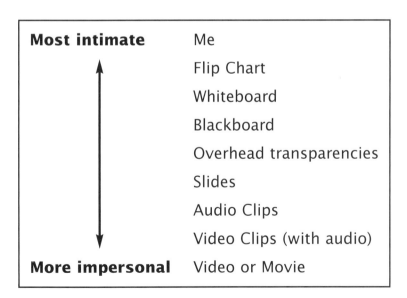

**Most intimate**    Me

Flip Chart

Whiteboard

Blackboard

Overhead transparencies

Slides

Audio Clips

Video Clips (with audio)

**More impersonal**    Video or Movie

*Figure 8–3.* Intimacy ranking of common audiovisuals. The audiovisuals you use can help make a more or less intimate connection with your audience. The most intimate connection is person to person, whereas the screening of a video is among the most impersonal.

persons. Any other audiovisual moves away from that direct connection. Flip charts are next in intimacy because they may retain clear vestiges of the interpersonal: your handwriting, the chart's movability, the real rather than projected image. The other less intimate AVs are all projections thereby distancing you more from your audience who are now asked to divide their attention between you and what is projected on the screen. Again, you do well to know your primary intention before selecting your audiovisual strategy.

How you use the audiovisual is as crucial as your choice of audiovisual. If you turn to the screen and read what is on each slide, if you introduce each new slide with words like "now this slide says . . . ," if you overuse animation effects, you are diverting attention from yourself and toward the slides. You are fracturing the interpersonal connection. If you maintain eye contact with your audience and continue your transmission with no break in the flow when a new slide appears, the slides augment your interaction and do not replace it. Like your gestures and your face, audiovisuals become powerful paraverbals that reinforce your intention. Make sure you remain the clear focus. All of these paraverbals help you to make a strong connection with your audience.

Intended meaning may start with phonemes and proceed to morphemes, words, and sentences, but meaning is packaged in wrappings that can stimulate any of the senses. We call these wrappings paraverbals. When brought to the conscious attention of the transmitter, when honed and shaped by a skilled communicator, paraverbals enhance meaning and make it far more likely that you will achieve your communication aims.

Although a seemingly infinite number of components exist in a transmission, there is only one connection—a unitary intention you have in mind when you choose to transmit to others. Your voice, body, face, and environment provide you with innumerable opportunities to say what you intend more emphatically, more precisely, more accurately. This paraverbal universe can be categorized in many ways. As briefly mentioned in a previous chapter, Dr. Jens Allwood (2002) discerns three ways to give expression: The primary ones are facial expression, gestures and the like; secondary ways include transmission extenders like cell phones, megaphones, and laptops; tertiary ways embody the furniture that accompanies the others—our tables and chairs, clothes, wallpaper, the feng shui, you might say of communication.

As a transmitter you have a choice about whether and how to utilize the paraverbal universe. You have less say in the decisions of your listeners as they try to make sense of that universe. Humans are meaning seekers. They will scour the world in search of a fuller understanding of what is being sent their way. What adroit communicators can do is make the world around the listener more accessible. Just as you select the words that most closely approximate what you intend to get across, so do you manipulate voice, face, gesture, body language, attire, and your showroom to transmit all you intend—from the self you seek to portray to the climate that is just right for the intended message to this person at this time.

Small talk and self-affirmation work together to set the stage for whatever intention is to come. Once the curtain opens you will be ready to report some data, engender a feeling, or create a conviction. The chapters that follow will explore these intentions in detail.

## Review of Key Ideas

- With both self-affirmation and small talk the information being transmitted is always secondary to the intention itself.
- First impressions are composed of both verbals and paraverbals, but paraverbals play an large role, whereas actual words are secondary. As I create a first impression, I am also setting a climate.
- A congenial climate is one that creates the emotions, the readiness, the energy that best suits the way in which I want my audience to listen, what I want my audience to retrieve and take with them from their encounter with me.
- Recent studies increasingly demonstrate that the brain responds in specific ways to different emotions in the voice, so the voice is crucial in creating the climate. A pleasant conversational tone puts my audience at ease. An accelerated rate of speech may indicate nervousness or uncertainty.
- If my voice is low and deliberate, I may be heard as authoritative or confident. If my tone is lively, my pitch raised a bit, my prosody intense, you might decide that I possess great conviction about my message. If I remove the intensity, you may well view me as much less passionate.

- With proper training, belt quality can be used as an effective, efficient technique for getting louder while speaking or singing to an audience.
- The biggest error made by those who want to cultivate an improved self image is the false face. Any alteration in your accustomed vocal practices runs the risk of constructing the false face, presenting yourself as inauthentic and less than thoroughly trustworthy.
- A vocal improvement should not be introduced into daily speech until it sounds natural.
- The voice is intimately bound up in self-image; it is a very personal possession. Deeply seated insecurities can migrate to judgments about how much you love or hate your voice.
- Some of the most common misperceptions about voice quality are that one's voice is too deep, too masculine (mostly from women); is too loud; sounds conceited.
- The environment has an effect on a listener's judgments and feelings about you and the climate you seek to create. Make sure you are positioned effectively with respect to the audience, that the room is suitable, that you have done all you can to make the space foster the desired climate.
- Face, gesture, and posture contribute to the climate, as does mode of dress. A major part of dressing right is meeting the expectations of your audience.
- Audiovisuals promote a particular climate, and the particular audiovisuals you select will reinforce certain intentions; they can be more or less intimate, more or less impersonal.
- There are three ways to give expression: The primary ones are facial expression, gestures and the like; secondary ways include transmission extenders like microphones; tertiary ways embody the furniture that accompanies the others, such as tables and chairs.
- Humans are meaning seekers. They will always search for fuller understanding.

# References

Allwood, J., 2002. Bodily communication dimensions of expression and content. In B. Granström, D. House, & I. Karlsson (Eds.), *Multimodality in language and speech systems* (pp. 7–26). Dordrecht, The Netherlands: Kluwer Academic.

Hills, L. S. (2006). Putting patients at ease with conversation. *Journal of Medical Practice Management, 22*(3), 168–170.

Johnstone T., van Reekum C. M., Oakes T. R., & Davidson R. J. (2006). The voice of emotion: An FMRI study of neural responses to angry and happy vocal expressions. *Social Cognitive and Affective Neuroscience, 1*(3), 242–249.

Klimek, M. M., Obert, K., & Steinhauer, K. (2005). *Estill voice training system level two: Figure combinations for six voice qualities workbook.* Pittsburgh, PA: Estill Voice International.

Reissland, N., Shepherd, J., & Herrera, E. (2001). Impact of intended emotion intensity on cue utilization and decoding accuracy in vocal expression of emotion. *Emotion, 1*(4), 381–412.

Rosenberg, G. G., Blake-Rahter, P., Heavner, J., Allen, L., Redmond, B. M., Phillips, J., & Stigers, K. (1999). Improving classroom acoustics: A three-year FM sound field classroom amplification study. *Journal of Educational Audiology, 7*, 8–28.

Willis, J. W., & Todorov, A. (2006). First impressions: Making up your mind after a 100-ms exposure to a face. *Psychological Science, 17*(7), 592–598.

Zebrowitz-McArthur, L., & Montepare, J. M. (2005). Contributions of a babyface and a childlike voice to impressions of moving and talking faces. *Journal of Nonverbal Behavior, 13*(3), 189–203.

# Chapter 9

# Informing Them

*To inform mankind is a bold effort of a valiant mind.*

—George Crabbe

*Interesting phenomena occur when two or more rhythmic patterns are combined, and these phenomena illustrate very aptly the enrichment of information that occurs when one description is combined with another.*

—Gregory Bateson

## Keys to Effectiveness in Information Exchange

Just about every time you open your mouth and voice words to others, information will be present. An information intention may not always be your principal intention, but it is pretty rare to send a message with no information whatsoever. So if just about all messages contain information, how do will you know when information is your primary intention? When seeking out your primary intention, the key question you will ask is a simple one: What do you want others to take away and retain from their encounter with you?

If you have a feeling intention, you mainly want your communication partner to reach a particular emotional state. If the intention is persuasion/direction, you want others to leave convinced of something, or you want them committed to doing something. If your intention is primarily informational, it is your strongest desire that others remember some things that you have transmitted to them —not necessarily act on them, not necessarily feel a certain way about them, not even necessarily believe them: just remember them.

Edward Snowden is an information technology professional whose job gave him access to large amounts of classified data from the National Security Agency of the United States. He leaked that data to the press in 2013. He explained his intention as simply informational. "My sole motive," he claimed, "is to inform the public as to that which is done in their name and that which is done against them." Sometimes even though people claim their intentions are purely informational, something in their transmission may lead you to become suspicious that a different intention may be in the foreground.

Even without knowing his tone, facial expression, or body language when transmitting those words, you might find it difficult to believe that Snowden had only an informational intention to transmit. It is certainly possible that he primarily intended for Americans to feel a certain way (shocked, aghast), act a certain way (consider halting collection of data on U. S. citizens), or be persuaded in a certain way (believe that what the government is doing is unconstitutional). Any of these intentions might seem more probable than merely an intention to inform—have us remember the information. If your message is truly informational, your intention is your listener's retention of the information.

In preparing a successful informational transmission, therefore, your critical first step is to figure out precisely and completely what it is that you want others to retain or record. All information is not created equal. Just because your intention is informational does not mean that every word you transmit is to be committed to memory. You might not care one bit if others recall a particular example you offered, but perhaps you do want them to be able to recite the principle being exemplified. There are four crucial aspects of a well-prepared informational message: clarity, precision, completeness, and accuracy.

Make sure your transmission is clear. Avoid ambiguous phraseology or vague wording. Use good grammar and sentence structure. Prefer the active voice: "You know the facts" not "The facts are known by you." Most importantly, know what you are going to say before you say it and transmit with precision. Make sure you say exactly what you mean. Follow these guidelines:

- Be brief. Avoid lengthy introductions, confusing examples, pointless rambling.
- Dispose of clutter. Do not use two words when one will do. Keep sentences short and to the point.
- Before the exchange begins, consider writing down your main points. If you cannot write it, you cannot speak it!
- Select words carefully. The verbals are critical since words carry the burden of meaning. Use words you know and develop a passion for choosing just the right word. It was Mark Twain who said that the "difference between the almost right word and the right word is really a large matter—it's the difference between the lightning bug and the lightning."

Send the complete transmission. A piece of information has a beginning, a middle, and an end. Make sure others hear all of what you want them to remember and that they can distinguish the "must remember" portion of the message from that which they do not need to recall. Teachers make this distinction all the time, especially when they say, "OK, this will be on the test. Remember it."

Frank, a safety manager, gave a one-hour safety presentation. Midway through he said, "Now, these are the four cardinal rules of safety. Break one of these and you will be terminated immediately." He recited the four rules and flashed a slide with the rules on it. He then asked the group: "Which of these four rules is it OK to forget?" A few chuckles ensued, but everyone knew the answer. They could forget the whole one-hour talk, but forgetting one of the cardinal rules was out of the question. Frank's informational intention was summed up, completed, quite neatly by the various ways in which he stressed the four cardinal rules of safety.

Finally, be accurate. Present fact as fact, opinion as opinion. A fact is something that can be shown to be true or to have happened. An opinion is something somebody may believe. Remember: If you are presenting an opinion to others and you want only for them to remember it (rather than believe it), then your intention is informational.

Fact: I went to the supermarket yesterday afternoon.

Opinion: That was the best supermarket in the state.

If you ask, "Now, do you know what I think of the supermarket?" and your friend answers, "Sure, you think it's the best one in the state," you have met an informational intention, even though your friend is repeating your opinion.

When Frank, the safety guy, informed his co-workers that they would be fired instantly for breaking a cardinal rule, he was offering them a motivation to remember the rules. The information intention requires work of the listeners: They must commit the information to memory. A receptive learner is one who is ready, willing, and able to hear and retain the intended information. If you are a receptive learner in a situation like this, you have a definable profile.

- Retention of the information serves some purpose for you, is of value to you. (Remembering the cardinal rules could save you your job, not to mention your life.)
- You perceive the transmitter as a reliable authority. (Frank is the safety manager; he should know.)
- The climate set by the transmitter is conducive to hearing and remembering this message. (This is a safety meeting; you expect to hear this kind of thing.)
- You understand the message and have been given the time and opportunity to store it in memory.

When you transmit information to others, they must make a connection with you as a reliable source for that information. If your professor is teaching you a course on voice disorders, you will have confidence in the reliability of her information if you know that she has a PhD in speech-language pathology, has treated individuals with voice disorders for many years, and has taught this course for ten years. Transmission of relevant credentials will improve your connection as a reliable source of the knowledge you are imparting. That is also an extremely helpful form of self-affirmation!

The ideal climate for transferring information has identifiable characteristics. It is businesslike, quiet, controlled, and comfortable. Everyone reading this book has experienced the typical classroom in which the transmission of information is the primary intention of the teacher. Teachers generally do seek a serious, quiet, and controlled environment. The classroom, unfortunately, can also generate climatic conditions that militate against learning and retention. Classrooms are often seen as boring, even oppressive. The question, then, is still out there: what is the ideal setting for the informational intention? What is the look, the feel, the sound?

## The Voice of Authority

Let us begin with the question, "What does an information intention sound like?" Your voice has a lot to do with creating the ideal setting for an informational intention. It was stated above that to be effective in your informational transmission, listeners should make a connection to you as a reliable source—someone who has authority to be providing the information.

Soon after Katie Couric took over the post of news anchor for CBS Evening News in 2006, ratings began to slip. Among the reasons given for the decline was that "viewers don't want to get their news from a female anchor." Do viewers really believe that the higher pitched woman's voice lacks the authority, the gravitas, to inform us of world events? Men's vocal pitch is on average half as high as women's, and lower pitch has been associated with interpersonal competitiveness and deference among males (Puts, Gaulin, & Verdolini, 2006). Listeners may also perceive lower pitch in terms of dominance (Puts et al., 2006). Dominance is not authority. Presentation coaches are aware that pitch can partner with other vocal qualities to enhance or reduce the perception that a speaker is in command of a subject.

Just as runners have an optimal running speed—if you run faster or slower you'll tire more quickly (Cavanagh & Williams, 1982)—so do speakers have an "optimal" (Fairbanks, 1960) or "best" (Boone & MacFarlane, 2000; Case, 1996) pitch for their voices. Whatever self you wish to affirm with your voice, remember that your own optimal pitch will be where you are most yourself.

Your optimal pitch is based on your age and gender, the make-up of your vocal anatomy; the size of your larynx; the length of your vocal tract; as well as the size, mass and stiffness of your vocal folds. Your optimal pitch should also be the most effortless for you to produce. Some people always speak at their optimal pitch. Some people do not. The pitch that you normally speak at is called your habitual pitch or speaking fundamental frequency (Boone, 1983). This is the pitch you have consciously or subconsciously decided you will use, sometimes to project the self you wish others to perceive.

The problem is, just like the runner, if your habitual pitch is too far from your optimal pitch, you may end up projecting a self you do not intend. Remember the false face discussed in the last chapter. A habitual pitch far from your optimal pitch may also result in a voice problem (Cooper, 1974; Van Riper & Irwin 1958; Wilson, 1962). These voice problems can manifest as muscle strain while talking and the perception of vocal fatigue at the end of a long day of talking. Treatment may include voice therapy to help you locate the pitch that is just right for you.

A voice disorder could also induce a maladaptive or compensatory change in habitual pitch. Mutational falsetto is a voice disorder that is characterized by an abnormally high pitch due to a technique-related issue (usually caused because individuals have not dropped their larynx during their voice change in adolescence) rather than a vocal fold lesion or other organic etiology. In voice therapy for the transgendered voice, speaking fundamental frequency is often targeted, though other paraverbals like mannerisms, body language, facial expressions, gait, and gesture have been found to have more of an impact on people's perception of gender than the voice (Gelfer, 1999), except, of course, when hearing the voice on the telephone.

In voice therapy, Cari rarely targets pitch directly. Changes in laryngeal position are much easier to facilitate and do not often leave clients feeling so far away from their habitual pitch. Often, achieving better vocal fold closure remedies the situation completely without direct changes to pitch or laryngeal position. Raising the larynx does draw a listener's perception to the higher frequencies that already exist in the voice. Dropping one's larynx creates the opposite effect. If the worry was that people perceived Katie Couric as less authoritative because her speaking pitch was too high, then an astute vocal coach may have instructed her to lower her larynx slightly.

If only changing viewers' perceptions was that easy. Couric's speaking pitch was most likely not the only factor in the viewers' skewed perceptions of who qualifies as an appropriate news anchor. Couric's paraverbals, as well as viewers' idea of what gender a news anchor should be, probably played a more important role than her pitch alone. It is also possible that she was just was not very good at the job, although her resume makes that possibility less likely.

There are definite characteristics that will signal to your audience that an expert is standing before them. When participants in the Presentation Practicum give feedback to their colleagues after presentations, they are consistent in their perceptions about what constitutes a confident, clearly expert presenter. The patterns that display a lack of confidence are every bit as pronounced. Here are some frequently noted practices that may reduce the listener's confidence in what a presenter is saying:

- Long pauses, accompanied by searching or "nervous" eyes
- Excessive "ums" or other fillers
- Shaking voice
- Loss of vocal intensity
- Uptalk (habit of ending phrases with rise in pitch to a major or minor key)
- Ending a phrase in a minor key (unless culturally acceptable)
- Pitch break (cracking voice)
- Speech frequently interrupted by swallowing
- Glottal fry (voice begins to creak, slack TVFBC)
- False starts (beginning, then starting over)
- Increasing rate of speech (talking too fast)
- Catch breath (noisy clavicular breath)
- Continuing to speak when out of breath
- Depending overly on notes or slides
- Apparent unfamiliarity with the slides or other AVs
- Inappropriate dress (too informal, garish, or dressy for the audience)

All these items are frequently cited by our workshop attendees as features likely to cause a lack confidence in the speaker. None of them have anything to do with immutable characteristics like gender or height. Although there is scant research about what constitutes credibility or authority in the voice, the perception of authority may have some relationship to a lower pitch (Gélinas-Chebat

& Chebat, 1996). The following guidelines will improve that perception no matter how high or low-pitched your voice:

- Know what you are about to say and how you are going to say it
- Think before you begin so you do not have to restart
- Maintain vocal strength and loudness (belt quality)
- Maintain open-anchored posture
- Remove fillers like "um"
- Exhale to REL if you feel as though you are "out of breath" or "cannot catch your breath"
- Add a little AES narrow to help a shaky voice
- Swallow occasionally but unobtrusively during speech
- Maintain a constant and deliberate rate of speech
- Phrase appropriately and take breaths at natural pauses
- Make sure you have a small glass of water nearby and take a sip when you need one
- Deep breaths should be limited; a quick exhale helps you take the right amount of air on your inhalation.
- Take your time; be deliberate, not rushed

There is such a thing as vocal compatibility with your audience. In general, when you receive information meant to be retained, you prefer to hear moderately lively inflection, an intensity that indicates interest, and a firm stress on key words. With an informational intention, you should use many declarative sentences delivered with a ring of sureness and ending at a lower pitch in a major key (Figure 9–1). You may introduce discussion with a question, but you should know the answer in advance and stand ready to affirm it when an audience member correctly recites it.

Vocal compatibility also varies with the specific audience. When our engineer friend, Joe, gave information to his peers, his voice pattern differed quite a bit from the exchange with his five-year-old nephew. He learned to add some of the inflection he uses with his nephew to liven up the exchange, but his vocal pattern stayed strong and firm with his colleagues. It is important to become aware of the expectations of your particular group of listeners. What works with one group can fall embarrassingly flat with another.

*Figure 9–1.* Signaling listeners with pitch change. **A.** Statement ending in a major key indicates that a declarative statement is being made. **B.** Statement ending in a minor key may cause feelings of uncertainty in listeners. **C.** If the speaker is not asking a question, a statement ending in a rise in pitch indicates a lack of confidence.

Marta, an excellent consultant, typically received rave reviews for her presentations on negotiation techniques, which she shared with corporate audiences. Her vocal quality was resonant, her speech articulate, humorous, and suffused with the light touch much appreciated by businesspeople. One day Marta delivered her talk on negotiation to a group of college professors who had never heard her before. She changed nothing in her voice and received highly critical feedback. This feedback indicated that the academically-oriented participants concluded that she lacked seriousness, so they did not take her seriously.

A few modifications to Marta's speech and voice might have served her better in the latter case. Although her vocal quality should have remained resonant, she might have considered a quality less lilting and more deliberate. While her intonation should have remained interesting and varied, she might have achieved more authority by using less pronounced changes in pitch. Her demeanor should have appeared a little less colloquial and a little more formal.

In his travels Lonnie has noted myriad regional differences that affect his approach when delivering information. Being from the Northeastern United States, Lonnie talks quite clearly but at a moderately rapid pace. When he spoke in Knoxville, Tennessee, the pace seemed anything but moderate. "Whoa," shouted a fellow in the back of the room. "When you New Yorkers talk so fast I can't keep up, I reach down and hold onto my wallet." The fact that Lonnie was from Philadelphia did not make the critique easier to take. Being seen as a fast-talking swindler was not exactly a feather in his cap, so he slowed his pace significantly. Of course, if he had adopted a "Knoxville pace" in Manhattan, his audience would have begun to lose interest within minutes.

Once you have settled on a vocal style appropriate to your informational intention and your audience's expectations, you will be in a position to create a verbal and paraverbal climate that helps assure success in making the interpersonal connection.

## The Learning Center

When information exchange is your intention, you want to generate an environment where learning and remembering are facilitated. It should evoke curiosity in your audience about the topic. It should motivate them to find out what you want them to find out. It should engage their intellect and elicit a strong desire to remember what they discover. It should constitute a true learning center.

The showroom in this instance is a kind of laboratory, a place where discoveries are made, conclusions are reached, and memorable information is compiled. As with any lab moderator, you control the experimental conditions so as to transmit the appropriate data. You come armed with illustrations of salient points and reasons the points are salient to this audience. The laboratory contains instruments and components that are suitable for any "experiments" you plan. The room and chairs accommodate general and small group sessions if such are envisioned. In a one-on-one situation, you take charge of the environment in much the same way You are asking your audience to retain information, commit it to memory, a task that, at minimum, requires some distance from noise and distractions.

You must know what kind of memory you want your audience to access. Perhaps it is nothing more than rote recall of a poem or a street address. A nonrote memory asks your audience to learn material in such a way that they can feed it back in their own words or summarize it. If you are transmitting a skill or technique, you need your listener to remember how to do it. Managers, therapists, and trainers frequently transmit new techniques to clients who must sometimes alter lifetime habits.

You, the presenter, are yourself an audiovisual aid. You should be fine-tuned to deliver the information intention. We have discussed the role of the voice in a successful transmission. Visuals like facial expression and eye contact must also be considered. The face should maintain an expression consistent with the meaning and purpose of the information being transmitted. If you are relating crucial instructions to help others avoid serious injury, you will adopt a serious, no-nonsense expression. If you are transmitting a recipe for fudge brownies, your countenance might lighten considerably.

As you give others the information you want them to remember, your eye contact should be direct but not piercing; you should glance away frequently for a second or two and then reconnect. Your eyes should remain "alive," engaged with your listener and with the topic rather than vacant or disconnected. If your eyes look otherwise you might drain your listener's energy away and distract your listener from the task of committing the information to memory.

Research is not abundant on the role of gestures in the effective transmission of information, but one study does suggest that certain concrete gestures can help a listener obtain more clarity about what the speaker intends (Holle & Gunter, 2007). Listeners can utilize the information contained in gestures to make speech less ambiguous. There is even evidence that the brain reacts differently to words accompanied by certain appropriate gestures compared to the same words delivered without the gestures (Cook, Duffy, & Fenn, 2013; Wu & Coulson, 2007).

Participants in the Presentation Practicum consistently identify the gestures they perceive as effective in information exchange. You should nod your head often to indicate the positive flow of information. You should keep your hands apart, open, and make full use of pulling gestures, the palms-up kind that indicates a welcoming attitude, gestures that invite your audience to listen, grasp, and retain. If you are presenting to a group, you should move freely about the room to keep the audience interested and maintain contact with all of them. When you make salient points, you should stop and plant yourself to emphasize definiteness. Everything about your face and body and movement should convey your firm objective that the audience receive and recall this information.

If your intention is informational, you want to accomplish two basic feats: to transmit the information effectively and to reinforce it powerfully. The audiovisuals you employ properly serve a reinforcing function. Your presentation should display slides that use a number of techniques to support your informational connection. Below are suggestions for slides and charts. These derive from surveys taken in our Presentation Practicum over the years, but they are consistent with recommendations from other noted authorities (Atkinson, 2005; Yaffe, 2008).

- Make sure all slides are easy to read, even in a well-lighted room.
- Use contrasting colors (like yellow font on dark blue background); avoid multicolored or textured backgrounds; avoid small print.
- Avoid putting too much on one slide or chart. Busy slides are cumbersome to read and can induce headaches over time.
- Consider replacing a busy slide with a handout.
- A wireless remote allows you to change slides from anywhere in the room; if equipped with a laser pointer, it can be used to reference details of a slide.
- Limit the use of animation effects; they can be distracting and annoyingly repetitive.
- Use bullet items like this one, with the main points summarized. Consider presenting them in "build" fashion one at a time as you recite them orally.

▪ Display a key word by itself or with an illustrative graphic as you discuss it.

▪ Use graphs and tables to illustrate statistical points.

▪ Use pictures to create useful associations that can maintain interest and help viewers remember key points. Slides and charts are visual; take advantage of that fact.

▪ Avoid reading from the slides, except on rare occasions for dramatic effect.

Here are some suggestions for interacting with slides.

▪ Maintain audience focus on you, not the slides. They are positioned behind you in a "supporting role." You should never be in the dark; this is your show, not a slide show.

▪ The screen should not inhibit your mobility. Move about the room as freely as if no screen appeared behind you, meanwhile avoid casting your shadow upon the screen.

▪ Do not announce a new slide with expressions like "next" or "now for the next slide." Audiences will know a new slide has appeared every time a new slide appears.

▪ Avoid mention of the slide when talking about what is on it. Do not say, "This slide shows the three main points of this talk." Say, "The three main points of this talk are . . . " Your audience will know you are talking about what is on the slide.

▪ Use a slide to present a central point or quote by flashing it in large type by itself. One technique for stressing its importance is to project the slide, turn towards it (your back the audience) and maintain silence while they read it. Another technique is to read it aloud word for word.

▪ Do not read slides word for word, except as a reinforcing device like the one in the previous bullet.

▪ Slides present summaries. You present the details with your voice.

▪ An illustration is best when it requires no accompanying commentary. A great picture is worth a thousand words, so let the picture do the talking. Silence can be as effective as speech.

No matter how well you prepare your slides and for what purpose, be aware of their limitations. Ian Parker's 2001 *New Yorker* article, "Absolute PowerPoint: Can a software package edit our thoughts?" provides an excellent overview of the history of the use of AVs and important caveats about computer-generated slides.

Videos are a popular medium for transmitting information during workshops and can be useful. The following are some points and suggestions concerning the use of videos to support your presentation:

- Your audience is quite familiar with video; it is not special at all. Americans spend many hours a week watching TV on a variety of screen types.
- If you are employing sound or video, make sure the video and accompanying speakers are functioning properly and you know how to make them work. Do this before you give your presentation.
- Make sure your videos are very well done and up to date. Dated, unprofessional looking clips draw groans and defeat your informational purpose (unless your video is historical or meant to be dated).
- Consider using short videos (under 30 seconds a clip and no longer than three minutes total) interspersed with live discussion; these tend to be far more reinforcing and interesting than longer ones.
- The most memorable videos make their point with a light touch and with effective humor; avoid heavy-handed moralistic approaches.

An infrequently used but sometimes effective AV is a prepared audio. Long before they were easily available, original recordings of famous speeches were taped by a now-retired history professor and prepared for playing to her class. Students were startled into wakefulness (and later recall) when the professor would begin her lecture on the entry of the USA into World War II by pressing a button under her desk. Booming out was FDR's famous "Date that will live in infamy" speech. Used sparingly and creatively, audio can reinforce your message dramatically.

No matter how well you plan, there will be challenges. Once, when delivering a performance management workshop to seasoned defense department managers, Ryan was confronted by a sardonic participant who asked, "What good are these techniques?"

When Ryan asked what the problem was, the dissenter said, "These skills work nicely here in tightly controlled role plays. Out there in the real world there are interruptions, personality clashes, the whole nine yards."

"Precisely," Ryan said, to the surprise of the participant. "We control conditions here to highlight and practice a skill or technique. I do not apologize for that; this is a learning lab, not the real world. If you were learning a technical skill, I'd also teach it under controlled conditions, even though the real world is a lot sloppier. Let's learn the technique under ideal conditions; then we can apply it to the real world." Ryan's non-apology struck precisely the right chord. The information being transmitted deserved a potent laboratory setting, and his audience got it.

A less successful workshop featured a group of internal auditors being taught how to deliver quarterly oral reports to their company's executive board. When Ryan asked why the apparent lack of interest, the class as one rejoined that these reports were a waste of time, that no one listened to them or cared about them, that they were a mere formality with no real point. Ryan, ultimately unable to pierce their armor of indifference, found that they had no motivation at all to learn and remember the skills or techniques. Although he could have shifted to the persuasive intention and tried to get them interested in learning to give oral reports, he was being paid to do this workshop, and he did the best he could. It was not a ringing triumph.

## The Informative Connection

Success at information sharing requires that you make the informative connection, which means you arouse your audience's interest sufficiently that they leave your presence remembering or committed to remembering the information you have transmitted. You access all the tools available in the verbal and paraverbal universe and deploy them cannily to inform them.

You build for your audience an edifice of knowledge. That is the key. When you are done, they know things they did not know before. It could be as simple as the directions to your house, as complicated as quantum theory, or as practical as how to change a tire. If it is an opinion, you have no interest in whether they buy it, only that they know it. If it is a fact, they come away in possession of a little more truth about the world.

You will have your best chance of success if your audience is somehow assured that this new knowledge will enrich them. If they really believe that, they will be highly motivated to learn and retain your information. If you transmit information with clarity, precision, completeness, and accuracy, your audience can turn that motivation into a listening energy equal to the task of acquisition and retention. If you boost the stimulant with powerful doses of creativity and competence, it is hard to imagine that they will fail to be enriched, not to mention informed.

Samantha, the attorney, was running late for the court appointment of her firm's largest client. She was yelling frantically at her Bluetooth device as her car idled drearily in heavy traffic. "I don't care where he is; get him on the phone." The missing phone mate was Ralph, an associate who just yesterday was chatting lazily with Samantha in her office. He was sharing information about a nifty short cut he knew to the very courthouse to which she was inching along. Although she nodded pleasantly, she neither received nor retained the information from Ralph as it held no importance for her. Not at that moment, at least. Now, trapped in a major traffic jam, she could not imagine any data more significant in the entire world than the Marauder's Map revealing Ralph's secret passageway to her destination. If only Samantha had known how vital that information would be fewer than 24 hours after that first failed transmission.

If only Ralph had figured out how to transform her into an enthusiastic recipient of his informational intention.

## Review of Key Ideas

- If my intention is primarily informational, my main objective that you remember some things that I have transmitted to you.
- In preparing a successful informational transmission, the first step is to figure out exactly what I want you to remember.
- There are four crucial aspects of a well prepared informational message: clarity, precision, completeness, and accuracy.

▪ Avoid ambiguity or vagueness. Use good grammar and sentence structure. Prefer active voice. Know what you are going to say before you say it.

▪ Make sure you say exactly what you mean. Be brief, write down main points, select words carefully, and transmit the entire message so the listener distinguishes what must be remembered.

▪ Be accurate; separate fact from opinion.

▪ The information intention requires work of the listeners: they must commit the information to memory. The profile of receptive learners may include these factors: retention of the information serves some purpose; reliable transmitter; the climate set by the transmitter is conducive to hearing and remembering; listeners understand and can store the information in memory.

▪ An environment conducive to informing is businesslike, quiet, controlled, and comfortable.

▪ Informers should be aware of vocal quality, speech characteristics, facial expressions and gestures appropriate to specific audiences.

▪ Informers should be aware of the guidelines for the use of audiovisuals like slide shows, video, and audio.

▪ Information exchange takes place most effectively in an environment that is free of noise and other distractions.

▪ The most intimate audiovisual aid is me, the person presenting.

▪ Maintain direct but not piercing eye contact; keep the eyes engaged.

▪ Prefer pulling gestures that indicate a welcoming attitude.

▪ Move freely about the room to maintain contact with the audience members and hold their interest.

▪ Observe the guidelines for effective use of presentation programs and other audiovisuals.

▪ Make sure informational transmissions are interesting and relevant to the audience.

## References

Atkinson, C. (2005). *Beyond bullet points: Using Microsoft PowerPoint to create presentations that inform, motivate, and inspire.* Redmond, WA: Microsoft Press.

Boone, D. R. (1983). *The voice and voice therapy.* Englewood Cliffs, NJ: Prentice-Hall.

Boone, D. R., & McFarlane, S. (2000). *The voice and voice therapy* (6th ed.). Needham Heights, MA: Allyn & Bacon.

Case, J. L. (1996). *Clinical management of voice disorders* (3rd ed.). Austin, TX: Pro-Ed.

Cavanagh, P. R., & Williams, K. R. (1982). The effect of stride length variation on oxygen uptake during distance running. *Medicine and Science in Sports and Exercise, 14*(1), 30–35.

Cook, S. W., Duffy, R. G, & Fenn, K. M. (2013). Consolidation and transfer of learning after observing hand gesture. *Child Development, 84*(6), 1863–1971.

Cooper, M. (1974). Spectrographic analyses of fundamental frequency of hoarseness before and after vocal rehabilitation. *Journal of Speech and Hearing Disorders, 39*(3), 286–297.

Fairbanks, G. (1960). *Voice and articulation drillbook.* New York, NY: Harper & Row.

Gelfer, M.P. (1999). Voice treatment for the male-to-female transgendered client. *American Journal of Speech-Language Pathology, 8*(3), 201–208.

Gélinas-Chebat, C., & Chebat, J. C. (1996). Voice and advertising: Effects of intonation and intensity of voice on source credibility, attitudes toward the advertised service and the intent to buy. *Perceptual and Motor Skills, 83*(1), 243–262.

Holle, H., & Gunter, T. C., 2007. The role of iconic gestures in speech disambiguation: ERP evidence. *Journal of Cognitive Neuroscience, 19*(7), 1175–1192.

Parker, I. (2001, May 28). Absolute PowerPoint: Can a software package edit our thoughts? *The New Yorker,* p. 76.

Puts, D. A., Gaulin, S. J., & Verdolini, K. (2006). Dominance and the evolution of sexual dimorphism in human voice pitch. *Evolution and Human Behavior, 27*(4), 283–296.

Van Riper, C., & Irwin, J. (1958). *Voice and articulation.* Englewood Cliffs, NJ: Prentice-Hall.

Wilson, K. (1962). Voice re-education of adults with vocal nodules. *Archives of Otology, Rhinology, and Laryngology, 76,* 68–73.

Wu, Y. C., & Coulson, S. (2007). Iconic gestures prime related concepts: An ERP study. *Psychonomic Bulletin and Review, 14*(1), 57–63.

Yaffe, P. (2008). How to use presentation slides to best effect. *Ubiquity, 9*(15).

# Chapter 10

# Persuading Them

*Now, the framers of the current treatises on rhetoric have constructed but a small portion of that art. The modes of persuasion are the only true constituents of the art: everything else is merely accessory.*

—Aristotle's *Rhetoric*

## Keys to Effectiveness in Persuasion and Direction

Although information infuses every transmission, informing may not be your primary intention. To uncover what you most want to transmit, you need to ask what it is that you want your audience to take away and hold on to after the encounter. Sometimes the answer is that you want them to walk away changed. You want the impact of your transmission to be that they leave with a changed mind, a changed heart, or changed plans. If that is true, persuasion/ direction is your intention. You want to persuade them to think a certain way, believe a certain way, or behave a certain way.

There is, of course, some element of persuasion in every transmission. As you saw in Chapter 9, when your intention is purely informational, you are still under the obligation to persuade the audience to see the oncoming information as enriching to them. Many high school teachers experience the frustration of "spending too much time trying to motivate the students to learn and not enough time teaching." In our paradigm, these teachers are complaining that they see the point of their transmissions as informational, but they are forced by student indifference to shift their intention to persuasion.

In any event, once you have ascertained that your intention is persuasion/direction, your first step is to determine what it is you want your audience to be convinced of or to do. Although you will be transmitting considerable information, often in the form of premises to your arguments, it is the conclusions that you want them to accept. In the case of direction, you want them to conclude that they will do something. A straightforward request is the simplest of this type of intention. "John, get me a bottle of water, will you?" You are using your voice to express a persuasion/direction intention. If John gets you the water, you have succeeded in your intention.

University admissions officers sometimes deliver talks to high school seniors where their main intention is to get those students to e-mail an admissions officer with a request for further information. If the admissions officer cares mainly that the students e-mail them and does not care as much that the students retain any of the information imparted, then the intention was persuasion/direction.

Before you embark on your transmission to your audience, you must be clear in your own mind that you want them to do something and that you will deem yourself unsuccessful if they fail to do it. Furthermore, you must be very clear in your own mind about just what it is you want them to do. If you want them to e-mail you, but it is just as good if they telephone you, that fact has importance because they have options and should know them. If you want them to e-mail you and will not respond if they telephone you, that caveat too is useful.

The other realm of the persuasive intention targets convictions and beliefs. Mary, a pharmaceutical sales representative, ultimately wants a physician to prescribe her company's product, but may be content early in the sales process that the good doctor admit that the product has advantages over that of a competitor. If the physician says, "Yes. I can see the advantages of your product," then Mary may believe that her persuasive intention was entirely met, at least for the time being. Similarly, those admissions officers sometimes want their audiences to take no action after a particular talk, but they do want suitable candidates to depart persuaded that they have qualities that match what the institution is looking for in a new freshman.

Of course, it is possible that the admissions officer wants to instill both a change of thinking and a commitment to an action, the gamut of persuasion/direction, in one interaction. If so, the admissions officer should be aware of that full intention and create a transmission likely to achieve all of it. You could very well have more than one intention in a presentation. You may indeed want your audience to be persuaded to a new way of thinking as well as have them retain certain information, thereby holding both an information intention and a persuasion/direction intention. That complexity is built into human communication.

When persuasion is all or even part of your intention in your transmission to others, there is one reality you always confront: You are asking them to change. The change may be small, as it is when they get you a bottle of water, or it may be momentous, as it is when you convince them to alter their philosophy of life or change careers or choose a college. Either way, your appeal must be equal to the tumult the change will bring about in them.

There are important guidelines to consider if you want to be persuasive.

- Make sure that the issue you raise is of importance to the listener and that you explicitly stress that importance. Studies show that the more significant the issue is to the listener, the more carefully the listener tunes in to the arguments you are making (Petty, Cacioppo, & Schumann, 1983).
- If you are arguing a point, make sure the rules of logic are on your side and that the premises really imply the conclusion. Ask yourself, would a reasonable person be convinced by my presentation? Am I offering a sound rationale for the listener to accept the new belief? Am I convinced the new belief is worth believing? Do I have supporting evidence or examples?
- Establish the benefits to the listener of converting to the new belief. There is no reason for your listener to shift to a new belief if the old belief is working just fine.
- Get what you can in a given interaction; do not push the listener beyond what the listener is ready to accept. If a listener cannot fully agree but admits your point makes sense, that is progress. Even when a listener resists your appeal, the listener sometimes begins doubting his or her own belief (Tormala, Clarkson, & Petty, 2006).

A prospective change in thinking can cause significant discomfort. Lonnie was in Sacramento, California, for the first time. He finished a meeting and was off in his rental car to an appointment in San Francisco. Lonnie reasoned flawlessly that he had merely to point his car toward the ocean and, before he knew it, he would be in that City by the Bay. Figuring out which direction to go was easy, as Lonnie, being from Philadelphia, had driven often to the ocean for vacations. So, fully confident, he headed east.

This is not a story about a persuasive person convincing Lonnie to drive across the American heartland in a weird quest for a misplaced ocean. Lonnie managed the feat all by himself. What is here illustrated is the discomfort of the eventual realization that wrong is right and right is terribly, terribly wrong. For as Lonnie drove confidently along, he soon enough noted a road sign informing him that Reno was 200 miles away. For a moment, his confidence was a little shaken.

Sometime later, a similar sign indicated that Reno was now 180 miles distant. Lonnie began to wonder. A definite change of thought was emerging. Yet Lonnie continued east until a third sign indicated that Reno was drawing even closer. Now Lonnie asked the question that turned the tide—and ultimately turned his car in the opposite direction: "What is the likelihood that a city in Nevada would pop up between two cities in California?" The likelihood was zero, and Lonnie searched out his error. It was as simple as it was preposterous: He was heading to the Atlantic Ocean rather than the Pacific Ocean.

Lonnie learned many lessons that day. He has since retained a keen awareness of what it is like to go through the extreme discomfort of finding out that what you once believed with absolute confidence was utterly mistaken and that your thinking had to take an entirely new direction—literally, in this case.

Often the most intractable challenges facing you as a persuader is the very human reluctance of your listeners to let go of an idea in which they have found comfort or familiarity over the years. Persuasion becomes virtually impossible if their framework for processing the premises is inadequate. Sixteenth century astronomy, for example, could not accept an earth spinning on an axis because it did not enjoy the benefit of Newton's insights about gravity and motion. "Surely if the earth were spinning at a dizzying speed, stones thrown straight up would land far away. And if the earth was wheeling around the sun, how could it keep the moon in tow?" (Gingerich, 2003, p. 82). This reasoning seemed impeccable.

Another difficulty in persuasion, as Lonnie's journey exemplifies, is the fact that your listeners may go through several stages on their way to accepting a new thought. Quite a bit of research has involved itself with stages of change in humans and groups, including the Transtheoretical Model (Prochaska, DiClemente, & Norcross, 1992), the Organizational Change Model (Glanz, Lewis, & Rimer 1996), and the classic Stages of Grief (Kübler-Ross, 1997/1969). If you are seeking to persuade your audience, you may be called upon to guide them through stages such as those listed below.

*Stage 1.* The comfort level they maintain with the old idea

*Stage 2.* Denial that the new idea poses any threat to the old idea

*Stage 3.* Doubt about the old idea; anxiety that it might not be sound

*Stage 4.* Anger at the prospect of changing to a new idea

*Stage 5.* Exploration of the benefits of accepting the new idea

*Stage 6.* Acceptance of the new idea

Go back and track Lonnie's likely progression through these steps as he drove himself to the realization that he would have to make a U-turn to attain his objective. If you have ever gone through a change in thinking like this, you may be able to recall most if not all of the six stages. The delicacy and complexity of the process makes it all the more critical to learn how to use the tools of effective interpersonal communication when the intention is persuasion/direction. Although the scope of this chapter does not permit an extensive examination of each stage, it is important to understand that the change under discussion usually involves a multistep process.

## Voicing Conviction

How do you "inflect belief"? How do you sound convincing and convinced? Aristotle, as you already are aware, defined rhetoric as "the faculty of observing in any given case the available means of [vocal] persuasion (Honeycut, 2007)." He meant a lot by that simple definition, but one of the things he meant was that there are some vocal characteristics that tend to be more persuasive than others. This book differentiates between persuasive intentions and feeling intentions. In this chapter we are discussing persuasion, an appeal to the rational faculty. The objective is not to "stir" or "move" the listener but to elicit agreement that a belief is sound or that the listener should perform a certain action.

There are vocal patterns and paraverbals to consider and patterns to avoid if persuasion/direction is the intention. Here are some frequently noted patterns that tend to diminish persuasiveness according to attendees at the Presentation Practicum. These less effective patterns can induce in a listener a sense of skepticism or suspicion about a person's sincerity or self-confidence (Page & Balloun, 1978). A few of these items are similar to some of those in Chapter 7 indicating a lack of confidence on the part of the presenter. You will also note some similarities with guidelines on the informational intention in Chapter 9.

- Lack of vocal strength; thin or stiff TVFBC
- Artificially high intensity; overstressing words
- Inaccurate word selection when stating a new belief
- Overly programmed or seemingly memorized statements
- Pitch break (cracking voice) and glottal fry (voice begins to creak, slack TVFBC)
- Strained or tight voice (may project desperation, uncertainty)
- Undermining insertions like sudden laughter or "yeah"
- False starts (beginning, then starting over)
- Rushing (not allowing listener time to digest points).

What is desired is a voice that calls, a voice that welcomes the listener to consider the new idea. These are voice strategies and paraverbals you may use when you want to be persuasive.

- Be deliberate but not mechanical or scripted. Use natural pauses.
- Project patience, not a memorized spiel.
- Maintain vocal strength, but keep a calm tone to impart a quiet confidence (Gélinas-Chebat & Chebat, 1996).

- Maintain an open, anchored posture.
- Utilize a resonant vocal quality and avoid the extremes of your pitch range.
- Allow the listener ample opportunity to express concerns.
- Use inflection to project rational thinking rather than soaring emotion. Keep intonation from rising excessively.
- Use appropriate stress to highlight key points of your argument.
- Exhale to REL if you feel you cannot catch your breath.
- Do not swallow anxiously during speech.
- Think before you begin so you do not lose the thread of your argument.

As you reach the end of your phrase when talking, you may at times feel yourself running out of air. To get to the end of the phrase you drop your pitch a little and then you hear a slight creak in your voice. That creaky sound, often referred to as "glottal fry," is slack TVFBC. This TVFBC condition usually occurs at the end of phrases (some people speak on it all the time) and is one of the most relaxed vocal fold vibratory patterns you can achieve. To create slack, you close or adduct the arytenoids and draw the vocal folds closer together without fully compressing them. This vocal fold approximation generates a relaxed, aperiodic vibratory pattern with no definite fundamental frequency and minimal air escape. For this reason you can hold out an "ah" on slack TVFBC for a long time.

To eliminate slack TVFBC from your speech, phrase more regularly so that you do not speak all the way to REL. If you feel the creak coming, try to add a little more air to end of the phrase. But remember, if you have no more air left you probably should have taken a breath long before. Adding narrow AES to your voice or tilting your thyroid to add sweetness to the end of your phrase, will also help to eliminate slack. Perform the siren exercises in Chapter 4. Maintain thin TVFBC while sirening down to your lowest pitches; keep your anchors and raise your eyebrows while you siren down your scale. You should try to generalize those strategies to short phrases. Although slack TVFBC may not be the most pleasing TVFBC condition to listen to during speech, it can be used as a facilitator to achieve vocal fold closure in individuals who have extreme muscle tension.

From these suggestions, you can certainly see the significance of vocal inflection, tone, and prosody in persuasion, but never lose sight of the importance of crafting your presentation effectively to convey an understanding of your persuasive goal. Failure to do so can upset your audience, as the following illustration shows.

Norabelle was an excellent presenter. As her company's director of operations, she was assigned the task of convincing stockholders at the semiannual meeting that the slight contraction in profits was due to needed capital expenditures and was a one-time event. She began with the upbeat statement, "Ladies and gentlemen, I am here today in the hope that I can put to rest any concern you may have about our recent marginal downturn in gross profits." Thus alerted that the talk would be persuasive in intent, the audience listened expectantly.

Norabelle had arrived well prepared. After her opening remark, she launched sensibly into a survey of recent financial performance. Since she saw this portion as informational background, she quickened her pace and clicked through the initial slides briskly. She was stunned when a stockholder called out, "Wait a minute!" Several others chimed in with, "Yeah, hold on," and, "What's going on here?"

"Excuse me?" Norabelle said perplexedly. A stockholder spoke for the group when he said that this was important and they wanted to follow carefully what she was saying. They were put off and even suspicious about her rushed style. What was she trying to hide? Was she trying to hurry past an embarrassing point? The reaction not only shocked Norabelle, it offended her. There were a few tense moments, to say the least.

Norabelle's error was to begin by alerting the stockholders of her persuasive intention on a matter of great importance to them, and then shift without warning to an informational aim. Her rate of speech increased. Her apparent flippancy defied her audience's every expectation. It was not enough to announce that she intended to persuade; she needed to follow through, not change intentions.

Speech-language pathologists also encounter the persuasive intention when they seek to convince wary clients of the need for voice therapy. As therapy proceeds, the clients may be further persuaded to make significant changes in their lifestyles. A fundamental change in both thinking and behavior is essential to clinical success. One of the speech-language pathologist's ultimate goals is to give clients the tools to become, in effect, their own clinicians.

There is, then, a sequence of persuasive intentions directed at the clients. The first intention is that they believe the therapy is a good idea for them. The second intention is that they consistently come to their scheduled appointments and participate. Third, they practice continuously and begin to use their techniques in everyday conversation. Finally, they arrive at the belief that they can do all this without the therapist and they can make real lifelong changes. The speech-language pathologist may set a modest objective early on to convince the clients to attend an initial therapy session. Following that session, the clinician may move to the more ambitious goals.

To accomplish this series of persuasive intensions, relevant and compelling arguments are developed and employed. The speech-language pathologist may call on research that demonstrates the effectiveness of the techniques, testimonials detailing earlier success stories, and a listing of benefits of therapy along with the possible consequences of avoiding therapy. These arguments constitute the logic of the case: why it is, in fact, persuasive.

Actors approach the logical challenge from a different perspective. One of their objectives is not to change belief but, as Coleridge suggested about poetry, to "suspend disbelief." The audience at a play knows that what is happening in the performance is not real life. They must hold this awareness in abeyance and accept that the action occurring onstage has its own honesty. The conflicts being portrayed have their own reality, and the narrative has its own truth. Theater people speak of "the fourth wall," the people watching and listening to the production. Persuasion is a constant intention piercing that fourth wall, from the actors to the audience.

Within that narrative, characters are themselves interacting, so persuasion can be going on at that level too, as can the other intentions. Romeo persuades Juliet of his love, and we too are convinced. Linda Loman asserts of her husband's life as a salesman that "attention must be paid," and we nod in agreement. Arguments are presented; a logic is pursued.

With the logic in hand, whether from a theater's stage, a classroom, or any setting in which you intend to convince others, you should next achieve a clear focus on appropriate climate setting.

## A Climate That Persuades

If you want to succeed in persuading, whether in a group or a one-on-one situation, you do well to give attention to climate. When you are seeking only to impart information, the climate you set may resemble a learning center or laboratory. When your intention is to persuade, the ideal climate initially is calm, relatively relaxed, but highly engaging. As the interaction proceeds, you may want to introduce elements of urgency or at least the sense that it is somehow vital that your listeners consider moving away from their belief and toward yours. Lonnie's excursion to the realization that he was not going to San Francisco certainly started in that calm, relaxed manner. Soon enough, the urgency of doubt about the wisdom of his 75-mile-per-hour easterly trip caught up with him and ultimately resulted in a U-turn, implying changes in both belief and action.

The climate, then, can vary throughout the exchange as you take your audience through the different stages leading to an acceptance of the new belief. Many factors come into play, not least their shifting attitudes as the persuasion process moves along. The strength of their attitudes too is an important factor in determining a suitable climate (Crano & Prislin, 2006). What you must keep in mind above all is the fact that they are unlikely to be persuaded by your suave voice, winning manner, or sincere tone. What will finally persuade them is the power of your argument, its logic, reasoning, and grounding in supporting data (Crano & Prislin, 2006; Tormala et al., 2006). Although a suitable vocal tone and delivery is enormously helpful, the verbals you employ, your content, is crucial to any success you hope to achieve in persuading or directing them.

The showroom for a persuasive intention will not look or feel much different from that described for informational exchanges (see Chapter 9). The surroundings should be quiet, softly lit, inviting but not cozy. Seats should be ergonomically comfortable; you do not want them contending with a backache while you are trying to convince them of a point. In a small group setting of, say, two or three, you and they should sit in the collaborative position or at a small round table (see Figure 4–8).

There are exceptions to this guideline. In one-on-one settings, speech-language pathologists and some other professionals typically assume the confronting or face-to-face position with their clients during voice therapy sessions. Although the speech-language pathologists' intention can swing from informational (when giving instructions) to persuasive/directive (when inciting clients to exhibit a practice) to feeling (when calming clients), the stress is often on persuading and directing. There is no success unless the clients try to perform the practice being taught and perform it in the correct position.

The confronting position allows speech-language pathologists to situate clients so that they are looking straight ahead and maintaining good posture and support. Clients should not attempt to perform a correct vocal technique with their head to one side, as the collaborative position necessitates. In voice therapy, the confronting position is the most intuitive position for the type of therapy the speech-language pathologists are conducting. To avoid an uncomfortable level of confrontation, speech-language pathologists can simply shift their chair slightly to the side while maintaining the face-to-face position.

Classrooms were set up traditionally to establish the authority of the instructor. While the students sit side by side, they are not "cozying" with each other. No, the students are situated so that each of them is in a confronting position with the teacher. Being side by side is entirely incidental. Originally, the professor or teacher was perched on an elevated platform and looked down upon the class; this positioning emphasized the professor's authority and made clear who would win the "confrontation."

In workplaces of the early 20th century, the supervisor (literally, "the one who looks from above") also sat or stood in an elevated position and gazed down on the workers, the better to detect slackers and assure that the supervisor's arguments were persuasive. In more recent times, such heavy-handed environments are often seen as diminishing the persuasiveness of the professors and supervisors: If their arguments are sound, why do they need the trappings of coercive authority?

The setting can change when the mode of persuasion changes. Sometimes the persuading requires a demonstration of some kind, and that may take communicators to the site where the demonstrating can take place. A car salesperson, for example, will sooner or later show prospects an actual vehicle that they may test drive; a science teacher will mix just the right chemicals to produce a desired reaction. If you are contemplating a demonstration to prove your point, to convince your listeners, you should make it as interactive as possible and give them every opportunity to participate. As you speak, you should pause frequently so they can ask questions; you should maintain a lively but deliberate pace that parallels the progress of the demonstration. You do not want to be seen as a kind of magician with sole access to the trick.

Mode of dress can further enhance the persuasive climate. The rules for what to wear are not much different from those that apply to the informational intention. Specialized garb like a chemistry instructor's lab coat or a preacher's stole can be effective in well-defined venues. It is vital that you avoid clothes or accessories that would make you seem less compatible with the audience and, therefore, less persuasive. Overdressing can have this effect—remember Lonnie's three-piece suit in Maui? An over abundance of make-up or fragrance can likewise reduce your standing.

Remember also that, no matter how effective you believe yourself to have been in persuading your audience, they may disappoint you later with an unexpected reversal. The comfort and familiarity of their old idea may draw them back from the new one you thought you had persuaded them to believe (Crano & Prislin, 2006). Depending on the situation, persuasion can be an extensive process. This is especially so when you are trying to alter a long-standing pattern of thought or behavior. Your dentist may convince you to brush your teeth in the opposite direction from your accustomed practice, but it can consume much time and effort to break the old habit and remake the new. As the persuader, your job is to persuade, that is, make the new option so clearly beneficial and superior that they will take the trouble to adopt it.

Speech-language pathologists, along with the authors of this book, typically seek to persuade clients to have an interest in maintaining a strong, healthy voice. These clients need to be convinced to modify a number of long-standing habits, including such lifestyle and dietary changes as avoiding tobacco, increasing water intake, managing heartburn or reflux, and resting the voice. The paragraph that follows presents a specific case against smoking, a case focusing on the voice. See if you accept the logic and find the arguments compelling.

The American Academy of Otolaryngology-Head and Neck Surgery states that 95% of individuals who have laryngeal squamous cell carcinoma are smokers (Fact sheet: Laryngeal cancer, 2007). Although laryngeal carcinoma is a multifactorial disease, research has shown that smoking is one of the most important factors in its occurrence in an individual (Garnett, 2001). Cigarette smoke may also affect the vocal folds in different ways. You know the voice: gravelly, rough, and low-pitched; we call it the "smoker's voice." This voice quality is caused by fluid building up in the superficial lamina propria called Reinke's space. The name of the voice disorder associated with excessive fluid build-up is Reinke's edema. Risk factors for developing Reinke's edema include the number of cigarettes consumed daily, as well as how long an individual has been exposed to cigarette smoke (Marcotullio, Magliulo, & Pezone, 2002). Smoking and inhaling second-hand smoke do nothing to help your voice. If you want to maintain the health of your voice, stop smoking if you smoke, and do not start if you do not smoke.

The paraverbal universe can significantly enhance your efforts at persuasion. Your face, gestures, and audiovisuals must work with you to lend that note of conviction to your transmission. You must remain in constant awareness that your aim is not so much to inform as to persuade. You do not merely add to your audience's storehouse of knowledge; you change the way they think about what they know. You may even be changing what they think they know.

Samantha, the lawyer, gained insight about her presenting style when she learned about the two types of gestures—palms up or pulling and palms down or pushing. She knew she employed pushing gestures excessively and trained herself to be more welcoming by using more of the pulling kind. She became very good at reaching out, palms up, and drawing her hands back toward her rib cage. Then, a surprise: Samantha began getting feedback that her style was not as persuasive as it used to be.

It turns out she was overusing the pulling gestures. They were fine when she said something like, "Let's consider how we would react in such a crisis." She continued pulling, however, during comments like, "Stop! Take a minute and think about this from the other perspective." In the latter case, a pushing gesture is indicated (imagine the gesture of a traffic cop saying "Stop!"). In a group setting, pushing gestures can serve a purpose similar to that served by the speech-language pathologist's confronting position with a client.

Samantha learned also to coordinate her face with her gestures. When switching to the pushing gesture, her facial expression would likewise shift, usually from an open, smiling aspect to a sober, tighter look, eyebrows lowered, lips closer together, eye contact intense and sure. She remained in the same position or moved only a step toward the audience when she was arguing a point. Her message was, "Look, I'm serious here, and I'm right." Ironically, she had always been quite effective at creating this impression with the pushing gesture. The trouble is, she went from overusing it to underusing it. Her listeners were every bit as quick to detect an inappropriate pulling gesture as an inappropriate pushing gesture. The inappropriate gestures also undermined her excellent vocal characteristics.

Face and gesture, along with the voice, should assertively transmit the commitment to persuade, a willingness to be patient through the process, an optimism that the change is superior to the previous state.

Audiovisuals and props should also synchronize with one's persuasive/directive intention. Demonstration items have already been considered. Slides designed for persuasion look and feel different from those that are effective in the transmission of information. Persuasive slides have a cut-to-the-chase feel. Compare the following two sentences.

"People who successfully complete a smoking cessation regimen will significantly reduce their chances of developing certain voice disorders."

"Stop smoking and save your voice."

The first sentence reflects what you might actually say to your audience, but the second sentence is far more suitable for the slide you use. This concise statement captures the persuasive essence of your message.

When Norabelle gave her presentation to her stockholders, she erred in shifting out of a persuasive mode and into a recitative informational mode. Her first slides were busy and overly informational. They alarmed shareholders seeking reasons and explanations amid the verbiage. As it turned out, Norabelle's later slides were excellent. They were crisp, unambiguous, logical—and persuasive.

She boasted an especially potent series of four slides highlighting the benefits of the capital investment that had dented profits. The first displayed photographs of the renovated spaces and new equipment. The next compared efficiency estimates after and before installation of the new purchases, in that order. The third slide was a bulleted summary of these benefits, and the last was a convincing six-month graph indicating that the upswing was already underway. After her rocky start, Nora's presentation was ultimately a hit with the wary investors.

## The Persuasive Connection

A wise philosophy professor once claimed that to persuade another of your conclusion, your argument must have three essential properties: logic, logic, and logic. In fact, studies give evidence that she was on the money. In *Rhetoric*, Aristotle named three grand divisions of rhetoric: ethos, pathos, and logos. Logos or logic is the appeal to the mind, the rational arguments you employ to move your listeners to an acceptance of what you want them to believe or do. Nowhere in all our discourse with one another is the rational argument so critical as it is in the pursuit of a persuasive intention. If what you are promoting is illogical or irrational, the probability that they will give it the nod is quite low, no matter how you dress it up.

Logic is intrinsic to the transmission. Once the logic is understood, it becomes compelling regardless of how it was transmitted. Take this syllogism:

All dogs are canines.

Fido is a dog; therefore,

Fido is canine.

The syllogism is absolutely valid, by which is meant that if the first two lines are true, the final line must necessarily be true. The argument is cogent, and its cogency depends entirely on the words and the logic behind the words.

Not that logic is all you need to be persuasive with your audience. Your voice must convey the cogency of the logic. When you state the two premises, that all dogs are canines and that Fido is a dog, speak in a fluid style without strong stress on any one word. Then, after a pause, say, "therefore," with emphasis and anticipation of the conclusion to come. Deliver the words, "Fido is canine," with extra strength and unarguable certainty.

There is one other element of the persuasive connection, and it is embodied in Aristotle's first rhetorical division, *ethos*, or credibility—the moral authority of the voice to convey the good character of the speaker. Specifically, if you would have your audience accept your persuasive efforts, it would be well that they trust you. The goals of aspiring persuaders are cogency and trust. Chapter 7 is devoted to the vital concept of credibility, which encompasses these goals.

Still, the finest and most credible practitioners of the persuasive arts know that there are limits. For one thing, you cannot persuade your audience of too much too soon. They will become overwhelmed by the accumulating challenge. Nor can you easily dislodge from their store of convictions a belief they hold so dear that it would cause them enormous anxiety even to consider changing it. Mike, the liberal we met earlier, argues and is sometimes influenced by Sacha, the conservative, and vice versa, but neither has ever seriously considered abandoning his or her core beliefs. Still, such a change is not impossible.

As a new project launched, consultant Lonnie stood before top managers of a very large organization. They were on the brink of adopting a comprehensively revamped performance management system, complete with a new merit pay process. When the executives impatiently asked the consultant how long it would take to get this process up and running, he answered, "If you can persuade the majority of employees to commit to this system wholeheartedly, if we here can persuade each other to drive this without flagging, we'll be operating smoothly under this new system in three years." He slowed his vocal pace, indicating that he will be patient and transparent.

Still, the executives were stunned. How could it take so long? Lonnie explained from his own experience what happens in each of the first three years when an organization of this size goes through such a major change. His voice was sympathetic but firm and determined. He persuaded them to embark on the three-year plan, knowing that the persuading had only just begun, both for the executives and for the bulk of the employees. A successful three-year implementation, guided by Lonnie at all levels of the organization, was the happy result.

Roland had always typed using only his index fingers. His daughter Jayleen was stunned that her dad never learned to type properly. He wrote for a living. Jayleen began lessons with her somewhat reluctant student and she was relentless. Dad would learn keyboarding if he knew what was good for him. After several weeks, he could actually use all 10 fingers in a painstaking search for a match between finger and key. At long last, Jayleen set her father free. He could improve by practicing on his own.

A few weeks later Jayleen came upon her dad at the computer and was distressed to see that he had reverted to the inefficient two-finger hunt and peck mode. "Sorry, honey," Dad said. "I just don't have the time to practice with 10 fingers until I get as fast as I am now with two fingers."

"You know you'll be much faster in the long run, Dad."

"Yes. But in the short run, I have a job to do."

Jayleen's logic was compelling, her arguments cogent. Her father agreed. Although she persuaded him that her logic was correct, she did not get him to change his behavior. For him the long-term benefits did not outweigh the short-term cost of learning to type with 10 fingers. He never did learn.

Andrea, a young mother, was teaching her five-year-old daughter, Belle, to play tennis. Five minutes into the first lesson, instructor and student were at wits' end. Onlookers turned away sadly as Mom began reciting all the wrong moves her daughter was making. Andrea's voice was high pitched and rapidly paced, projecting impatience and frustration. "Follow through; hold the racket up higher; don't point the racket down; elbow in; you're swinging too late." Andrea finally gave up. Clearly, her daughter just did not know how to follow instructions.

Strangely, when Belle enrolled a month later in a tennis class with other five-year-olds, she became a star pupil. Her instructor took a very different approach. His voice was always lower in pitch and never rushed. Early on, he taught Belle to swing the racket with no regard whatsoever for where the ball went. He even cheered when Belle whacked it into the net! A few lessons later, he began to instruct her on how to hold the racket, then how to follow through. Andrea finally noticed that the coach taught Belle everything Andrea had tried to teach—just not all at once. One of the limits of persuasion/direction dawned on Andrea: You cannot learn faster than you can learn.

What these stories illustrate is one final component of effective persuasion. That component is the empathy you have for the people you are trying to persuade. In a case like Belle's, you need a clear, accurate feel for where she is developmentally and the ability to project that feel vocally. That sense is crucial for speech-language pathologists, trainers, teachers, coaches, tutors, parents, managers—anyone desirous of imparting a complex skill or set of ideas. That sense will dictate your pace, timing, and how you sequence the transmission. Taking it step by step will reduce frustration on both sides and multiply opportunities to celebrate success over failure.

Jayleen had her logic all worked out and it was almost without flaw. The one flaw was that an argument can be absolutely cogent in general but not apply in one particular case. Jayleen's father could not be convinced to take the time to convert his keyboarding style, as his work demanded a higher output than he would have mustered while learning to type with 10 fingers. He knew he would be a better typist in the long run, but it was not the long run that worried him.

Lonnie had to convince an impatient upper management team to give their new system three full years. What he became in this instance was an effective persuader and on more than one level. He had to employ his powers of persuasion and vocal skills in a targeted, sensitive fashion, mindful of the motivations and resistance points of various audiences at various times during the long implementation.

In both of these illustrations, you can see a process embedded in much of the persuading you undertake—the process of negotiation. Effective negotiation implies a back and forth situation, where two or more parties move toward agreement or conflict resolution. Persuasion often has a central role.

Whether you are involved in a complicated negotiation process or a simple need to make a convincing point, the output of an effective persuasion/direction intention is always the same: a compelling argument delivered compellingly. Its ingredients are logic, character, poise, empathy, and patience driven by the inexorable power of the human voice to make the persuasive connection.

## Review of Key Ideas

■ There is some element of persuasion in every transmission, but once I have ascertained that my intention is persuasion/

direction, I must determine what it is I want you to be convinced of or to do.

- When persuasion is all or even part of my intention in my transmission to you, I am asking you to change.
- Guidelines for persuasion include several factors: The issue you raise is of importance to the listener; the rules of logic are on your side; the listener will benefit from the change; you do not pursue more than the listener is willing to give.
- If I am seeking to persuade you, I may also be called upon to guide you through six stages: (1) Comfort with the old idea; (2) denial that the new idea is better than the old idea; (3) doubt about the old idea; (4) anger at the prospect of changing; (5) exploring the new idea's benefits; and (6) acceptance of the new idea.
- The following are vocal patterns to avoid in persuasion/ direction: thin voice, overstressing words, poor word selection, programmed statements, pitch break and glottal fry, strained voice, sudden laugh, false start, and rushing.
- The following are voice and speech guidelines in persuasion/direction: Be deliberate but not mechanical; maintain vocal strength with a calm tone; pause frequently; project rational thinking rather than soaring emotion; inhale inaudibly; do not swallow anxiously; and think before you begin.
- When my intention is to persuade, the ideal climate initially is calm, relaxed, and highly engaging; urgency can appear later; the climate can vary through the various stages leading to acceptance of the new belief.
- The confronting position is the most intuitive position for the type of therapy the speech-language pathologist is conducting.
- Persuaders should avoid clothes or accessories that seem incompatible with their audience, for example, overdressing or wearing too much make-up.
- Paraverbals must be used wisely. Face and gesture should transmit the commitment to persuade, a willingness to be patient, and an optimism that the change is superior to the previous state.
- Audiovisuals and props should also synchronize with my persuasive/directive intention. If what I am promoting is

illogical or irrational, the probability that you will give it the nod is quite low no matter how I dress it up.
■ Logic is intrinsic to the transmission. An illogical argument will rarely persuade.
■ The twin goals of effective persuaders are cogency and trust.
■ Empathy is a key component of persuasion. I need an accurate feel for where the listener is developmentally, I need to know that a listener's priorities will not trump my intention, and I need to know motivations and resistance points throughout the process.

# References

Crano, W. D., & Prislin, R. (2006). Attitudes and persuasion. *Annual Review of Psychology, 57,* 345–374.

Fact sheet: Laryngeal cancer. (2007, April 8). Retrieved from http://www .entnet.org/healthinfo/ throat/Throat_Cancer.cfm

Garnett, J. D. (2001). Tobacco and laryngeal pathology. *West Virginia Medical Journal, 97*(1), 13–16.

Gélinas-Chebat, C., & Chebat, J. C. (1996). Voice and advertising: Effects of intonation and intensity of voice on source credibility, attitudes toward the advertised service and the intent to buy. *Perceptual and Motor Skills, 83*(1), 243–262.

Gingerich, O. (2003). Truth in science: Proof persuasion and the Galileo affair. *Perspectives on Science and Christian Faith, 55*(2), 80–87.

Glanz, K., Lewis, F. M., & Rimer, B. K. (1996). *Health behavior and health education: Theory, research, and practice* (2nd ed.). San Francisco, CA: Jossey-Bass.

Honeycutt, L. (Compiled, 2011). *Aristotle's Rhetoric.* Retrieved from http:www.rhetoric.eserver.org/aristotle/

Kübler-Ross, E. (1997). *On death and dying.* New York, NY: Scribner. (Original work published 1969.)

Marcotullio, D., Magliulo, G., & Pezone, T. (2002). Reinke's edema and risk factors: Clinical and histopathologic aspects. *American Journal of Otolaryngology, 23*(2), 81–84.

Page, R. A., & Balloun, J. L. (1978). The effect of voice volume on the perception of personality. *Journal of Social Psychology, 105*(1), 65–72.

Petty, R. E., Cacioppo, J. T., & Schumann, D. (1983). Central and peripheral routes to advertising effectiveness: The moderating role of involvement. *Journal of Consumer Research, 10*(2), 135–146.

Prochaska, J. O., DiClemente, C. C., & Norcross, J. C. (1992). In search of how people change: Applications to addictive behaviors. *American Psychologist, 47*(9), 1102–1114.

Tormala, Z. L., Clarkson, J. J., & Petty, R. E. (2006). Resisting persuasion by the skin of one's teeth: The hidden success of resisted persuasive messages. *Journal of Social Psychology, 91*(3), 423–435.

# *Chapter 11*

# Moving Them

*Those that will not hear must be made to feel.*
— German proverb

*Poetry is when an emotion has found its thought and the thought has found words.*
— Robert Frost

## Keys to Effectiveness in Addressing Emotion

No matter what you mean to say, there is one intention you can never completely dismiss, and that is feeling. This chapter's focus is on the feeling intention when it is the primary intention, but in every transmission a feeling intention is present. You always want your audience receptive to what you are communicating to them, and receptivity is a feeling-state. Although receptivity is preferable most of the time, hostility is also a feeling intention your audience may receive. You cannot interact without feeling, because without feeling you would be without the motivation to interact. Feeling may not be your core intention, but it is there.

Sometimes, however, feeling is your core intention. When the feeling intention takes center stage, the interaction can be challenging and sometimes volatile.

One of the most popular and well-regarded American speeches of the 20th century is the "I Have a Dream" speech of Rev. Dr. Martin Luther King, Jr. Early in the speech delivered on a blistering

August day in 1963, Dr. King seemed clearly in persuasive mode as he spoke of redeeming a check written long ago to African Americans and returned marked "insufficient funds." Midway through, the preacher shifted into a new genre and began one of the great oratorical crescendos ever launched as he recited, "My country 'tis of thee . . . " He spoke of his dream in ringing repetitions and soared to his finale quoting,the spiritual, "Thank God Almighty, we're free at last!"

Research suggests that rising vocal intonation can increase a listener's involvement or inclination to respond "yes" instead of "no" (Barath & Cannell, 2001). Rarely has the human voice elicited such a powerful "yes" over so many years as did Dr. King on the day his seminal speech was filmed. Some irreducible combination of words, environment, voice, and gesture created a moment that gripped the feeling center of a nation and never let go. We step into this exploration with humility and a keen appreciation of the power of human emotion.

As with all the intentions, you begin by determining that indeed it is a feeling you wish to impart over any other aim. College admissions officers usually agree that their very first talk to prospective students and their parents has a high feeling component. Although the presentation is brimming with information and has many persuasive elements, recall of that information or a change in beliefs is less crucial than the positive feelings students and parents experience about the school. Here is a typical paragraph of a college admissions talk to high schoolers and their parents.

"Thomas Jefferson, author of the Declaration of Independence and our third president, founded our university over 200 years ago. Our community has maintained his tradition of the highest standards of higher education, and, if those standards are important to you, you too will want to consider joining this community."

The paragraph contains a lot of information, but how important is it to the speaker that you retain all that data? Persuasion is there too: If you have strong educational standards, you will be interested in our school. The feeling intention, although never explicit, is also pretty obvious. This presenter wants the audience to feel excited, enthused, maybe even a little awestruck, at the idea of attending this great university.

Which intention is foremost? Imagine you could achieve only one of the three mentioned previously. Outcomes could be (1) the high schoolers and parents remember information about Jefferson and standards; (2) they are persuaded that college applicants with high standards might consider this school, or (3) they are truly inspired to look more seriously into this option for college. In workshops Lonnie has conducted, actual admissions officers confronted with these choices chose the third, almost unanimously.

This result is not a surprise. In general, it is quite common to find feeling intentions at the forefront in the initial stages of an interaction. A noted presentation expert (Wyeth, 2014) suggests several surefire openings to capture the attention of an audience. Notice the high feeling component of each of these sample quotes.

"How many of you have ever wondered where your next meal is coming from?"

"Marketing technical products is too important to leave to marketers."

"Every hour in Gaza a child is dying of artillery fire and missiles."

Advertisers know the importance of the feeling intention. Most commercials on video have strong emotional content. These ads assume that the viewer is being introduced to the product. It is possible to conceive that the only information advertisers want their viewers to retain is the name of the product. Beyond that, all efforts are expended to get the viewer to feel a certain way about the product or simply to associate a certain set of emotions with the product. This aim is crucial in the few seconds you might take to look at a commercial before viewing an Internet clip.

Emotion-related states seen as valuable associations include pleasure, camaraderie, patriotism, and popularity. Look for them in the next 15-second ad that pops up while you are awaiting a video you just clicked on. Even before widespread use of the Internet, TV commercials began to depend more and more on emotional stimuli (Hazlett & Hazlett, 1999).

Those who provide automated voice services have an interest in vocal styles that form the basis of emotional expression, the voice quality and the words that tend to evoke from listeners specific emotional interpretations, like "welcoming" and "hostile" (Maffiolo & Chateau, 2003). The most famous of these voices, Carolyn

268     Your Voice Is Your Business

Hopkins, was interviewed on Public Radio's *Here and Now* on March 10, 2015 (Hobson, 2015). She explained why her voice is in demand at airports and rail stations around the world. "I try to make it clear, concise, and friendly." She is certainly giving information and often persuading people to "stand on the right and pass on the left" of the moving walkway, but her friendliness and upbeat quality set her apart.

Salespeople certainly understand the feeling intention. Randall was an excellent life insurance sales rep. At his first meeting with a young married couple, he began with a few questions. How many children did they plan on having? Did they know the projected cost of college when those kids reached 18 years of age? Did they know the average savings of a father of four who tragically dies after ten years of marriage? Randall recited statistics about the financial situation of uninsured families who lose a wage earner. It sounded dry, dense with data, entirely informational.

If you agree that the agent had an informational intention, you cannot be blamed. You also cannot be more wrong. Randall had one and only one aim, to evoke an emotion. Something between stark terror and extreme dread would work nicely. His intonation—low-pitched, declarative; his pacing—even, uninterrupted; and his loudness level—confidential, intimate, low intensity—all these effects served to enhance the chilling nature of the transmission. Randall's success is very much dependent on how accurately he pinpoints the feeling response he is seeking and how effectively he elicits it. The same is true for you during your feeling transmissions.

Ask yourself, just how do you want your listeners to feel as you begin transmitting? What feelings do you want your listeners to have during the transmission? What feeling do you want your listeners to experience as the listeners leave? What enduring feeling would you like them to retain? If you can get clear answers to those questions and if those answers form the primary aim of your transmission, then you have a feeling intention.

Sometimes there is a progression of feelings that you are seeking. You may begin by acknowledging the other person's resistance to a message you have, then move to reduce that resistance, and finally replace it with a more open-minded feeling. You might save the actual persuasion (a different intention) for your next encounter.

Lonnie certainly had a feeling intention when he dealt with the unsympathetic outlook of the executives confronting the prospect of a three-year implementation of a new performance management system. Lonnie had to move them from an attitude of "No way it's going to take that long" to "OK, help us understand why it will take three years." If he could not get them to that point, he would not have been in a position to persuade them; their resistance would have short-circuited his efforts.

Lonnie was fortunate to have achieved this feeling intention and then moved to persuasion within the same meeting. But what might have happened had he not addressed the feeling issues early on? There is evidence that we are so predisposed to accept emotional cues that we will give credence to even false physiological feedback (i.e, if it is consistent with the emotion we believe a person is transmitting) (Gray, Harrison, Wiens, & Critchley, 2007). Here are some likely consequences of a failure to take on a feeling intention immediately when it is called for.

- Mild resistance can harden into outright hostility. This could easily have happened with the upper managers with whom Lonnie was consulting in the previous chapter.
- Unchecked fear can spread through a group and grow into panic. University admissions officers who dismiss one parent's concerns about sending their child to an urban campus might see the dread spread among the audience all out of proportion to the seriousness of the issue.
- Initial fears or frustrations can also morph into anger. Norabelle, the director of operations, saw that happen when she ill-advisedly shifted from persuading to informing (see Chapter 10). Ironically, she had already achieved a valuable feeling intention. The investors arrived at the meeting in an anxious state, and Norabelle quickly reduced that anxiety and made them receptive to a positive interpretation. Still, the investors were skittish. By failing to recognize the feeling tone of the group, Norabelle almost lost it all.
- Indifference does not melt into interest by itself. Middle school students with no curiosity at all about history may need persuading at some point, but if they are met with an enthusiastic teacher capable of transporting them to the romance and excitement of a bygone era (a feeling intention), the path to persuasion may be cleared nicely.

To connect with others emotively, you must know what emotions your listeners are experiencing as you begin your transmission.

While empathy can be helpful, it is not empathy but savvy that is called for here. You must ask, what is this person feeling? What is the person likely to be feeling? You may call upon your own experience in similar situations; you may look for cues to possible feeling-states; you might even ask the other person what he or she is feeling. Once you have connected with the other's feeling-state, you are in a position to plot your next move. And it better be genuine. Emotionally, you must take a person from where that person is to where you want the person to be.

In one sense, there are an almost infinite number of feeling-states to which you may want to move your audience. In another sense, there is really only one and that is receptivity. You want your listeners receptive to your message. The thing is, receptivity is different in different circumstances. Randall the insurance guy finds the customer most receptive when the customer is scared stiff. Lonnie's upper managers need to feel less certain that a performance management system can be hurried into existence. Those history students need to be on the edge of their seats anticipating the adventure to come. Norabelle's stockholders need to be fearful enough to want to hear her explanation but not so panicky that they shut her down.

If you know your feeling intention, you still might not achieve it. If you do not know your feeling intention, however, you almost surely will not achieve it. Once you do know your intention, success is possible, and success will come with much greater frequency if you know how to state your emotional case.

## Putting Feeling in Your Voice

Begin, as always, with voice. Examples of effective voicing of emotion vary greatly. At one end there is Dr. King's soaring intonation and increasing intensity as he seeks to stir his audience. Then there is Randall the insurance rep whose low, intimate, recitative style strikes cold fear into the hearts of young parents everywhere. One lesson is that fear is not always most effectively evoked by a hideous scream; passion is not always elicited by a whispering intensity. The detection of an emotion in your voice by no means guarantees that your audience will experience that same emotion. Still, there are some reliable vocal guidelines.

In their review of the literature on voice and emotion, Murray and Arnott (1993) discerned specific vocal effects commonly associated with basic feeling states like anger, happiness, sadness, fear, disgust. The distinctions they noted are illustrative of people exhibiting a particular emotion but may not be ideal for a speaker evoking the feeling.

First of all, there is a difference between steady and strident. Steady is measured, strong, unwavering; strident is clamorous, shrill, pressing, discordant. One is just enough, the other too much. The voice seeking to establish a feeling tone should remain steady but never strident. Maintain and even strengthen vocal intensity when reaching for an emotional payoff, but do not explode out of the pitch range within which your voice sounds natural. Never stop sounding like yourself. Here are a few useful stratagems.

- Do not get so loud you feel vocal strain. Dr. King achieved considerable intensity during the "Dream" speech, but he never sounded like a different person, never showed strain even at his loudest. Do not force air or push when getting loud.
- If you have decided to build to a crescendo, start at a low intensity and low pitch so that your voice has a wide margin within which to swell. The high intensity voice is best used to excite an audience, to stir, to move, to create a passionate response. Such a reaction should be sought infrequently.
- Support the high intensity voice (e.g., belt) with an open, anchored posture, a quick exhale, or if needed, a small inhale.
- If you feel a tickle, scratch, or cough in your voice, reevaluate your technique because you are doing something wrong.
- Avoid screaming, growling, or cracking.
- Use your high intensity voice sparingly and with specific intention; overuse will make the listening experience tedious, annoying, or, at best, ordinary.
- Be open to voice evaluation and voice therapy by a voice care team; they may significantly enhance your ability to achieve the vocal effects you envision.

Other feelings are more subtle. You may be experiencing exactly what you want your audience to feel, but that does not mean you are getting them to feel it. Think about notable tear-inducing movies. When Oskar Schindler wept near the end of

*Schindler's List* because he was unable to save more lives than he did, we cried along with him. In the 1946 movie *It's a Wonderful Life*, the director boasts at least four emotional climaxes, each one calibrated to make a grown man cry—women, too.

Lonnie sometimes ends his workshop on listening with the heartfelt story of a little girl he knew who succumbed to leukemia. There is rarely a dry eye in the audience when he finishes, yet Lonnie's voice remains strong and matter of fact in the telling. So potent is the story itself that any vocal embellishments would actually detract from the emotional impact. The straight informational style works best although the feeling intention is front and center.

Our trial attorney, Samantha, has learned to modulate tone and intensity for a wide variety of feeling intentions. A witness who is nervous may need to be put at ease by a slow pace, soothing tone, and even pitch, with intensity well under control. A witness being cross-examined might be treated to a more rapid-fire interrogation with higher intensity; the intention might be to cause feelings of doubt in the witness about what they thought happened.

In closing statements to juries, Samantha sometimes exhibits high intensity and inflection, even including a touch of sarcasm. In those instances she wants the jurors to look upon her opponent's case as unsupported or ludicrous. Different circumstances can require a very different style. She may desire nothing more than that the jury feel empathy or pity for her client, in which case her vocal intensity decreases to a near whisper, while her intonation is intimate and confidential. Selecting the wrong feeling intention at this point in the proceedings can be harmful to Samantha's purpose.

## The Climate That Feels Just Right

While your voice does its part, the universe of paraverbals should also align with your feeling intention. Begin by imagining the climate that is ideal for the success of your transmission. Then shape the sensory world to conform as closely as possible to that ideal state.

The progression to the ideal feeling-state is an evolution. Your task is to build a paraverbal bridge from where your audience is when you start to where you want them to be when the conversation is done. If your audience comprises parents who are apprehensive about campus safety, your bridge will carry them to a less anxious state where their worries, if not totally dispelled, are significantly reduced. If they are a jury who supposes your client looks guilty, build a bridge to a state where they feel more comfortable with the way your client looks and sounds. The enormity of the bridge-building challenge depends on the depth of your audience's emotion and the distance of their current emotion from the one you seek to evoke.

Let your eyes summon a power equal to the challenge. Often this means looking your audience right in the eyes with precisely the emotion you seek to impart. Samantha does this when the soft and glistening glow of empathy suffuses her glance at a jury and she says, "Try to imagine yourself going through what he went through. Try!" Lonnie uses the same glance when he relates the tragic story of the beloved little girl who died too young; he peers at his audience with dry-eyed stoicism. Norabelle gazes intently, then switches on the light of self-confidence that announces to worried stockholders, "All is well; your management team is in control."

Facial expression follows suit. The more anxious your audience is, the more emphatic will be their response to an emotional cue in your face (Holmes, Richards, & Green, 2006). The slight smile may call them to empathize. The broad smile may simply say, "Lighten up!" A brief nod of the head can bring them up alongside of you emotionally, and you all can venture on together. Gestures complement; that nod is reinforced by a beckoning pulling gesture. Below are some visual cues that can indicate specific feeling tones.

- Eye contact is important, but just as important in feeling messages is eye expression.
- Raised eyebrows can show surprise, joy, or fear, depending on differences in total facial expression. The open-mouthed, about-to-scream look indicates terror, whereas a closed-mouth gaze can relate that you are pleasantly surprised.
- Lowered eyebrows can show confusion, anger, or deep thought, depending on total facial expression. With lips slightly parted, chin askew, you might be indicating that you are thinking it over, meanwhile a frown will show displeasure. The furrowed brow can simply show that you are concentrating hard on what is being said.

- Looking away can indicate many things depending on context. If you look off to the side and down during a moment of high emotion, you might be perceived as gathering your strength or as somewhat overwhelmed by it all.
- Pulling gestures in a feeling context usually invite your listener to experience the emotion. A well-placed pushing gesture can say to your communication partner hold on, wait, consider what is being felt. Strong gestures violating the effectiveness zone (between the waist and the shoulders), even a clenched fist, can occasionally be effective in conveying passion or conviction.
- If you are not sure about the feeling tone of your face and gesture, try performing them alone in front of a mirror; ask if the image matches what you think you are conveying. Viewing a video of yourself can also be very instructive.

Audiovisuals designed to complement a feeling intention require a great deal of forethought. A frequent error among presenters is the use of unsuitable slides to support a feeling intention. Computer-generated slides are frequently prepared as information carriers. It is frighteningly easy for you to take the Word document of your talk and copy and paste it chunk by chunk into a deck of slides. What you end up with is a slideshow every bit as boring as your outline, only harder to read.

Instead of defaulting to informational slides ask, what image would convey your feeling intention with vividness and clarity? Your task is to transmit a feeling, not a logical inference, not a status report. Perhaps there are props that would serve your purpose better than slides. Maybe now is the moment for a well-placed story or even a joke—if it reinforces your feeling intention. Possibly it is time to push the envelope and take a risk.

David was a well-regarded lecturer on the topic of workplace stress. He had a finish that never failed to leave the audience saying, "I'll be darned if I'm going to put up with one more minute of undue stress." He began by asking everyone to stand up. They did. Then he told them to imagine the ugliest, slimiest, heaviest, most disgusting monster wrapped like a stole around the back of their necks. He built up the image until they could feel the monster's hot breath in their ear.

"That's the stress you carry around with you all day at work," David said. He then commanded them to reach behind their head, grab the monster, throw it to the ground, and scream out, "Get off my back!!" As the laughter and buzz died down, David asked rhetorically, "Now. How did that feel?" He knew the answer: like a big load off the back.

When Lonnie teaches negotiation skills, one of his objectives is a clear feeling intention: he wants his listeners to muster the chutzpah to initiate negotiations in everyday commerce—with hotel reservationists, rental car agencies, airlines—just as they do with car dealers. He tells three stories in succession, all of them located in a marketplace where bargaining is the norm. One transpires in Tijuana, Mexico; one in Mumbai, India; and one in Little Italy in South Philadelphia, Pennsylvania.

Each story has a different point, but they all elicit the same feeling: that bargaining, the assertive act of challenging the sticker price, is normal. In discussion, the feeling is reinforced as participants recount instances in which they negotiated a better deal than the first offer. People typically leave the workshop determined to overcome their trepidation and challenge the sticker price a lot more often.

Toward the conclusion of his workshop, Lonnie makes a very different emotional appeal. His topic is integrity, and his pitch is that it is better to maintain integrity when negotiating than to use manipulation and deception. Lonnie's feeling intention is modest: encourage receptivity to hearing the definition of integrity and the reasons for maintaining it. He begins by asking participants to bring to mind the person who has the highest credibility of anyone they know. During discussion the participants come to realize that the people they visualized have a very high integrity quotient and that they are much admired.

With these exceptional role models in mind, Lonnie then says, "Let me list some of the benefits of maintaining your own integrity. He lists a few, then asks, "How many parents are out there?" Most hands go up. "OK, here's a benefit for you." His voice gets lower, more confidential. On the screen is one word, "Integrity." He takes a step toward them. "Your kids will love you when they're little. But that's no big deal. Our kids always love us when they're little. No, the benefit is this. Your kids will not only love you when they're small; they will respect you when they grow up and can look you right in the eye."

The picture of that two-year-old growing to eye level and looking at Dad or Mom with respect is the most effective visual in the whole workshop. And it never appears on a slide. Your ability to select the right mix of communication techniques to achieve your feeling intention improves with practice. In the brief situations depicted below, consider effective ways to create the right emotional connection with the audience. There can be more than one right answer to each of the questions. They are designed to get you thinking about achieving a feeling intention in a variety of settings.

1.  You are coaching a golfer on changing his swing so as to avoid slicing a long drive. You are at a tee on a driving range. The golfer says his slice is not that bad, but you think he must work on this before moving on to other improvements. You begin talking to him.
    - What is your feeling intention at this moment?
    - What is the first thing you say?
    - Describe your tone of voice as you say it.
    - Consider your gestures, posture, and positioning.
    - What props or AVs would you use and how would you employ them?
    - What would make the environment more conducive to the achievement of your intention?

2.  You are an admissions officer at an urban college speaking about campus safety to a group of concerned parents of prospective new freshmen. A parent raises her hand and says, "I'm from a rural area. I don't think I could stand it if I felt my child was in danger of being assaulted."
    - What is your feeling intention at this moment with this parent? What about the rest of the audience?
    - What is the first thing you say?
    - Describe your tone of voice as you say it.
    - Consider your gestures, posture, and positioning.
    - What props or AVs would you use and how would you employ them?
    - What would make the environment more conducive to the achievement of your intention?

3. You are an athletic coach. You are in the locker room. Your team is about to play the initial game of the state playoffs. This is the first time your school has ever been in the playoffs. You step in front of them. Their eyes are wide as they look to you.
   - What is your feeling intention at this moment?
   - What is the first thing you say?
   - Describe your tone of voice as you say it.
   - Consider your gestures, posture, and positioning.
   - What props or AVs would you use and how would you employ them?
   - What would make the environment more conducive to the achievement of your intention?

4. You are a technical expert instructing a person on the way to get started with a new smart phone. The person is elderly and has just decided to purchase and learn to use one. You are standing in the middle of a busy store.
   - What is your feeling intention at this moment?
   - What is the first thing you say?
   - Describe your tone of voice as you say it.
   - Consider your gestures, posture, and positioning.
   - What props or AVs would you use and how would you employ them?
   - What would make the environment more conducive to the achievement of your intention?

5. You are a sales manager at a pharmaceutical company. You are in a conference room talking to the 20-person sales force about the launch of a new drug. The company has high hopes for this drug and wants the reps to discuss it with every general practitioner in the region. The outreach will begin immediately.
   - What is your feeling intention at this moment?
   - What is the first thing you say?
   - Describe your tone of voice as you say it.
   - Consider your gestures, posture, and positioning.
   - What props or AVs would you use and how would you employ them?
   - What would make the environment more conducive to the achievement of your intention?

## The Feeling Connection

You will not find it difficult to create or extinguish a feeling in your audience. What is difficult is to create or extinguish the particular feeling you intend to create or extinguish. The previous exercise likely gave you some perspective on this challenge. You need to know where they are coming from emotionally and just how emotional they are about it. You further need to know where you wish to take them emotionally and how far away that is for them. Then you must know how to marshal the verbals and paraverbals that will be up to the job.

Getting them to feel a certain way is a legitimate intention, but it is subject to manipulation and underhandedness. After all, con man is short for confidence man, a person whose intention is to trick you into feeling that he can be trusted so you will look the other way as he robs you blind. We have grown wary of advertisers, salespeople, and politicians whose workplace is our feelings, whose feeling intentions too often arouse our suspicion. How do I seek to achieve my feeling intentions without manipulating or deceiving?

The answer is remarkably simple: Do not manipulate or deceive. Feeling intentions should be as straightforward and transparent as informational or persuasive intentions. If at any time your audience wants to know what your intentions are, you should be quick to tell them honestly and completely. You should have nothing to hide; this is an act of communication like any other.

Still, there is power in creating or extinguishing a feeling. It can make a jumpy group of investors relaxed enough to endure a downturn in gross profits. It can transform an impatient covey of top executives into willing partners in a three-year implementation. It can generate smiles, frowns, laughter, and, yes, even tears. It can steel the nerves of the timid and cause tremors of anxiety in the resolute.

With that power comes risk. If you push them too far, they might recoil to a feeling-state that is worse than when you began. If you misjudge the depth of their feeling, you might evoke anger rather than solidarity. You can even be too successful. A football coach might meet the feeling intention of exciting his quarterback to a fever pitch prior to kickoff. In fact, he might get the player so excited that the player loses complete control of his passing arm and throws three or four interceptions. A choral director might so thoroughly impress upon her *a capella* choir the high stakes of their performance in the regional finals that they nervously sing completely off-key.

If you are smart, you remain prepared to make modifications during your transmission, especially when it comes to your feeling intentions. Adjust the intensity throughout the interaction; make sure the connection is strong but does not get out of hand. You are always at liberty to gauge the intensity by asking questions. "So, how are you feeling about this so far?" "Are you still worried?" "Do you feel differently now?"

University admissions officers are sometimes surprised that the heart of so many of their presentations is a feeling intention. The comment of one was revealing:

Actually, I have several feeling intentions. I want the parents to walk away feeling that this is a school that will not just educate but take good care of their child; they should feel relieved as much as anything else. There are also students out there who are not a good match for our school. Still, I want them to walk away feeling positive about the school, so they'll tell their younger sister that this might be the school for them. And, finally, the real prospective students, they should go home feeling, well, just feeling like they want to visit our university or come back, that something will be missing for them if they never get to the campus.

Now, there is a set of intentions you should be proud to achieve if you were an admissions officer. The desired intentions may not be easy, but you have a voice, you have the words, and you have a universe of paraverbals at your command. You only need to get a feel for them.

## Review of Key Ideas

■ A feeling intention is present in every communicative transmission. A feeling intention can be your core intention or it can be secondary to another primary intention.

- The feeling intention is crucial in advertising; great efforts are expended to get you to feel a certain way about a product or idea.
- Those who provide automated voice services have an interest in vocal styles that form the basis of emotional expression, the voice quality and the words that tend to evoke from listeners specific emotional interpretations.
- To connect with others emotively, you must know what emotions your listeners are experiencing as you begin your transmission.
- Once you have connected with the other's feeling-state, you are in a position to achieve your other objectives.
- The following are strategies for voice use to deliver a feeling intention effectively: Do not get so loud you feel vocal strain; support the high intensity voice with an open, anchored posture; avoid feeling a tickle, scratch, or cough in your voice; avoid screaming, growling, or cracking; use high intensity voice sparingly; be open to voice evaluation and voice therapy.
- The following are guidelines for facial expression: Make eye contact, be aware of eyebrow positioning use pulling gestures to invite your listener to experience emotion, practice facial expression and gesture in a mirror if you feel unsure about the message you are conveying.
- Audiovisuals designed to complement a feeling intention require a great deal of forethought. Instead of defaulting to informational slides ask yourself what image would convey your feeling intention with vividness and clarity.
- Do not manipulate or deceive. Feeling intentions should be as straightforward and transparent as informational or persuasive intentions.

# References

Barath, A., & Cannell, C. F. (1976). Effect of interviewer's voice intonation. *Public Opinion Quarterly, 40*(3), 370–373.

Gray M. A., Harrison, N. A., Wiens, S., & Critchley, H. D. (2007). Modulation of emotional appraisal by false physiological feedback during fMRI. *PLoS One, 2,* 546.

Hazlett R. L., & Hazlett, S. Y. (1999). Emotional response to television commercials: Facial EMG vs. self-report. *Journal of Advertising Research*,
*39*, 7–23.

Hobson, J. (2015, March 10). *Meet the voice of hundreds of airports, sub-
ways and theme parks.* [Interview with Carolyn Hopkins, public service announcer]. Available at http://hereandnow.wbur.org/2015/03/10/
voice-carolyn-hopkins

Holmes, A., Richards, A., & Green, S. (2006). Anxiety and sensitivity to eye
gaze in emotional faces. *Brain and Cognition, 60*(3), 282–294.

Maffiolo, V., & Chateau, N. (2003). The emotional quality of speech in
voice services. *Ergonomics, 46*(13–14), 1375–1385.

Murray, I. R., & Arnott, J. L. (1993). Toward the simulation of emotion in
synthetic speech: A review of the literature on human vocal emotion.
*The Journal of the Acoustical Society of America, 93*(2), 1097–1108.

Wyeth, S. (2014). *The most powerful ways to start a presentation.* Retrieved
from http://www.inc.com/sims-wyeth/all-s-well-that-begins-well-the-
power-of-first-impressions.html

# Chapter 12

# Summing Up

*Free expression is the base of human rights, the root of human nature and the mother of truth. To kill free speech is to insult human rights, to stifle human nature and to suppress truth.*

—Liu Xiaobo, Chinese human rights activist

*It usually takes me more than three weeks to prepare a good impromptu speech.*

—Mark Twain

## A World Connected

When the television series *Star Trek* aired in the 1960s, projections of humans a couple of centuries from now were imagined. They had made enormous strides in space travel. Traveling at warp speed they could hop from solar system to solar system in a matter of days. Starships had their own ecosystems complete with magical food dispensers, earth-level gravity, and all the oxygen anyone could want. People could even use a transporter to hop from ship to planet by having their molecules disassembled here and reassembled there.

Communication had advanced tremendously as well. People had flip phones with, amazingly, headshots of the person they were talking to! Books were completely replaced by what looked like portable electronic tablets. Flat-screen monitors adorned walls every-where, and folks were able to view each other while they spoke.

Now, nearly a quarter of the way through the 21st century, the creative minds behind *Star Trek* would notice quite a bit of progress, but it would not be uniform progress.

Space travel has not met the mark set by the series, nor is it making great strides in that direction. We went to the moon dur-ing the first run of *Star Trek* and have never sent a person that far since. There is no warp speed or likelihood of such an invention. Our space station supports life with a limited oxygen supply but no gravity. And there is certainly no Thomas Edison about to regale us with the first transporter beam.

The communication side, however, has seen marked progress. Every one of the innovations mentioned has been invented, mass produced, and deployed worldwide. In some cases, our century has already surpassed the imagined communication technology of the *Star Trek* universe.

We have phones with live video of the other party; you might call it face time or something like that. In fact, phones send all kinds of written and spoken messages anywhere in the world. Instantly. Those same phones are full-fledged computers networked with millions of other computers by something we call the Internet. *Star Trek*'s measly phones were, well, phones. And archaic flip phones at that. Captain Kirk was never once seen viewing a movie on his communicator, whereas you could watch an episode of *Star Trek* on your phone right now if you so desired.

Books have not been replaced by electronic tablets, but they could be and quite easily. We are quickly merging phone and tab-let and laptop and desktop. They are all computers with access to a world at least as interconnected as the world portrayed in *Star Trek* ever was. While space travel lags woefully behind the curve, communication technology has in many ways leapt beyond Gene Roddenberry's wildest imagination—and he had a pretty wild one.

You might argue that the reason for this is simple. The technol-ogy for improved communication capability has been more accessi-ble than the technology required for advances in interstellar planet hopping. True enough, but that fact does not explain the enormous explosion of communication devices and designs in our time.

Our need as humans to connect with each other is utterly insatiable. The drive to communicate may be the strongest drive we possess. Kirk said space was the final frontier. Perhaps he was wrong. Maybe the final frontier is the chasm that exists between one human mind and another; maybe communication is the bridge.

As much connection as technology has brought, literally, to our fingertips; as easy as it now is to access mountains of information, to make contact with people across the globe, to see and hear and learn—still we are brought back to that direct, eyeball-to-eyeball transaction that requires only ears to hear, eyes to see, and a voice to send our truth across.

With all the video conferencing capability imaginable, global corporations insist on filling airplanes daily with people traveling 18 hours to meet up with their associates, shake hands, sit around a table, and strike an accord. In 2015 U. S. Secretary of State John Kerry was in tense international negotiations in France. He broke his leg in a biking mishap and had to use video conferencing to continue the talks. This option was seen as unfortunate. Why?

A newborn's first cry is not an intentional act of communication, nor is its first exposure to light and shadow a sightseeing tour. But this is where seeing and speaking begin. A mother hearing that cry is moved to pick up the child, warm it, cuddle it, and feed it. The child thrives. Communication in this inaugural moment is a matter of survival. Mother and child may be the primordial connection, the real beginning of communication. This special connection is called bonding, and we know it involves every one of the five senses, even the sense of smell. When a 71-year-old high stakes negotiator says it is unfortunate that he cannot meet in person, he may be referencing his earliest moment of connection, one he has learned to trust above all.

Our metaphors reveal our preference for in-person encounters. We stay "in touch" by cell phone or text, although we are not actually close enough to touch. The word "contact" means at root "to touch with." You say you did not "hear" from your friend, even if you mean that he did not email you. "I'll reach out to you soon." "We'll speak tomorrow." "Let's visit by phone." "If he's here, I'll sniff him out." All the senses are called into service to express our predisposition to meet face to face.

When you improve any aspect of your ability to transmit or receive direct communication with another person, you are honing what may be your most highly valued human competency.

## Giving Voice

To a degree never available to us before this era, the voice and its astounding proficiency are becoming clear. The science of voice reveals a mechanism distinctly human in its structure and myriad capabilities.

The structure begins with the vocal folds, those tiny curtains of tissue moving the air nearby as they vibrate into your resonating chambers, creating the unique sound of your very own voice. A single vocal sound calls into play bones, muscles, and organs throughout your torso and head, from the diaphragm and lungs providing breath that vibrates the folds to the oral and nasal cavities expanding a soft buzz into a full-bodied vocal utterance.

Mastering the use of the voice in everyday conversation requires years of devoted effort. A child says her first recognizable word at one year, but recognizable grammatical structures do not arise until almost three years. Pronunciation too comes gradually and only after much work and practice. The child eventually forms complete sentences and can differentiate among statements, questions, commands, and exclamations. Comprehending the notion that the sound of the word "table" refers to that piece of furniture over there is an incredibly complex mental feat. It requires the child to understand symbolic meaning: This word means that object.

Yet humans invariably do comprehend language, a monumental achievement that gives access to all human history, science, philosophy, literature, and song. As you acquire your own voice, you are enabled to hear and perceive the voices of all who speak. No wonder the word "voice" carries so many connotations of personal stature, power, and decision.

Once you learn to use your voice in speech and song, in oratory, drama, or conversation, it becomes one of your most precious possessions. The fact that so many people take so little care of their voices is astonishing, especially since the proper way to care for the voice and to avoid vocal harm is well known among speech-language pathologists and many who teach voice. Much of their advice is found throughout this book.

Preserving a healthy voice is the beginning. Learning to use the voice to transmit meaning and intention requires a solid grasp of the physical mechanism involved in producing various vocal qualities. With that fundamental knowledge, you can benefit enormously from training on techniques for producing those qualities, along with practice in effective and healthy use of the voice.

The result is a voice that says what you want to say in the way you want to say it, a voice that remains resilient and fresh. Radio personalities who depend entirely on their voices for their livelihoods know full well the importance of these outcomes. Those who use their voices frequently like teachers, actors, singers, and drill sergeants are also aware of the value of good and healthy vocal use. The point is, the same can be said for those others who simply employ their voices in everyday life. They too speak daily and wish to maintain a hearty voice.

It is all a matter of awareness of vocal power and a willingness to work at increasing it.

## A Look, A Gesture

The deaf community relies on visuals to achieve their interpersonal communication goals. Sign language combines with facial expression and body language to generate a rich and full vocabulary and syntax.

For the hearing, such visuals often accompany voiced words and sentences to enhance and clarify meaning, add nuance, and confirm intentions. Along with vocal inflection, intonation, and prosody, these enhancements are called paraverbals. Paraverbals transmit meanings that can be learned and used proficiently to get your point across.

That point is the message you intend to relay. The 5 Intentions covered in this book are self-affirmation, small talk, information, persuasion, and feeling. Even though more than one of these can exist in any given message, you usually have a primary intention; the verbals and paraverbals you choose can be employed to transmit that intention accurately and powerfully. Getting listeners to perceive precisely what you intend is the sum and substance of communication. It results in shared meaning and common understanding.

## Speaking Truth

Every message contains, at its heart, a singular truth about the person formulating the message. You are not a keyboard, not just a vehicle carrying the message forth. You are the source, the origin of the message. It speaks to you, your personality and your character. People learn not only about your transmissions when they receive your messages, they learn about you. Your character is embedded in the things you communicate.

Communicate from a standpoint of knowledge, and others will realize that, when you speak, what you say is grounded and demonstrable. You are intelligent and informed. Communicate as a person competent to discuss the matter, and they will expect sound advice and proper technique. You are skilled and able. Communicate from a standpoint of experience, and they will pay a visit to your reality rich with the fruits of a worthwhile journey. You are mature and assured.

Finally, communicate with integrity, and they will feel the courage and commitment of human wholeness. You are who you are, devoid of subterfuge, manipulation, or underhandedness. You regard the connection of communication as precious, vital, and inviolable.

A few conclusions can be derived from this portrait of exemplary interpersonal communication. First, it is essential to our species. If a caregiver does not hear that infant's first cry, does not feed and warm and care for the newborn, survival is not possible. We are social animals with a powerful need to make contact with our kind. Without that contact very little can happen, neither a looming skyscraper protruding from the Dubai desert nor a friendly game of checkers on a park bench in Peoria.

Second, communication is our birthright. Our sensory organs have evolved wondrously to enable speech to be emitted and heard, articulated and understood. The deaf find the hands, the body, and the eyes quite suitable for making effective contact. Our brains are finely tuned to the nuances of words, grammar, syntax, and paraverbals. In truth, our brains increasingly appear to be built for making contact with others. Getting ourselves across is, simply, what we do.

Third, communication is not just essential, not only natural for us, communication is difficult. It takes years to learn, a lifetime to refine. Language begins in sign and symbol, so two communicators are already once removed from the thought one is attempting to transmit to the other. Direct thought transference is not currently possible, so there is no foolproof way to guarantee that what you heard is what was meant.

Recognizing this chasm that exists between one person and another, we introduce all manner of means to make our meaning clearer, our nuances more apparent. We use words, sentences, grammar, and syntax. We inflect words with intonation, emphasis, and prosody. We incorporate visuals like gesture, facial expression, even the clothes we choose to wear. We design three-dimensional spaces to indicate intention.

If prose does not do the trick, we resort to poetry. Nonfiction has its truth and fiction another kind of truth. Drama, dance, song, art, all collaborate to extend our reach as communicators. What may have begun as a grunt echoing from the depths of an ancient cave has evolved into a vast centuries-old library of literature, history, theater, cinema, and art.

Communication is difficult. Misunderstanding may happen more often than understanding. But we soldier on because communication is our birthright. Even ignoring someone is an act of communication; we cannot evade it. That is because communication is essential to us. We are hooked on it. We are contact addicts.

Our current era makes this fact abundantly clear. Information abounds from the phone in our pocket, to the flat screen in the neighborhood pub, to office computer. We are awash in a bombardment of data from every corner of the globe from every conceivable human motivation.

Yes, communication is essential, natural, and hard. Perhaps this book has provided a path to help you succeed more often at it. Perhaps you have renewed your commitment to the integrity necessary to engage in authentic interaction. All that is left is to decide which interactions are important enough to win your attention and engagement. To whom will you speak? To whom will you listen? Whom will you believe?

That is where we leave you because those decisions are entirely in your hands.

# Glossary

***Abduct.*** Open.

***Adduct.*** Close.

***Aryepiglottic (AES) narrow.*** Also known as epilaryngeal narrowing; epiglottis is pulled posteriorly toward the arytenoid cartilages.

***Arytenoid cartilages.*** Pair of cartilages found in the posterior part of the larynx and attached to the vocal folds.

***Audience failure.*** A communication breakdown that occurs when not all the right people are in on a conversation.

***Basement membrane zone (BMZ).*** Area of the vocal folds that secures the epithelium to the superficial lamina propria; susceptible to injury and often the site of nodules.

***Bernoulli effect.*** As air passes through a narrowed constriction created by two masses, the velocity of the air increases and causes a negative pressure, pulling the two masses together.

***Content failure.*** A communication breakdown caused by the communication of incorrect or insufficient information.

***Credibility.*** Quality of being someone who can be believed and believed in; often built on perceived honesty, responsiveness, trustworthiness, and ability to stay informed.

***Cricoid cartilage.*** Signet-shaped structure that rests on top of the trachea.

***Cricothyroid (CT).*** Primary vocal fold tensor that works antagonistic to the adductors of the vocal folds and can pull the thyroid cartilage forward, stretching the vocal folds and increasing pitch.

***Deep lamina propria.*** The most durable of all layers of the vocal folds, consisting of mostly collagenous fibers.

***Epiglottis.*** Elastic cartilage that acts as a flap, diverting food and liquid away from the airway and into the esophagus during swallowing, thus protecting the vocal folds.

***Epithelium.*** The thin, most superficial layer of the vocal folds that is covered in mucosa.

***Ethos.*** Credibility; the moral authority of the voice to convey good character.

*False vocal folds.*   Paired tissues located directly above the vocal folds that serve to protect the vocal folds.

*Feeling.*   Communication intention where the speaker's purpose is to change how the listener feels about something; appeals to emotion.

*Flexible laryngoscope.*   Flexible fiberoptic tube that is inserted into the nasal passage, passed through the velopharyngeal port, and positioned above the vocal folds to view the structure and function of the larynx.

*Frequency.*   Number of cycles per second vocal folds vibrate; measured in Hz.

*Fundamental frequency (F0).*   Lowest frequency in a complex wave.

*Glottis.*   Space between the vocal folds.

*Habitual pitch.*   Pitch at which an individual typically speaks.

*Harmonics.*   Various frequencies that comprise a complex, periodic sound wave.

*Information exchange.*   Communication intention in which the speaker's main purpose is to transmit information to the listener without trying to change the listener's opinion.

*Infrahyoid muscles.*   Muscles that lower the larynx.

*Integrity.* Quality of oneness when what an individual projects on the outside matches what they are on the inside.

*Intensity.*   Dynamic of phonation related to the amplitude of vocal fold excursion (during vibration) and subglottal pressure (during the closed phase of vibration).

*Interarytenoid (IA).*   Large muscle in the posterior part of the larynx that runs from one arytenoid cartilage to the other; adducts vocal folds.

*Intermediate lamina propria.*   Layer of the vocal folds composed of elastic fibers likened to "soft rubber bands."

*Jitter.*   Perturbations of frequency; deviation from true periodicity.

*Laryngologist.*   Otolaryngologist with specialized fellowship training in laryngology and all things related to the voice.

*Laryngology.*   Study of the larynx or voice box.

*Lateral cricoarytenoid (LCA).*   Paired muscle that runs from the cricoid cartilage to the muscular process of the arytenoids; adducts vocal folds.

*Logos.*   Logical and sound argumentation.

*Loudness.*   Perceptual correlate of intensity.

*Morpheme.*   Smallest unit of meaning in language.

*Occasion failure.*   A communication breakdown due to a delay in the request for or delivery of information.

*Optimal pitch.*   The most effortless pitch for an individual to produce based on his or her age, gender, and vocal anatomy; speaking habitually at a pitch other than the optimal pitch may cause voice problems.

*Otolaryngologist.*   Ear, nose, and throat physician; also known as an ENT.

***Paraverbals.*** Voice, tone, gestures, and facial expressions, serving to enhance the meaning of verbal communication; may include clothing selection and other communication signals.

***Pathos.*** Speaker's power to stir the emotions.

***Persuasion.*** Communication intention in which the speaker's purpose is to change how the listener thinks about something.

***Phonation.*** Process of making sound via vocal fold vibration.

***Pitch.*** Perceptual correlate of frequency of vocal fold vibration.

***Posterior cricoarytenoid (PCA).*** Paired muscle that sits outside, posteriorly, and courses from the cricoarytenoid lamina to the muscular process of the arytenoids; sole abductor of the vocal folds, working primarily to open the vocal folds for breathing.

***Prosodic fluency.*** Ability to vocalize sentences in a manner that fills them with the meanings you intend.

***Prosody.*** Vocal inflection.

***Purpose failure.*** A communication breakdown in which the objective of communication is muddled, inappropriate, or not achieved.

***Recurrent laryngeal nerve (RLN).*** Branch of the Vagus nerve that provides motor information to the intrinsic muscles of the larynx.

***Resonator.*** Something forced into vibration by another vibratory source; in human voicing, the vocal tract.

***Rhetoric.*** The voice in use to persuade others.

***Rigid laryngoscope.*** Rigid tube inserted into the mouth to view the larynx; excellent for close, clear viewing of the mucosal wave and appearance of the vocal folds.

***Self-affirmation.*** Communication intention in which the speaker's main purpose is to seek validation or affirmation of his or her self-concept by gaining a listener's attention.

***Shimmer.*** Perturbations of amplitude.

***Siren.*** Gliding up and down in pitch on an "ng" sound.

***Slack true vocal fold body cover.*** Irregular pattern of vocal fold vibration; sometimes called "glottal fry."

***Small talk.*** Communication intention in which information exchanged is often trivial and for the purpose of relationship building, climate setting, or relaxation.

***Stiff true vocal fold body cover.*** Audible airflow and quiet; sometimes called "breathy."

***Stroboscopy.*** Light source used to visualize vocal fold motion during vibration.

***Superficial lamina propria.*** Also known as Reinke's space; gelatinous, loose, and pliable portion of the vocal folds located toward the midsection of the vocal folds.

***Superior laryngeal nerve (SLN).***   Branch of the Vagus nerve that provides sensory information for the larynx, as well as motor information to the cricothyroid muscle.

***Suprahyoid muscles.***   Muscles that raise the larynx.

***Thesis.***   Purpose of essay or speech; what the speaker intends to get across when he or she sets out to speak at a particular moment.

***Thick true vocal fold body cover.***   Loud and clear; characterized by a large mucosal wave.

***Thin true vocal fold body cover.***   Quiet and clear; characterized by a small mucosal wave.

***Thyroarytenoid (TA).***   Fan-shaped muscle of the vocal folds that runs from the thyroid cartilage in the front to the arytenoids in the back; adducts vocal folds.

***Thyroid cartilage.***   Paired cartilage fused at the midline that sits above the cricoid and contains prominence commonly known as Adam's apple; houses and protects the vocal folds.

***Trachea.***   Cartilaginous tube that provides the pathway to the lungs.

***Vagus nerve.***   Tenth cranial nerve responsible for both motor and sensory information in the larynx.

***Vocal cord dysfunction (VCD).***   Also known as paradoxical vocal fold motion disorder (PVFMD); vocal folds reflexively close during breathing when they would typically remain open.

***Vocal folds.***   Commonly known as vocal cords; layered folds of tissue about the size of a thumbnail that vibrate together in a wave-like motion.

***Vocal ligament.***   Band of tissue used to position the vocal folds and support vocal fold vibration at high pitches; composed of intermediate and deep lamina propria.

***Vocal tract.***   Hollow spaces in the throat, head, and nasal cavities.

***Vocology.***   Study of voice.

***Voice therapy.***   Learning and repatterning of behaviors that reestablish adequate vocal fold closure patterns and balance airflow and subglottal pressure during vocal fold vibration.

# Index

# C

Carcinomas
  laryngeal, 101
  smokers and, 254–255
Carreras, José, 101
Cartilages, laryngeal, 37–39
Caruso, Enrico, 138
Chenoweth, Kristin, 203, 205
Cicero, 138
Climate setting
  small talk and, 161
  tips on, 202
Collaborating position, 132
Common meaning, 150–152
Communication
  audience failure and, 141
  authoritative, 229–234
  as birthright, 288–289
  connection
    successful, 147–150
    through meaning, 145–146
  content failure and, 140–141,
    144
  direction, 163–164
  effective, 140
  feeling as, 164–166
  guidelines, 227–228
  information exchange as,
    162–163
  Intentions of Communication,
    147
  interpersonal, 219
  missed connection and, 139–145
  multiple intentions and, 166–170
  occasion failures, 140, 144
  persuasion, 163–164
  purpose failure, 141–142
  refining, 289
Competency
  credibility and, 188
  experience and, 188–189
  integrity and, 189

Confronting position, 132–133
Connection
  common meaning and, 150–152
  communication and missed,
    139–145
  completing, 215–221
  feeling, 278–279
  kinds of, 147–150
  modes of, 146–147
Consistency, credibility and, 191,
  193
Content failure, 144
  communication and missed,
    140–141
Couric, Katie, 229
Cozying position, 132, 133
Cranial nerves, 43–46
Credibility, 179–183
  competency and, 188
  consistency and, 191, 193
  forethought and, 191–192, 194
  honesty and, 190, 192
  is not, 183–186
  knowledge and, 188
  loyalty and, 192
  payoffs, 192–195
  perceptions of, 190–192
  pillars of, 188–189
  proxy, 186–188
  reliability and, 191
  responsiveness and, 190–191
  of the voice, 137
Credible self, 179–183
Credo, points of, 189
Cricoid tilt, 122
Cricothyroid (CT ), 40–41
Cry, 89
CT (Cricothyroid), 40

# D

Deaf community, gestures and, 287
Declaration of Independence, 266

Streep, Meryl, 200, 207
Stress, 114–115
Students, receptive, 228
Superficial lamina propria, 47, 48
Superior laryngeal nerve (SLN), 46
Suprahyoids, 42
Syntax, 139

**T**

TA (Thyroarytenoid), 41
Tensor veli palatine, 73
Thick true vocal fold closure, 61
Thin closure, 61
*Thinking in Pictures*, 112
Thought, voice a, 13–16
Thyroarytenoid (TA), 39
Thyrohyoid, 43
Tidal
   breathing, 31
   volume, 29, 34
True Vocal Folds: Body Cover
   (TVFBC), 118–119, 125,
   249
Truth, speaking, 288–290
TVFBC (True Vocal Folds: Body
   Cover), 118–119, 125, 249
Twang, 89
Tyler, Steven, 203

**V**

Vague working, 226
Vagus nerve, 43–44
Valsalva maneuver, 52
VCD (Vocal cord dysfunction), 49
Velopharyngeal port, 73
Velum, 72–75
Verbals, 110
Videostroboscopy, 95–96
Vocal choice, 88–89
Vocal cord dysfunction (VCD), 49
Vocal fold paralysis, 100

Vocal folds
   abduction, 69
   airway protection, 53–54
   anatomy, 46–48
   benign lesions, 100–101
   biomechanics, 48, 48–54
   change with age, 86
   closure, 61–62
   cover of, 47
   development, fundamental
      frequency and, 87
   dimorphism, 86
   false, 68–69
   hygiene strategies, 98
   in older women, 87
   production, myoelastic
      aerodynamic theory of,
      56–57
   pulmonary function, 48–50
   pushing and pulling, 51–53
   qualities, 89
   sound, voice and, 12
   typical, 85–87
   tracts, 26, 64–66
   anatomy, 66
Voice
   in action, 137–139
   authoritative, 229–234
   awareness, 101–103
   care team, 94–97
   center, 95
   choice of, 88–89
   defined, 23
   distant, 173–177
   as a dynamic system, 24–25
   evaluation, 95
   giving, 286–287
   lack of knowledge about, 89–92
   medical management, 100
   optimal pitch, 229–230
   putting feeling in, 270–272
   qualities, 89
   recognition technology, 9